Elementary Linear Algebra

Elementary Linear Algebra

Marvin Marcus and Henryk Minc

Department of Mathematics
University of California, Santa Barbara

The Macmillan Company
Collier-Macmillan Limited, London

Second Printing, 1969

Library of Congress catalog card number: 68–11004

The Macmillan Company
Collier-Macmillan Canada, Ltd., Toronto, Ontario

Printed in the United States of America

To Rebecca and to Catherine

Preface

This book is intended for use at the freshman and sophomore levels as a standard two-quarter or one-semester course in linear algebra and matrix theory. If certain sections are omitted as suggested below, the book is entirely suitable for an introductory one-quarter course as well. Linear algebra has in recent years moved from the graduate level to the upper division undergraduate level and most recently it has become a part of the first two years of training in most colleges and universities. As a matter of fact, many high school students come into the freshman year having acquired some knowledge of 2×2 and 3×3 matrix algebra.

Our plan in the organization of this book is to introduce relatively few concepts and discuss them at several levels of abstraction. For example, vectors (two-dimensional) are first introduced as translations of the plane (Section 1.4), then as n-tuples (Section 1.6), and finally as elements of an abstract vector space (Section 4.1). Similarly, the all-important notion of an inner product is first introduced for vectors in a plane (Section 1.5), then for complex n-tuples (Section 4.3), and finally for abstract vector spaces (Section 5.2). Throughout, we motivate our approach by geometric examples. Thus in Chapter 2 matrices appear as a natural tool for studying linear transformations on spaces of n-tuples. In Section 5.1 we are led to the theory of congruence through the problem of classification of conics.

Chapter 1 begins with a leisurely treatment of sets, functions, and vectors in the plane. For a student who is adequately prepared, the first five sections can be omitted. However, the last section of this chapter is essential for the rest of the book. It is here in the context of the concrete vector spaces of n-tuples that most of the fundamental ideas first appear—e.g., linear dependence, bases, and dimension.

In the first two sections of Chapter 2 we develop the algebra of matrices and define the inverse of a square matrix. The product of two matrices is introduced in terms of the composition of two linear transformations. In Section 2.3 we derive the fundamental Hermite normal form of a matrix which is then used to analyze systems of linear equations. Rank is defined in terms of the linear independence of rows.

In Chapter 3 we define determinants inductively and thereby avoid developing the theory of permutations. We then show how rank and the nonvanishing of subdeterminants are related.

These first three chapters comprise what normally can be covered in one quarter. This material is sometimes taught concurrently with a course in calculus in some institutions.

Chapters 4 and 5 deal with the analysis of certain important classes of matrices and linear transformations. Chapter 4 begins by describing the postulates for an abstract vector space and defining linear transformations on abstract vector spaces. Matrices appear here as representations in terms of bases, and similarity of matrices is an analytical expression for a change of bases. Some instructors may choose to omit all of Section 4.1 with the exception of the definition of similarity of matrices (Definition 1.6). Section 4.2 deals with the problem of reducing a matrix to diagonal or triangular form by similarity. The concepts of characteristic roots and characteristic vectors appear here as natural devices for completing this analysis. We then go on to the classical Cayley-Hamilton theorem. In Section 4.3 the standard inner product in the space of n-tuples is introduced. This leads naturally to the definitions of unitary and orthogonal matrices. The reduction of hermitian, skew-hermitian, and unitary matrices by unitary similarity is carried out here in detail.

Section 5.1, Chapter 5, is concerned with the reduction of quadratic forms to a sum and difference of squares. Sylvester's law of inertia is proved and examples of congruence reduction to diagonal form are worked out in detail. Section 5.2 reintroduces the concept of the inner product in its abstract setting and contains a proof of the Cauchy-Schwarz inequality for the general inner product. This section may be omitted in a one-semester course in view of the fact that the concept of an inner product appears at several places earlier in the book.

The present book substantially differs from our *Introduction to Linear Algebra*. Here we are addressing ourselves to an audience of students whose mathematical background is less extensive and therefore the scope of this book is more limited. For example, we do not develop here the general theory of normal matrices nor do we present the more sophisticated spectral properties of linear transformations. Also, the general version of the Laplace expansion theorem and the Binet-Cauchy theorem have not been included. Moreover, the pace of the exposition is appreciably slower in *Elementary Linear Algebra*. In general, we believe that this book can be easily used by students who have had no mathematics beyond second year high school algebra, whereas our earlier book presupposes a level of maturity one would expect to find among sophomore science and engineering students.

We are indebted to our colleague Professor Adil Yaqub and to the editorial staff of The Macmillan Company for their valuable suggestions.

We also wish to express our sincere thanks to the following people who have assisted in the technical preparation of this book: Mrs. Wanda Michalenko, Mrs. Virginia Brimer, Mrs. Louise Kraus, Miss Amy Mok, Miss Nancy Peacock, Miss Alice Rosen, and Miss Susan Katz.

M. M

H. M

Numbering System

Each of the chapters is divided into sections. Thus the third section of Chapter 2 is numbered 2.3. Definitions, theorems, and examples are separately numbered within a section. Thus Theorem 3.4 is the fourth theorem in the third section. We refer to a theorem (definition, example) by this number and, if necessary, by the chapter number.

The asterisks in the table of contents refer to parts of sections that can be omitted either because of their difficulty or their peripheral importance.

Contents

Chapter 3.   Determinants

Chapter 4.   Characteristic Roots

Chapter 5. Quadratic Functions

Elementary Linear Algebra

1

Introduction to Vector Spaces

1.1. SETS

The most widely used concept in mathematics at every level is that of a set of objects. The word "set" is not defined in terms of more primitive concepts and will be used synonymously with words such as "collection," "totality," "family," "aggregate," etc. The elementary notion that goes with the idea of a set is that of set membership, that is, of an object belonging to a set or not belonging to it. We write

$$x \in S \tag{1}$$

and read it as "x is an element of the set S," if x is a member of S or x belongs to S. If it is not true that x belongs to S, we write

$$x \notin S. \tag{2}$$

Sets are usually described in one of two ways. The first of these is by simply writing down all the objects which belong to the set; the second is by making some kind of descriptive phrase that designates the objects in the set. For example, the set consisting of the even integers between 1 and 11 can be written

$$S = \{2, 4, 6, 8, 10\}. \tag{3}$$

The braces are suggestive of the idea that we are considering the integers

1

2, 4, 6, 8, and 10 as the totality of members of S. On the other hand, we could designate the set S by the following notation:

$$S = \{n \mid n \text{ is an even integer between 1 and 11}\}. \tag{4}$$

This latter notation is read as follows: S is the set of all n such that n is an even integer between 1 and 11. That is, the vertical bar is read "such that" or "for which." The notation in (4) permits us to talk about sets which contain more than a finite number of elements. Thus we can conceive of the set of all even integers E. It is quite clear that we could write E as

$$E = \{n \mid n = 2k, k \text{ an integer}\}. \tag{5}$$

Thus E is the set of all n such that n is twice some integer.

There are two important ways of combining sets to produce new ones. The first of these is *union* and the second is *intersection*. Thus if S and T are two sets, their union is just the set of all the items that belong to either S or T (or possibly both). As an example, if $S = \{2, 3, 4\}$ and $T = \{2, 3, 5\}$, then the union of S and T is just the set $\{2, 3, 4, 5\}$. Note that we do not count 2 and 3 as appearing twice. The notation for the union of S and T is

$$S \cup T \tag{6}$$

and is read "S union T." Another primitive way of combining sets is intersection. If S and T are two sets, their intersection is the set which consists of precisely those items belonging to both S and T. Thus if S and T are the sets in the immediately preceding example, their intersection is just the set $\{2, 3\}$. The notation for the intersection of two sets S and T is

$$S \cap T \tag{7}$$

and is read "S intersection T." Now suppose that S and T are two sets which have no element in common. For example, $S = \{2, 3, 4\}$ and $T = \{5, 6, 7\}$. If we are to talk about the intersection of S and T in this case, then we must introduce a logical device called the *empty set*. Thus the empty set is the set which has no member. This idea is philosophically related to the number zero which one encounters in elementary arithmetic. It is simply a convention that allows us to do "arithmetic" of sets without having to constantly talk about exceptional situations. That is, we want to have available the answer when we subtract 3 from 3 in the same way that we want to have available the answer when we intersect two sets with no common element. The notation for the empty set is $\varnothing$. Thus in the case of the above example we can write $S \cap T = \varnothing$.

Sometimes we shall have occasion to consider intersections and unions of more than two sets. In fact, we might very well be confronted with a situation in which we would like to look at the common elements or the elements in any of an infinite collection of sets. For example, consider the set S_j whose elements are the nonnegative numbers in the interval between 0 and $1/j$, including 0 but excluding $1/j$, i.e.,

$$S_j = \left\{ x \mid 0 \leq x < \frac{1}{j} \right\}, \qquad j = 1, 2, \ldots.$$

This is an infinite collection of sets: There is one S_j for each integer $j = 1, 2, \ldots$. These sets can be pictured as shown in Fig. 1. Clearly the

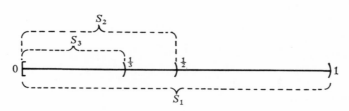

Figure 1

union of these sets, i.e., the totality of numbers lying in any one of the S_j, is just S_1. This is because S_1 contains the elements in all the S_j. On the other hand, the intersection of all the S_j is the set consisting of the single number zero. This is because whatever positive number we take, however small, some S_j has its right-hand end point to the left of that number and thus does not contain the number. Zero is the only number which is not excluded by this argument, and surely zero belongs to every one of the S_j. We write

$$\bigcup_j S_j = S_1, \qquad \bigcap_j S_j = \{0\}.$$

In general, we shall use the notations $\bigcup_j S_j$ and $\bigcap_j S_j$ to designate the union and intersection of a collection of sets, respectively.

Our final elementary notion concerning sets is that of *inclusion*. Thus in the preceding example we remarked that each S_j is contained in S_1. This means simply that every number in a given S_j is also in S_1. In general, if we have two sets S and T for which every element of S is an element of T, we say that S is *contained* in T or *included* in T, or that S is a *subset* of T; we write

$$S \subset T. \tag{8}$$

Formally this means that $x \in T$ whenever $x \in S$. We say that the two sets S and T are equal, written $S = T$, if $S \subset T$ and $T \subset S$; i.e., S and T consist of precisely the same elements. The following inclusions are immediate from the definition:

$$\varnothing \subset S \cap T \subset S,$$

$$S \cap T \subset T,$$

$$S \subset S \cup T,$$

and

$$T \subset S \cup T.$$

Quiz
Answer *true* or *false*:

1. If $\{0\}$ is the set consisting of the integer 0, then $\{0\} = \varnothing$.
2. The intersection of the two sets of numbers, $\{x \mid 0 \le x \le 1\}$ and $\{x \mid \frac{1}{2} < x \le 1\}$, is the set of numbers $\{x \mid \frac{1}{2} < x \le 1\}$.
3. If $S_j = \{x \mid 0 \le x \le 1/j\}$, where j takes on all values 1, 2, 3,..., then $\bigcap_j S_j = \{0\}$.
4. If S is any set, then $S \cap S = S = S \cup S$.
5. If S contains n elements and T contains m elements, then $S \cap T$ has p elements in it, where p is smaller than both m and n.
6. If S has m elements and T has n elements, then $S \cup T$ has at most $m + n$ elements in it.
7. If S and T are the sets in the preceding example and $S \cap T \ne \varnothing$, then $S \cup T$ has at most $m + n - 1$ elements in it.
8. If R denotes the set of rational numbers, that is, the set of all fractions whose numerators and denominators are integers, then $\sqrt{2}$ is not an element of R.
9. If R is the set of rational numbers and E is the set of even integers, then $E \cap R = E$.

10. If R is the set of rational numbers and $S = \{x \mid x = n\sqrt{3},\ n\ \text{an integer}\}$, then $S \cap R = \varnothing$; that is, the set of all integer multiples of $\sqrt{3}$ has nothing in common with the set of rational numbers.

Exercises

1. Show that for any two sets S and T, $S \subset S \cup T$ and $S \cap T \subset S$.

2. Try proving that if R is the set of rational numbers, then $\sqrt{2} + \sqrt{3} \notin R$. (Although this exercise is not too difficult, it shows that even though the idea of set membership is very simple, its verification in any particular instance may be bothersome.)

3. Let $S_1 = \{2, 4, 6, 8, 10, 12, 14\}$, $S_2 = \{-1, 0, 2, 4, 6\}$, and $S_3 = \{\sqrt{2}, \sqrt{3}, -5, 4\}$. Find $S_1 \cap S_2$, $\bigcap_{i=1}^{3} S_i$, $\bigcup_{i=1}^{3} S_i$, $(S_1 \cap S_3) \cup S_2$, $(S_1 \cup S_3) \cap S_2$, and $S_1 \cup (S_2 \cap S_3)$.

4. Either prove, or show to be false by example, the following statements: If S_1, S_2, and S_3 are any sets, then

$$S_1 \cup (S_2 \cap S_3) = (S_1 \cup S_2) \cap (S_1 \cup S_3),$$
$$S_1 \cap (S_2 \cap S_3) = (S_1 \cap S_2) \cap S_3,$$
$$S_1 \cup (S_2 \cup S_3) = (S_1 \cup S_2) \cup S_3,$$
$$S_1 \cap (S_2 \cup S_3) = (S_1 \cap S_2) \cup (S_1 \cap S_3).$$

1.2. RELATIONS AND FUNCTIONS

In ordinary English we sometimes use the word "function" in the same way as we do in mathematics. Thus we may say that one's weight is a function of the amount of food one consumes, that the brightness of the day is a function of the cloud cover, etc. In other words, we associate an item in a set in some specified way with each of the items in another designated set. It may be the case, however, that such a specification is not uniquely defined. For example, consider Fig. 2. Any vertical line intersects this circle in two points (we assume that our vertical lines are not tangents or do not miss the circle altogether). Hence we cannot sensibly say that the second coordinate, i.e., the projection on the vertical axis of the point of intersection, is a function of a, simply because we have not specified which of the two numbers b and c we mean. This leads us to a somewhat more general concept than that of a function—the idea of a *relation*.

Before making our formal definitions, we introduce an important way of combining sets.

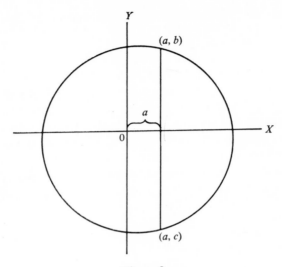

Figure 2

Definition 2.1. (**Cartesian product, relation**). *If X and Y are sets, consider the following totality of pairs:*

$$\{(x, y) \mid x \in X, y \in Y\}, \tag{1}$$

i.e., *the set* (1) *is just the set of all ordered pairs in which the first of the ordered pair is an element of X and the second of the ordered pair is an element of Y. The set* (1) *is called the* **cartesian product** *of X and Y and is denoted by*

$$X \times Y. \tag{2}$$

If R is a subset of X × Y, then R is called a **relation** *on X to Y.*

Thus a relation on X to Y is just a set of pairs of objects, the first of each pair from X, the second from Y. In Fig. 2 if we think of X as being the horizontal axis and Y the vertical axis, then $X \times Y$ is just the set of all points in the plane; the circle is a subset of $X \times Y$ and hence is a relation.

Definition 2.2. (**Functions**). *If X and Y are sets and f is a relation on X to Y in which every element of X occurs in some pair of f in such a way that no two different pairs in f have the same first member, then f is called a function on X to Y. We write this as*

$$f: X \to Y. \tag{3}$$

*If (x, y) belongs to f, y is called the **value** of the function at x and we write it*

$$y = f(x). \tag{4}$$

Thus a function is a set of pairs of the form (x, y), $x \in X$, $y \in Y$, in which y is completely determined once x is given. Usually in elementary mathematics the function f is given in some computable way, i.e., a formula is given so that one may obtain $f(x)$ from x by "turning a crank." For example, consider the function $f: X \to X$ given by $f(x) = 2x + 5$, where X is the set of all real numbers. Given an x we can compute $f(x)$ from the formula. A familiar way of looking at the function f is in terms of its graph, Fig. 3, with respect to a pair of mutually perpendicular lines.

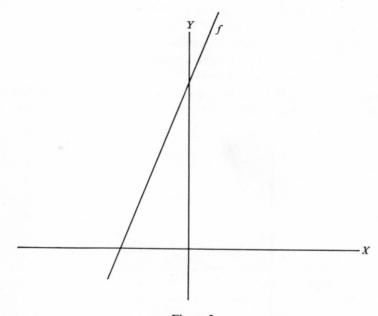

Figure 3

Functions which are more familiar to us have certain special names, although we may not be able to compute their values for any particular x in the same way as we did in the preceding example, e.g., $f(x) = \sin x$, $f(x) = e^x$, and $f(x) = \sqrt{x}$. We may argue that in these last three examples we can look up values in a table; that is, given x we can leaf through a table for the sine function and find $\sin x$. But the number in the table is usually not a precise value, and it is doubtful, in fact, whether any one knows the 200 millionth digit in the decimal expansion of sin 11°. One should see from these remarks that it is better to have a concept of function defined without reference to any mechanism for generating the values of the function.

The set X of first members of pairs in the function f is called the *domain* of the function. The set of all function values $f(x)$, $x \in X$, is called the *range* of f and is sometimes written $f(X)$. If $f: X \to Y$ there is no reason to think that the range of f is all of Y. Thus if $f(x) = x^2$ and X and Y are both the set of nonnegative integers, we know that the range of f is not all of Y; i.e., 5 is not the square of an integer. In the event that the range of f is all of Y, we say that f is *onto* Y. For example, suppose X and Y both are the set of all points in the plane and $f: X \to Y$ is the function which associates to each point $P = (x_1, x_2)$ the point $f(P) = (x_1 + 3,$ $x_2 + 1) = (y_1, y_2) = Q$. Clearly any point Q in the plane can be obtained as a value of the function f at some appropriate P. For example, if $Q =$ $(0, 0)$, then we want to find a point $P = (x_1, x_2)$ for which $x_1 + 3 = 0$, $x_2 + 1 = 0$, and we have immediately that $P = (-3, -1)$. The function depicted by the arrow in Fig. 4 has a special name. It is called a *vector*.

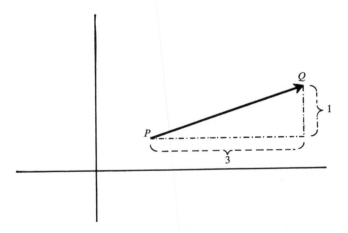

Figure 4

In Sections 4 and 5 we shall discuss in greater detail the properties of such functions, but it suffices to say here that a vector is just a function whose domain is the plane, whose range is the plane, and for which the function value $f(P)$ is obtained from P by adding to the coordinates of P some fixed (i.e., independent of P) numbers.

Some functions have the property that it is possible to recapture x given the function value $f(x)$. Thus, for example, if $f(x) = x^2$ and f is a function whose domain is the set of nonnegative real numbers X, then given any nonnegative real number y, we know that we can find an x such that $f(x) = y$. This value of x is, of course, denoted by $\sqrt{y}$. Note that if the domain of this function were the set of all real numbers instead of just the set of nonnegative real numbers, we would not be able to find a unique x for which $f(x) = y$, e.g., $f(2) = f(-2) = 4$.

Definition 2.3. (*1-1 function, inverse function*). *Let f be a function, $f : X \to Y$, whose domain is X and suppose that whenever $f(x_1) = f(x_2)$ it follows that $x_1 = x_2$. Then f is said to be 1-1 (read "one to one"). If f is 1-1 and onto Y, then the function $g : Y \to X$ whose elements are all pairs of the form $(f(x), x)$ is called the **inverse** of f and is written $g = f^{-1}$. We have $f^{-1}(f(x)) = x$.*

We should observe that the relation g on Y to X as defined in Definition 2.3 is indeed a function. This follows immediately. For, suppose two pairs in g have the same first element, i.e., $(f(x_1), x_1)$ and $(f(x_2), x_2)$ are in g and $f(x_1) = f(x_2)$. Then because f is 1-1 it follows that $x_1 = x_2$ and g satisfies the definition of a function. It is clear that this little argument would fail if f were not 1-1.

We consider some examples of inverse functions. Suppose X is the set of all nonnegative real numbers and Y is the interval consisting of all those y satisfying $0 \le y < 1$. Let $f: X \to Y$ be defined by $f(x) = x/(1 + x)$. To compute f^{-1}, the inverse of f, we have to convince ourselves that f is indeed 1-1. But if $f(x_1) = f(x_2)$, then $x_1/(1 + x_1) = x_2/(1 + x_2)$, i.e., $x_1 + x_1 x_2 = x_2 + x_1 x_2$, and it follows that $x_1 = x_2$. By definition, f^{-1} is the set of all pairs of the form $(f(x), x)$, i.e.,

$$f^{-1} = \{(f(x), x) \mid x \in X\}. \tag{5}$$

Although (5) is a perfectly adequate description of f^{-1}, it is not particularly easy to work with. We would really like to have a formula which tells us how to compute the function value $f^{-1}(y)$ given $y \in Y$. In other words, we want to write f^{-1} in the form

$$f^{-1} = \{(y, f^{-1}(y)) \mid y \in Y\}.$$

Now $f^{-1}(y) = x$, where x is uniquely specified by $f(x) = y$ (remember that f is 1-1). Hence y is $x/(1 + x)$ or

$$x = (1 + x)y,$$

$$x - xy = y,$$

$$x(1 - y) = y,$$

$$x = \frac{y}{1 - y}.$$

Hence $f^{-1}(y) = y/(1 - y)$ for any $y \in Y$.

As another example consider the function (in this case, vector) $f : X \to X$, where X is the plane and $f(P) = Q$ for $P = (x_1, x_2)$ and $Q = (x_1 + 3, x_2 + 1)$. It is obvious that f is 1-1 and onto. To find a formula for f^{-1} we write $P = f^{-1}(Q)$, so that given $Q = (y_1, y_2)$, we want $f^{-1}(Q) = P = (x_1, x_2)$. But $f(P) = Q$, so that $(x_1 + 3, x_2 + 1)$ is equal to (y_1, y_2) or $x_1 = y_1 - 3$ and $x_2 = y_2 - 1$. Hence $f^{-1}((y_1, y_2)) = (y_1 - 3, y_2 - 1)$ for any point (y_1, y_2) in X.

There is an important way of combining functions which essentially amounts to performing their actions in succession. Thus suppose we have two functions $f : X \to Y$ and $g : Y \to Z$. Then we can define a function

$$h : X \to Z,$$

called the *composite* or the *product* of g and f, whose value for any $x \in X$ is given by

$$h(x) = g(f(x)). \tag{6}$$

The function h is written

$$h = gf; \tag{7}$$

that is, g and f are simply juxtaposed.

It should be emphasized that the value of the composite (i.e., the product) of g and f for a number x does not mean the product of the function values at x, i.e., $(gf)(x)$ is not generally equal to $g(x)f(x)$. For example, if $f: X \to X$ (where X is the set of real numbers) is defined by $f(x) = 2x + 5$ and $g: X \to X$ is defined by $g(x) = x^2 - 2$, then

$$(gf)(x) = g(f(x))$$
$$= g(2x + 5)$$
$$= (2x + 5)^2 - 2$$
$$= 4x^2 + 20x + 23,$$

while

$$g(x)f(x) = (x^2 - 2)(2x + 5)$$
$$= 2x^3 + 5x^2 - 4x - 10.$$

Composition of functions is easily seen to be an *associative* operation. This means that if f and g are given as above and are onto Y and Z, respectively, and if $k: Z \to W$, then

$$k(gf) = (kg)f. \tag{8}$$

To establish (8) is very simple. Take any x in X. The value of the left side of (8) is $k(gf)(x)$, which is $k(g(f(x)))$ from the definition of gf. On the other hand, the value of the right side of (8) is $kg(f(x))$, which by the definition of the product of k and g is just $k(g(f(x)))$. Thus (8) is established.

We now apply the idea of function composition to the idea of inverse function. Thus suppose $f: X \to Y$ is a 1-1 function, $Y = f(X)$, and let $g = f^{-1}$,

$$f^{-1}: Y \to X.$$

Then $gf(x) = g(f(x))$. But the value of g at $f(x)$ is just x, because g consists of all pairs of the form $(f(x), x)$, $x \in X$. Thus we have $(gf)(x) = x$. We can turn the argument around and show that $(fg)(y) = y$ for all $y \in Y$. We define a special function on X as follows:

$$I_X: X \to X$$

in which $I_X(x) = x$ for every $x \in X$. The function I_X is called the *identity function* and our preceding remarks show that

$$f^{-1}f = I_X \quad \text{and} \quad ff^{-1} = I_Y.$$

As another instance of function composition suppose that X is the plane; $f: X \to X$ and $g: X \to X$ are two functions (vectors) given by

$$f((x_1, x_2)) = (x_1 + 3, x_2 + 1),$$
$$g((x_1, x_2)) = (x_1 + 5, x_2 - 7).$$

We compute from the definition (6) that

$$\begin{aligned}
h((x_1, x_2)) &= g(f((x_1, x_2))) \\
&= g((x_1 + 3, x_2 + 1)) \\
&= ((x_1 + 3) + 5, (x_2 + 1) - 7) \\
&= (x_1 + (3 + 5), x_2 + (1 - 7)) \\
&= (x_1 + 8, x_2 - 6).
\end{aligned}$$

We should observe that the product of g and f was obtained by adding the 3 and 5 that occurred in the first coordinates and adding the 1 and -7 that occurred in the second coordinates. We omit the calculations but the reader should verify that in this case

$$gf = fg.$$

However, even though f and g are both functions on X to X, it is not generally true that $fg = gf$; i.e., function composition, although associative, is not in general *commutative*. For example, if f is the function in the example we just considered and $g: X \to X$ is the function whose value at any point (x_1, x_2) is given by

$$g((x_1, x_2)) = (x_1^2, x_2^2),$$

then

$$\begin{aligned}
fg((2, 0)) &= f(g((2, 0))) \\
&= f((4, 0)) \\
&= (4 + 3, 0 + 1) \\
&= (7, 1),
\end{aligned}$$

whereas

$$gf((2, 0)) = g(f((2, 0)))$$
$$= g((5, 1))$$
$$= (25, 1).$$

Quiz

Answer *true* or *false*:

1. The set $S = \{(x, y) \mid x^2 + y^2 = 1\}$ is a relation in the plane.
2. The set S in Question 1 is a function.
3. If $T = \{(x, y) \mid y \geq 0\}$, then $S \cap T$ is a function, where S is the set in Question 1.
4. The set T in Question 3 is a function.
5. The set T in Question 3 is a relation.
6. If $f : X \to X$ is a function onto X, then f is 1-1.
7. If $f : X \to X$ is a 1-1 function, then f is onto X.
8. If X is the set of nonnegative real numbers, then $f(x) = x^2/(1 + x^2)$ is a 1-1 function.
9. In Question 8, f is onto X.
10. If $Y = \{y \mid 0 \leq y < 1\}$ and f is the function in Question 8 then $f^{-1}(y) = \sqrt{y/(1 - y)}$.

Exercises

1. Let $f : X \to Y, g : Y \to Z$ be 1-1 onto functions. Prove that if $h = gf : X \to Z$, then h^{-1} exists and $h^{-1} : Z \to X$ is given by $h^{-1} = f^{-1}g^{-1}$.
2. If X is the set of nonnegative real numbers and $f : X \to X$ is given by $f(x) = \sqrt{x} \geq 0$, show that $f^{-1}(x) = x^2$.
3. Let $f : X \to Y$ and $g : X \to Y$ be functions for which $f(X) = g(X)$, i.e., functions with the same range. Show by constructing an example that it does not follow that $f = g$.
4. Let X be the plane and let $f : X \to X$ be a function defined by $f(P) = Q$, where $P = (x_1, x_2)$ and $Q = (x_1 + x_2, x_1 - x_2)$. Find a similar formula for $f^{-1}((x_1, x_2))$.
5. If $X = \{x_1, x_2, x_3\}$, write down the six possible 1-1 functions on X to X.
6. If X is the set in Exercise 5, how many functions $f : X \to X$ are there?

1.3. LINEAR FUNCTIONS

In this section we introduce the class of linear functions. These constitute the main items that one studies in linear algebra. Linear functions are much simpler in structure than the functions encountered in courses in

Calculus. However, it will be seen as we proceed that linear functions have an extensive, interesting, and important theory connected with them. It is safe to say that Linear Algebra is one of the few really successful mathematical disciplines.

Let X be the set of all real numbers, i.e., the ordinary line, and define the function $f : X \to X$ by

$$f(x) = ax + b, \tag{1}$$

where a and b are two fixed real numbers, e.g., f could be given by $f(x) = 2x + 5$. We all know that if we draw a pair of perpendicular lines and graph the set of all points $(x, f(x))$, i.e., graph f, then the resulting set is a straight line. Note in Fig. 5 that both the vertical axis and the horizontal

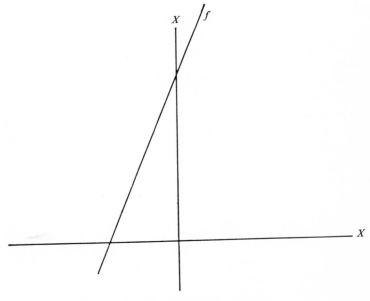

Figure 5

axis have been called X. In other words, the representation in Fig. 5 is obtained by plotting pairs of numbers $(x, f(x))$ with respect to the given pair of perpendicular lines. This is just a convenient representation and there is no reason to think that it is the only one. We could draw a representation for f as shown in Fig. 6, in which the real number line X has

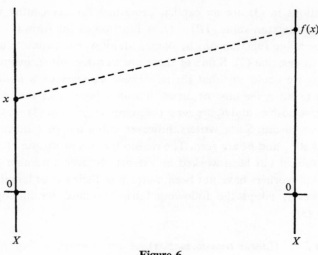

Figure 6

been drawn twice and in which we have connected each x with its function value $f(x)$.

A function of the form (1) is called an *affine function* on the line to itself. It is also called a *linear function*.

Now let X be the ordinary plane, i.e., $X = \{(x_1, x_2) \mid x_1 \text{ and } x_2 \text{ are real numbers}\}$. We are going to define a function on X to itself which will look something like the function (1) but will now have pairs of numbers as function values. Thus let a_{11}, a_{12}, a_{21}, a_{22}, b_1, and b_2 be six fixed real numbers. Define

$$f(P) = Q, \tag{2}$$

where $P = (x_1, x_2)$ and $Q = (a_{11}x_1 + a_{12}x_2 + b_1, a_{21}x_1 + a_{22}x_2 + b_2)$. Before we go on, let us make a few remarks about the subscripts that appear here. They are just convenient notational ways of keeping track of the coordinates we are working with. Thus if we set $Q = (y_1, y_2)$, our notation tells us that to get y_1 we multiply x_1 by a_{11}, x_2 by a_{12}, and add these two numbers to b_1. The first subscript 1 on an a tells us that we are calculating y_1, the first coordinate of Q. The second subscript on an a tells us which coordinate of P we are to multiply with that a. The subscript on a b tells us which coordinate to add to. Thus (2) can be written

$$
\begin{aligned}
y_1 &= a_{11}x_1 + a_{12}x_2 + b_1, \\
y_2 &= a_{21}x_1 + a_{22}x_2 + b_2.
\end{aligned}
\tag{3}
$$

The equations in (3) are an explicit procedure for associating with the point P the function value $f(P) = Q$. A function of the form (3) is called a linear or affine function on the plane. Many words beside "function" are used to describe (3). Some of these are *transformation, mapping,* and *map.* Thus we could say that (3) is a *linear mapping* or a *linear transformation* or an *affine map* or an *affine transformation* of the plane into itself. In case both b_1 and b_2 are zero, the mapping given by (3) is sometimes called *homogeneous.* Some writers, however, call a mapping linear only in the case that b_1 and b_2 are zero. The reason for this profusion of words is that this subject has been worked on extensively over a number of years and research workers have not been uniform in their use of language. We shall, however, adopt the following fairly standard terminology with respect to (3).

Definition 3.1. (*Linear transformation*). *A transformation f of the plane into itself is called* **a linear transformation** *if there exist fixed numbers* $a_{11}, a_{12}, a_{21},$ *and* a_{22} *such that if* $P = (x_1, x_2)$ *and* $f(P) = (y_1, y_2)$, *then*

$$y_1 = a_{11}x_1 + a_{12}x_2,$$
$$y_2 = a_{21}x_1 + a_{22}x_2. \tag{4}$$

In other words, a linear transformation has the form (3), in which b_1 and b_2 are both zero. Thus

$$f((x_1, x_2)) = (3x_1 + 2x_2, 5x_1 + 8x_2)$$

is a linear transformation, whereas

$$g((x_1, x_2)) = (3x_1 + 2x_2, 5x_1 + 8x_2 + 7)$$

is not a linear transformation. A transformation which is given by (3) will be called an *affine transformation.* Thus every linear transformation is an affine transformation but not conversely.

Let us consider next some special cases of affine transformations. We saw in the preceding section that a vector v is a function of the form (3), i.e., v is a function on the plane in which $v(P) = Q$, where if $P = (x_1, x_2)$, then $Q = (x_1 + h, x_2 + k)$ for some fixed numbers h and k. Thus a vector is an affine transformation of the plane in which $a_{11} = 1$, $a_{12} = 0$, $b_1 = h$, $a_{21} = 0$, $a_{22} = 1$, $b_2 = k$. As an example of a linear mapping of the plane into itself, consider the function that associates with each point P the point Q obtained by rotating P counterclockwise about the origin through a fixed angle θ (Fig. 7). Let us show that such a function is indeed linear.

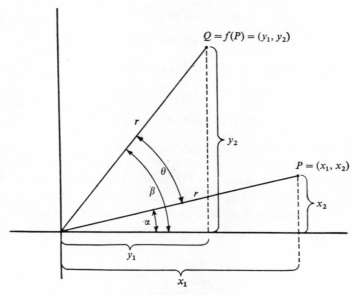

Figure 7

To do this let r denote the distance of the point P from the origin. Since we are rotating P about the origin, the point $Q = f(P)$ is also at a distance r from the origin. We see from Fig. 7 that $x_1 = r \cos \alpha$, $x_2 = r \sin \alpha$, $y_1 = r \cos \beta$, and $y_2 = r \sin \beta$. Now $\beta = \alpha + \theta$ and hence, using the elementary formulas for the sine and cosine of the sum of two angles, we have

$$\cos \beta = \cos \alpha \cos \theta - \sin \alpha \sin \theta,$$
$$\sin \beta = \sin \alpha \cos \theta + \cos \alpha \sin \theta.$$

It follows that

$$\begin{aligned}
y_1 &= r \cos \beta \\
&= r(\cos \alpha \cos \theta - \sin \alpha \sin \theta) \\
&= \cos \theta (r \cos \alpha) - \sin \theta (r \sin \alpha) \\
&= (\cos \theta) x_1 - (\sin \theta) x_2 .
\end{aligned} \tag{5}$$

Similarly,

$$y_2 = r \sin \beta$$
$$= r(\sin \alpha \cos \theta + \cos \alpha \sin \theta)$$
$$= \sin \theta(r \cos \alpha) + \cos \theta(r \sin \alpha) \tag{6}$$
$$= (\sin \theta)x_1 + (\cos \theta)x_2.$$

If we combine (5) and (6) we have the formulas

$$y_1 = (\cos \theta)x_1 - (\sin \theta)x_2,$$
$$y_2 = (\sin \theta)x_1 + (\cos \theta)x_2, \tag{7}$$

and this has precisely the form (4), in which $a_{11} = \cos \theta$, $a_{12} = -\sin \theta$, $a_{21} = \sin \theta$, and $a_{22} = \cos \theta$. In other words, given the angle θ, we can obtain the explicit representation (7) for the linear transformation which describes a counterclockwise rotation θ around the origin.

Suppose we consider a rotation in a counterclockwise direction around the origin through 45°. As we know, $\cos 45° = \sin 45° = \sqrt{2}/2$ and thus the formulas (7) become

$$y_1 = \frac{\sqrt{2}}{2} x_1 - \frac{\sqrt{2}}{2} x_2,$$
$$\tag{8}$$
$$y_2 = \frac{\sqrt{2}}{2} x_1 + \frac{\sqrt{2}}{2} x_2.$$

In other words, if we denote by T the function that maps the point $P = (x_1, x_2)$ into the point $Q = (y_1, y_2)$, where y_1 and y_2 are given by (8), then T constitutes a counterclockwise rotation through 45°.

Next suppose we are given a curve in the plane by some equation, say

$$g(x_1, x_2) = 0. \tag{9}$$

For example, if $g(x_1, x_2) = x_1^2 + x_2^2 - 1$, then (9) denotes the unit circle, or if $g(x_1, x_2) = x_2 - x_1^2$, then (9) represents a parabola. We can rewrite (9) as

$$g(P) = 0, \tag{10}$$

where

$$P = (x_1, x_2).$$

The type of problem we want to solve is the following: on what curve do the points $Q = T(P)$ lie when P lies on the curve given by (10)? Let us solve this problem for the straight line given by the choice $g(x_1, x_2) = ax_1 + bx_2 + c$, and the rotation T through 45° given by equations (8). Let $Q = (y_1, y_2)$, where y_1 and y_2 are given by equations (8). If we solve (8) for x_1 and x_2 we obtain

$$x_1 = \frac{y_1 + y_2}{\sqrt{2}},$$

$$x_2 = \frac{y_2 - y_1}{\sqrt{2}}. \tag{11}$$

Therefore $Q = (y_1, y_2)$ is of the form $T(P)$, where $P = (x_1, x_2)$, if and only if the relations (11) hold. Thus if $g(P) = 0$, i.e., $ax_1 + bx_2 + c = 0$, then substituting the relations (11) we have

$$a\left(\frac{y_1 + y_2}{\sqrt{2}}\right) + b\left(\frac{y_2 - y_1}{\sqrt{2}}\right) + c = 0$$

or

$$\left(\frac{a}{\sqrt{2}} - \frac{b}{\sqrt{2}}\right)y_1 + \left(\frac{a}{\sqrt{2}} + \frac{b}{\sqrt{2}}\right)y_2 + c = 0. \tag{12}$$

The totality of points Q satisfying (12) clearly constitutes a straight line. Thus we see that a rotation through 45° will map a straight line into a straight line. Of course, one expects this to happen from simple geometric considerations.

The idea in the preceding example is very useful as a tool for recognizing curves given by algebraic relations between their coordinates. We know from geometry that a rotation about the origin is not going to change the shape of a curve but merely its position with respect to the axis system. In other words, the curve will be of the same "type" before rotation as after. Let us use this idea to discover the nature of the curve whose coordinates satisfy

$$g(x_1, x_2) = x_1^2 + x_2^2 - x_1 x_2 - 1 = 0. \tag{13}$$

We try to determine the angle θ so that counterclockwise rotation through θ will permit us to recognize the shape of the curve given by (13). Returning to (7), if we multiply the first equation on both sides by $\cos \theta$ and the second equation by $\sin \theta$ and add, we obtain

$$x_1 = (\cos \theta)y_1 + (\sin \theta)y_2. \tag{14}$$

If we multiply the first equation of (7) by $\sin \theta$, the second equation by $\cos \theta$, and subtract, we get

$$x_2 = (-\sin \theta)y_1 + (\cos \theta)y_2. \tag{15}$$

In other words, $Q = (y_1, y_2)$ is of the form $T(P)$ for $P = (x_1, x_2)$ if and only if (14) and (15) hold. Now in (13), if we make the substitution indicated by (14) and (15), we get

$$(y_1 \cos \theta + y_2 \sin \theta)^2 + (-y_1 \sin \theta + y_2 \cos \theta)^2$$
$$- (y_1 \cos \theta + y_2 \sin \theta)(-y_1 \sin \theta + y_2 \cos \theta) - 1 = 0. \tag{16}$$

Simplifying (16) we have

$$y_1^2 + y_2^2 + y_1^2 \sin \theta \cos \theta - y_2^2 \sin \theta \cos \theta$$
$$+ (\sin^2 \theta - \cos^2 \theta)y_1 y_2 - 1 = 0. \tag{17}$$

We choose θ so that the coefficient of $y_1 y_2$ is 0 in (17). It is easy to see that this is the case if $\theta = 45°$. Then (17) becomes

$$y_1^2 + y_2^2 + \tfrac{1}{2}y_1^2 - \tfrac{1}{2}y_2^2 - 1 = 0$$

or

$$3y_1^2 + y_2^2 - 2 = 0. \tag{18}$$

We know from elementary analytic geometry that the curve (18) is an ellipse. Thus the original curve (13) is also an ellipse.

Quiz

Answer *true* or *false*:

1. The function $f(x) = x^2$ is an affine transformation of the real line into itself.
2. The function $f(x) = x$ is a linear transformation of the real line into itself.
3. The function T mapping the plane into itself and given by $T((x_1, x_2)) = (3x_1 + x_2, x_1 + x_2)$ is a linear transformation.

4. The function which sends each point P in the plane into its mirror image across the horizontal axis is a linear transformation:

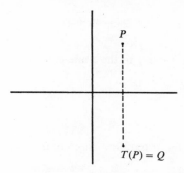

5. The function which sends each point P into its reflection through the origin is a linear transformation:

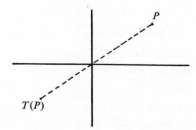

6. Every vector is a linear transformation of the plane.

7. Every vector is an affine transformation of the plane.

8. No vector is a linear transformation of the plane.

9. Any linear transformation of the plane must send the origin $(0,0)$ into the origin.

10. The function which maps every point in the plane into its projection on the horizontal axis is a linear transformation.

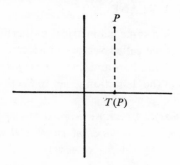

Exercises

1. If T is the linear transformation given by $T(P) = Q$, $P = (x_1, x_2)$ and $Q = (y_1, y_2)$, where

$$y_1 = x_1 + x_2,$$
$$y_2 = x_1 - x_2,$$

find the image of the curve in the plane consisting of those points (x_1, x_2) satisfying

(a) $x_1 + x_2 - 1 = 0$;
(b) $x_1^2 = 0$;
(c) $x_1^2 - x_2^2 = 0$;
(d) $x_1 - x_2^2 = 0$.

2. Let S and T be two linear transformations of the plane given by

$$T: \quad \begin{aligned} y_1 &= a_{11}x_1 + a_{12}x_2, \\ y_2 &= a_{21}x_1 + a_{22}x_2, \end{aligned}$$

$$S: \quad \begin{aligned} y_1 &= b_{11}x_1 + b_{12}x_2, \\ y_2 &= b_{21}x_1 + b_{22}x_2. \end{aligned}$$

Then show that the composite function TS is a linear transformation of the plane given by

$$TS: \quad \begin{aligned} y_1 &= (a_{11}b_{11} + a_{12}b_{21})x_1 + (a_{11}b_{12} + a_{12}b_{22})x_2, \\ y_2 &= (a_{21}b_{11} + a_{22}b_{21})x_1 + (a_{21}b_{12} + a_{22}b_{22})x_2. \end{aligned}$$

3. Using the result of Exercise 2, show that the composite, or product, of two counterclockwise rotations T and S about the origin through angles θ and ϕ, respectively, is a counterclockwise rotation about the origin through an angle $\theta + \phi$.

4. Using the distance formula for the points in the plane, show from formulas (7) that if P and P' are two points and $T(P) = Q$, $T(P') = Q'$ are their images under the rotation given by (7), then the distance between Q and Q' is the same as the distance between P and P'.

1.4.   VECTORS IN A PLANE

In this section we develop some geometrical properties of the special functions on the plane that we called vectors in Section 1.3. In what follows, R denotes the set of real numbers and the plane is just the cartesian product $R \times R$. We recapitulate the definition given in Section 1.3.

Definition 4.1.   (***Vectors***). *A **vector** v denoted by $v = [a_1, a_2]$, where a_1 and a_2 are two real numbers, is a function on $R \times R$ that maps each point $P = (x_1, x_2)$ into the point $(x_1 + a_1, x_2 + a_2)$.*

We denote the value of v at $P = (x_1, x_2)$ by v_P, or $v_{(x_1, x_2)}$, or $[a_1, a_2]_P$, or $[a_1, a_2]_{(x_1, x_2)}$. Thus we write

$$v_P = [a_1, a_2]_{(x_1, x_2)} = (x_1 + a_1, x_2 + a_2). \tag{1}$$

If $u = [a_1, a_2]$ is a vector, then the numbers a_1 and a_2 are called the *first coordinate* and the *second coordinate* of u, respectively. Now suppose that $v = [b_1, b_2]$ is another vector and that $u = v$. Recall that two functions u and v are equal if and only if $u_P = v_P$ for each $P = (x_1, x_2)$ in $R \times R$. Thus $u = v$ implies that

$$(x_1 + a_1, x_2 + a_2) = (x_1 + b_1, x_2 + b_2),$$

and therefore that $a_1 = b_1$ and $a_2 = b_2$. In other words, two vectors are equal if and only if their coordinates are equal.

Example 4.1. Let $v = [-4, 3]$. If P is the point $(4, 1)$ and Q is $(3, -1)$, then v_P is the point $(0, 4)$ and v_Q is the point $(-1, 2)$, i.e., $v_P = (0, 4)$ and $v_Q = (-1, 2)$ (Fig. 8). Clearly the lines joining P and v_P and Q and v_Q,

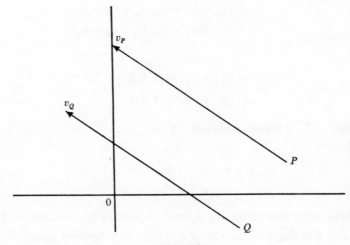

Figure 8

denoted respectively by Pv_P and Qv_Q, are parallel and each of length 5.

In general, if $v = [a_1, a_2]$ and P, Q are any points, then the segments Pv_P and Qv_Q are parallel and of the same length, $\sqrt{a_1^2 + a_2^2}$. One can say that a vector translates each point through the same distance and in the same direction. If we know the image of any single point under v we can determine v. In fact, if $v_{(x_1, x_2)} = (y_1, y_2)$, then $v = [y_1 - x_1, y_2 - x_2]$. This remarkable fact shows how "well-behaved" vector functions are and allows us to give a simple graphical representation of vectors. We represent a vector v by an arrow joining any point P in the plane to its value $v_P = Q$. We can denote v without ambiguity by $\overrightarrow{PQ}$. Thus $v = \overrightarrow{PQ}$ means that $v_P = Q$, and this, as we have seen, completely determines v. The fact that a vector in a plane is completely determined by a direction and by a length of an arrow leads to a multitude of applications in physics, where vectors are used to represent forces, moments, velocities, accelerations, etc. We shall not pursue these important, but specialized, applications of vectors.

Let $u = [a_1, a_2]$ and $v = [b_1, b_2]$ be vectors. Consider the composite function of u and v. It is customary to denote the composite function of u and v by $u + v$ instead of uv and call it the *sum of vectors* u and v. Thus if u and v are defined as above and $w = u + v$, then, for any point (x_1, x_2),

$$
\begin{aligned}
w_{(x_1, x_2)} &= (u + v)_{(x_1, x_2)} \\
&= u_{(x_1 + b_1, \, x_2 + b_2)} \\
&= (x_1 + b_1 + a_1, x_2 + b_2 + a_2) \\
&= (x_1 + a_1 + b_1, x_2 + a_2 + b_2).
\end{aligned}
$$

Hence

$$
\begin{aligned}
w &= [a_1 + b_1, a_2 + b_2] \\
&= [b_1 + a_1, b_2 + a_2].
\end{aligned}
$$

Definition 4.2. (Vector addition). *If* $u = [a_1, a_2]$ *and* $v = [b_1, b_2]$ *are vectors, then*

$$
\begin{aligned}
u + v &= [a_1 + b_1, a_2 + b_2] \\
&= v + u.
\end{aligned}
$$

If we again represent vectors by arrows originating at O we obtain Fig. 9. The vector u is $\overrightarrow{Ou_0}$ and the vector v is $\overrightarrow{Ov_0}$. It is obvious from the figure that $u + v$ is represented by the diagonal $\overrightarrow{OS}$ of the parallelogram Ou_0Sv_0. Note that S is the value $(u + v)_0$, since

$$
\begin{aligned}
(u + v)_0 &= u_{v_0} \\
&= u_Q \\
&= S.
\end{aligned}
$$

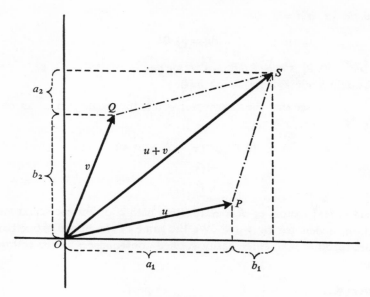

Figure 9

Example 4.2.

(a) Let $u = [a_1, a_2]$; then

$$u + u = [a_1 + a_1, a_2 + a_2]$$
$$= [2a_1, 2a_2].$$

We denote $u + u$ by $2u$.

(b) Let $2v = [c_1, c_2]$. Find v. Set $v = [b_1, b_2]$. We then have

$$2b_1 = c_1 \qquad \text{and} \qquad 2b_2 = c_2$$

or

$$v = [\tfrac{1}{2}c_1, \tfrac{1}{2}c_2].$$

These examples suggest the following definition.

Definition 4.3. (*Scalar multiplication*). *If d is a real number and* $u = [a_1, a_2]$ *is a vector, then the* **scalar product** *of d and u, written du, is the vector defined by*

$$du = [da_1, da_2].$$

In particular, if d = 0, then

$$0u = [0, 0].$$

*The vector [0, 0] is called the **zero vector** and is denoted by 0_2 or, where no confusion is likely to arise, simply by 0.*

It is easy to see that the zero vector is just the identity function on the plane. If $P = (x_1, x_2)$, then

$$[0, 0]_P = (x_1 + 0, x_2 + 0)$$
$$= (x_1, x_2)$$
$$= P.$$

The set of real vectors on $R \times R$, together with addition and scalar multiplication, is denoted by $V_2(R)$. We list some of the above properties of vectors together with some easily verified consequences in the following theorem.

Theorem 4.1.
  (a) *The sum of two vectors is a vector.*
  (b) *If u, v, and w are vectors, then*

$$u + v = v + u \ (commutativity),$$
$$(u + v) + w = u + (v + w) \ (associativity).$$

  (c) *There exists a vector, the zero vector $0 = [0, 0]$, satisfying*

$$u + 0 = u$$

  for any vector u.
  (d) *For any given vector u there exists a unique vector v such that*

$$u + v = 0.$$

  The vector v is denoted by $-u$.
  (e) *If d is a real number and u is a vector, then du is a vector.*
  (f) $0u = 0_2$.
  (g) $1u = u$.
  (h) $(-1)u = -u$.
  (i) *If c and d are real numbers and u and v are vectors, then*

$$(c + d)u = cu + du,$$
$$c(u + v) = cu + cv,$$
$$(cd)u = c(du).$$

All these statements follow immediately from the definitions. For example, it is easy to see that if $u = [a_1, a_2]$ is any vector, then $-u = [-a_1, -a_2]$.

Example 4.3. We use vector addition and scalar multiplication to obtain the following remarkable representation of vectors in the plane. Let $i = [1, 0]$ and $j = [0, 1]$, and let $u = [a_1, a_2]$ be any vector. Then

$$u = a_1 i + a_2 j. \tag{2}$$

That is, any vector can be represented as a sum of scalar multiples of the vectors i and j. Moreover, this representation is unique, since if $u = a_1 i + a_2 j$ and $u = b_1 i + b_2 j$, then

$$[a_1, a_2] = [b_1, b_2],$$

and thus $a_1 = b_1$ and $a_2 = b_2$. There is no reason, of course, to suppose that the vectors i and j are in any way special. In fact, the above example is a special case of a more general situation.

Definition 4.4. (*Linear combinations*).

(a) *If u and v are nonzero vectors and $u = tv$ for some real number t, then u and v are said to be **parallel**. We write $u \parallel v$ if u is parallel to v, and $u \nparallel v$ if u is not parallel to v.*

(b) *If u and v are any vectors and s and t any real numbers, then the vector $w = su + tv$ is called a **linear combination** of u and v.*

In the preceding example we showed that any vector can be expressed in a unique way as a linear combination of the vectors i and j.

Theorem 4.2. *Let u and v be nonzero vectors, $u \nparallel v$. Then any vector w can be expressed uniquely as a linear combination of u and v.*

Proof. Let $u = [a_1, a_2]$, $v = [b_1, b_2]$, and $w = [c_1, c_2]$. We have to find real numbers s and t such that

$$w = su + tv, \tag{3}$$

i.e., such that

$$
\begin{aligned}
[c_1, c_2] &= s[a_1, a_2] + t[b_1, b_2] \\
&= [sa_1, sa_2] + [tb_1, tb_2] \\
&= [sa_1 + tb_1, sa_2 + tb_2].
\end{aligned}
$$

In other words, we want to solve the equations

$$sa_1 + tb_1 = c_1,$$
$$sa_2 + tb_2 = c_2 \tag{4}$$

simultaneously for s and t. We know from elementary algebra that the system of equations (4) has a unique solution if and only if $a_1 b_2 - a_2 b_1 \neq 0$. In that case

$$s = \frac{c_1 b_2 - c_2 b_1}{a_1 b_2 - a_2 b_1}, \qquad t = \frac{a_1 c_2 - a_2 c_1}{a_1 b_2 - a_2 b_1}.$$

Suppose, on the contrary, that $a_1 b_2 - a_2 b_1 = 0$. Since $[b_1, b_2] \neq 0$, not both b_1 and b_2 can be zero. If $b_1 \neq 0$, then $(a_1/b_1)b_2 = a_2$ and $u = (a_1/b_1)v$, contradicting our hypothesis that $u \nparallel v$. A similar contradiction follows if $b_1 = 0$ but $b_2 \neq 0$.

We conclude this section with some applications of vectors to simple geometrical problems.

Example 4.4.
(a) Let $A = (a_1, a_2)$, $B = (b_1, b_2)$ be two points, $a_1 \neq b_1$, and suppose that $P = (x_1, x_2)$ is a point on the straight line through A and B. We express P as a value of a vector defined in terms of A and B. We know from similar triangles that

$$\frac{x_2 - a_2}{x_1 - a_1} = \frac{b_2 - a_2}{b_1 - a_1}, \tag{5}$$

or, for some number t,

$$x_1 = t(b_1 - a_1) + a_1,$$
$$x_2 = t(b_2 - a_2) + a_2. \tag{6}$$

We can express the equations (6) as a single vector equation. Let $w = [x_1, x_2]$, $v = [b_1, b_2]$, and $u = [a_1, a_2]$. Then (6) can be expressed in the form

$$w = t(v - u) + u. \tag{7}$$

Note that $P = w_0$, and therefore

$$P = w_0 = (t(v - u))_0 + u_0. \tag{8}$$

It is easy to verify that (8) also holds when $a_1 = b_1$. In particular, if $u = 0$, then

$$P = w_0 = (tv)_0. \tag{9}$$

   (b) Let $Q = (c_1, c_2)$ be a given point and let v be a given nonzero vector. We obtain a formula for any point P on the line through Q parallel to v as a value of a vector at the origin (Fig. 10). If we set $r = [c_1, c_2]$, then $r_0 = Q$ and we have for some number t,

$$\begin{aligned} P &= (tv)_Q \\ &= (tv)(r_0) \\ &= (tv + r)_0 \\ &= (r + tv)_0. \end{aligned}$$

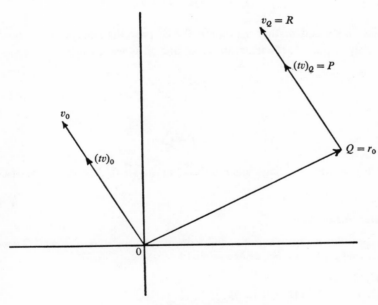

Figure 10

In other words,

$$\overrightarrow{OP} = \overrightarrow{OQ} + t\overrightarrow{QR}.$$

(c) Let $A = (a_1, a_2)$ and $B = (b_1, b_2)$ be points not collinear with O. Consider the parallelogram $OACB$. We show by use of vectors that the diagonals intersect at the midpoint of OC. Set $u = [a_1, a_2]$ and $v = [b_1, b_2]$. Then $A = u_0$, $B = v_0$, and $C = (u + v)_0$. Thus any point on the diagonal OC is the value of $s(u + v)$ at O for some s, and any point on the diagonal AB is the value of $u + t(v - u)$ at O, for a suitable number t. The two diagonals intersect at a point for which

$$(s(u + v))_0 = (u + t(v - u))_0 .$$

Now, two vectors agree at O if and only if the two vectors are the same. Hence

$$su + sv = u + tv - tu$$

or

$$(1 - s - t)u = (s - t)v.$$

Since $u \nparallel v$ and neither u nor v is 0, the preceding equality can hold if and only if both coefficients are zero, and thus we must have

$$1 - s - t = s - t = 0;$$

i.e.,

$$s = t = \tfrac{1}{2}.$$

In other words, the diagonals intersect at $(\tfrac{1}{2}(u + v))_0$, the midpoint of OC.

Quiz
Answer *true* or *false*:

In the following questions u, v, and w denote vectors, A, B, C, P, and Q denote points, and a_1, a_2, b_1, b_2, denote numbers.

1. $[2, 5] = [5, 2]$.
2. $[2, 5] + [1, 3] = [1, 3] + [2, 5]$.
3. If $u_P = v_P$ for one point P, then $u = v$.

4. If $v_{(y_1, y_2)} = (x_1, x_2)$, then $v = [y_1 - x_1, y_2 - x_2]$.

5. $u_{v_P} = v_{u_P}$ for any vectors u and v and any point P.

6. If $u_P = u_Q$, then $P = Q$.

7. $\overrightarrow{AB} + \overrightarrow{BC} + \overrightarrow{CA} = 0$.

8. If $i = [1, 0]$ and $j = [0, 1]$, then

$$(a_1 i + a_2 j) + (b_1 i + b_2 j) = (a_1 + b_1)i + (a_2 + b_2)j.$$

9. If $u \parallel v$ and $v \parallel w$, then $u \parallel w$.

10. If $u \nparallel v$ and $v \nparallel w$, then $u \nparallel w$.

Exercises

1. Show that $\overrightarrow{AB} + \overrightarrow{BC} = \overrightarrow{AC}$, $\overrightarrow{PQ} - \overrightarrow{PR} = \overrightarrow{RQ}$, and $-\overrightarrow{PQ} = \overrightarrow{QP}$.

2. Let u and v be vectors, t be a real number, and $A = u_P$, $B = v_A$, and $C = (u + tv)_P$. Show geometrically that the ratio of the length of AC to the length of AB is $|t|$.

3. Use the method of Example 4.4(c) to prove that medians of a triangle trisect each other.

4. Let $u = [3, 5]$, $v = [2, 1]$, and $w = [-2, 3]$. Find numbers s and t such that $w = su + tv$.

5. Show that $\overrightarrow{AB} = \overrightarrow{PQ}$ if and only if AB and PQ have the same length and either AB and PQ are collinear or parallel.

1.5. INNER PRODUCT OF VECTORS IN A PLANE

We saw in Section 1.4 that a vector v in the plane is completely determined by "its geometric representation," i.e., the line segment joining any point P to its image v_P. The line segment in turn can be completely specified by its length and, in case $v \neq 0$, by its direction. By direction we mean the angle Pv_P makes with any fixed direction, e.g., with the positive direction of the horizontal axis. Thus let $v = [a_1, a_2]$ be a vector different from 0. Let $A = v_0$ and let N be the foot of the perpendicular through A to the horizontal axis; i.e., N is the point $[0, -a_2]_A$ or, equivalently, the point $[a_1, 0]_0$ (Fig. 11). Then if θ is the angle NOA defined to be between $-\pi$ and π radians, (i.e., between $-180°$ and $180°$), we have

$$\cos \theta = \frac{ON}{OA},$$

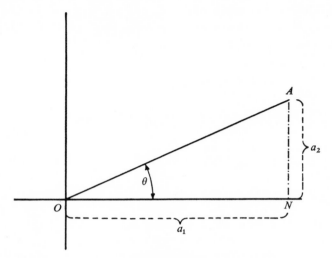

Figure 11

and therefore

$$\cos \theta = \frac{a_1}{\sqrt{a_1^2 + a_2^2}}.$$ (1)

We say that θ is the *angle* between v and the positive direction of the horizontal axis, or the angle between v and the vector $i = [1, 0]$. Similarly, the *length* of v is defined as the length of any of its geometric representations, i.e., as the distance through which v translates any point in the plane. The length of v is denoted by $\|v\|$. Hence if $v = [a_1, a_2]$ as before, then $\|v\|$ is the distance from O to $v_0 = A$:

$$\|v\| = \sqrt{a_1^2 + a_2^2}.$$ (2)

Of course, $\|v\| = 0$ if and only if $v = [0, 0]$. Also, combining (1) and (2) we have

$$\cos \theta = \frac{a_1}{\|v\|}.$$ (3)

Example 5.1.
   (a) Let $v = [-1, \sqrt{3}]$. Then

$$\|v\| = \sqrt{(-1)^2 + \sqrt{3}^2} = 2,$$
$$\cos \theta = -\tfrac{1}{2},$$

and therefore

$$\theta = \frac{2\pi}{3} \text{ radians}$$

$$= 120°.$$

(b) Let the function $f: V_2(R) \rightarrow V_2(R)$ be defined by

$$f([a_1, a_2]) = [a_1 \cos \alpha - a_2 \sin \alpha, \quad a_1 \sin \alpha + a_2 \cos \alpha] .$$

Let $v = [a_1, a_2]$. Then we compute

$$\|f(v)\| = ((a_1 \cos \alpha - a_2 \sin \alpha)^2 + (a_1 \sin \alpha + a_2 \cos \alpha)^2)^{1/2}$$

$$= (a_1^2 \cos^2 \alpha + a_2^2 \sin^2 \alpha + a_1^2 \sin^2 \alpha + a_2^2 \cos^2 \alpha)^{1/2}$$

$$= (a_1^2 + a_2^2)^{1/2}$$

$$= \|v\| .$$

Also, if $v \neq [0, 0]$, then the cosine of the angle between $f(v)$ and the vector i can be computed using (3). Thus if θ is the angle between v and i, we have

$$\frac{a_1 \cos \alpha - a_2 \sin \alpha}{\|f(v)\|} = \frac{a_1 \cos \alpha - a_2 \sin \alpha}{\|v\|}$$

$$= \frac{a_1}{\|v\|} \cos \alpha - \frac{a_2}{\|v\|} \sin \alpha$$

$$= \cos \theta \cos \alpha - \sin \theta \sin \alpha$$

$$= \cos(\theta + \alpha).$$

Hence the effect of the function f is to rotate every vector in the plane through the angle α, thereby leaving its length unchanged.

In many cases, it is important to evaluate the angle between two vectors as we did in Example 5.1(b). Let $u = [a_1, a_2]$ and $v = [b_1, b_2]$ be two non-zero vectors and let θ be the angle between them. That is, θ is the angle $u_0 O v_0$ (assumed to be between 0 and π radians, i.e., between 0° and 180°).

Let α and β be the angles between u and i and between v and i, respectively. Then

$$\cos\theta = \cos(\alpha - \beta)$$

$$= \cos\alpha\cos\beta + \sin\alpha\sin\beta$$

$$= \frac{a_1 b_1 + a_2 b_2}{\sqrt{a_1^2 + a_2^2}\,\sqrt{b_1^2 + b_2^2}},$$

i.e.,

$$\cos\theta = \frac{a_1 b_1 + a_2 b_2}{\|u\|\,\|v\|}. \tag{4}$$

The numerator of the fraction on the right side of (4) is a function of great interest in the theory of vectors. We enshrine it in the following definition.

Definition 5.1. **(Inner product).** *The (standard) **inner product** in $V_2(R)$ is the function f which assigns to each pair of vectors $u = [a_1, a_2]$ and $v = [b_1, b_2]$ the number $f(u, v)$ according to the formula*

$$f(u, v) = a_1 b_1 + a_2 b_2.$$

*It is customary to write (u, v) instead of $f(u, v)$ for the inner product of u and v. The **length** of v is the nonnegative number $(v, v)^{1/2}$. This definition is equivalent to (2); the length of v is denoted, as before, by $\|v\|$. If $\|v\| = 1$, then v is called a **unit vector**.*

Note that the inner product does not define "multiplication" of vectors in an ordinary sense, namely, the inner product of two vectors is not a vector but a real number (numbers are sometimes called "scalars"; in fact, the inner product is sometimes called the "scalar product").

Example 5.2. Let $u = [3, -2]$ and $v = [1, 2]$. Then

$$(u, v) = 3 \times 1 + (-2) \times 2 = -1,$$

$$\|u\| = \sqrt{3^2 + (-2)^2} = \sqrt{13},$$

$$\|v\| = \sqrt{1^2 + 2^2} = \sqrt{5};$$

from (4) the cosine of the angle between u and v is

$$\frac{-1}{\sqrt{65}}.$$

Definition 5.2. (**Orthogonality**). *Two vectors u and v are said to be **orthogonal** if $(u, v) = 0$. This means that nonzero vectors are orthogonal if and only if the angle between them is a right angle.*

For example, the vectors $[2, 1]$ and $[3, -6]$ are orthogonal. Also, the zero vector is orthogonal to any vector in $V_2(R)$.

We now state some properties involving the inner product that are fairly obvious geometrically. Nevertheless, these properties are very important. Moreover, their counterparts for more general types of vectors which we shall introduce in Section 6 do not always have an immediate geometric interpretation.

Theorem 5.1. *Let u, v and w be vectors in $V_2(R)$ and let α and β be real numbers. Then*

　(a) $(u, v) = (v, u)$;
　(b) $(\alpha u, v) = \alpha(u, v)$;
　(c) $(u + v, w) = (u, w) + (v, w)$;
　(d) $\|u\| > 0$, *unless* $u = 0$, *in which case* $\|u\| = 0$;
　(e) $\|\alpha u\| = |\alpha| \, \|u\|$ *(where $|\alpha|$ denotes the absolute value of α)*;
　(f) *("Cauchy inequality")*

$$|(u, v)| \le \|u\| \, \|v\|; \tag{5}$$

　　equality can occur in (5) if and only if one of the vectors is a scalar multiple of the other (i.e., either $u = \alpha v$ or $v = \alpha u$ for some real number α);
　(g) *("Triangle inequality")*

$$\|u + v\| \le \|u\| + \|v\|; \tag{6}$$

　　equality can occur in (6) if and only if one of the vectors is a nonnegative scalar multiple of the other (i.e., either $u = \alpha v$ or $v = \alpha u$ for some nonnegative real number α).

Proof. We leave the verifications of **(a)**, **(b)**, **(c)**, **(d)**, and **(e)** as exercises for the reader. To prove the last two inequalities set $u = [a_1, a_2]$ and $v = [b_1, b_2]$. Then (5) is equivalent to

$$(a_1 b_1 + a_2 b_2)^2 \leq (a_1^2 + a_2^2)(b_1^2 + b_2^2); \tag{7}$$

i.e.,

$$(a_1^2 + a_2^2)(b_1^2 + b_2^2) - (a_1 b_1 + a_2 b_2)^2 \geq 0. \tag{8}$$

Now, the left side of (8) simplifies to

$$a_1^2 b_2^2 + a_2^2 b_1^2 - 2a_1 a_2 b_1 b_2 = (a_1 b_2 - a_2 b_1)^2, \tag{9}$$

which, of course, is always positive except when $a_1 b_2 - a_2 b_1 = 0$. Hence the inequality (8) holds and therefore (5) holds. Now, if (5) is equality it follows that (8) is equality and

$$a_1 b_2 = a_2 b_1. \tag{10}$$

If $b_2 \neq 0$, we set $\alpha = a_2/b_2$. Then (10) gives $a_1 = \alpha b_1$ and we have $[a_1, a_2] = \alpha[b_1, b_2]$, i.e., $u = \alpha v$. If $b_1 \neq 0$, we set $\beta = a_1/b_1$ and obtain $u = \beta v$. If b_1 and b_2 are both 0, then $v = 0$ and $v = 0u$. Conversely, if $u = \alpha v$, then from (b) and (e) we compute

$$|(u, v)| = |(\alpha v, v)|$$
$$= |\alpha(v, v)|$$
$$= |\alpha| \, \|v\|^2,$$

while

$$\|u\| \, \|v\| = \|\alpha v\| \, \|v\|$$
$$= |\alpha| \, \|v\|^2.$$

Thus (5) is equality. The same conclusion follows if $v = \alpha u$.

We now prove inequality (6). We have

$$\|u + v\|^2 = (u + v, u + v)$$
$$= (u, u + v) + (v, u + v)$$
$$= (u, u) + (u, v) + (v, u) + (v, v).$$

The last two equalities follow by (c). Thus by (a) and (5),

$$\|u + v\|^2 = \|u\|^2 + 2(u, v) + \|v\|^2$$
$$\leq \|u\|^2 + 2\|u\| \|v\| + \|v\|^2 \tag{11}$$
$$= (\|u\| + \|v\|)^2,$$

which is (6). Now suppose that (11) is an equality. Then $(u, v) = \|u\| \|v\|$, which, by (5), can hold only if $(u, v) \geq 0$ and either $u = \alpha v$ or $v = \alpha u$ for some real number α. But if $u = \alpha v$, then

$$(u, v) = (\alpha v, v)$$
$$= \alpha \|v\|^2;$$

if $v = \alpha u$, then

$$(u, v) = (u, \alpha u)$$
$$= \alpha \|u\|^2.$$

In either case $(u, v) \geq 0$ only if $\alpha \geq 0$. Thus for equality we must have either $u = \alpha v$ or $v = \alpha u$, in which $\alpha \geq 0$. Conversely, if $u = \alpha v$ and $\alpha \geq 0$, then

$$\|u + v\| = \|\alpha v + v\|$$
$$= |1 + \alpha| \|v\|$$
$$= (1 + \alpha)\|v\|,$$

since $\alpha \geq 0$. Thus (6) is an equality. If $v = \alpha u$, the conclusion follows in the same manner.

Inequalities (5) and (6) are quite obvious from a geometric point of view. The Cauchy inequality simply states that the absolute value of the cosine of an angle cannot exceed 1 [see (4)]. The triangle inequality expresses in the language of vector algebra that the length of a side of a triangle cannot exceed the sum of lengths of the other two sides. However, as we shall see in Section 1.6, both these inequalities apply also in the case of vectors that have no geometric representation in the plane or in three-dimensional space.

Example 5.3. **Prove that**

$$\|u - v\| \geq | \|u\| - \|v\| |. \tag{12}$$

Set $w = u - v$. Then, by (6),

$$\|u\| = \|w + v\|$$
$$\leq \|w\| + \|v\|$$
$$= \|u - v\| + \|v\|,$$

i.e.,

$$\|u - v\| \geq \|u\| - \|v\|.$$

Similarly, we can prove that

$$\|v - u\| \geq \|v\| - \|u\|.$$

But $\|u - v\| = \|v - u\|$, and therefore

$$\|u - v\| \geq max(\|u\| - \|v\|, \|v\| - \|u\|)$$
$$= | \|u\| - \|v\| |.$$

In Section 1.4 and the present section we defined vectors in a plane and related concepts and we developed some of their properties. It is clear that a similar theory can be developed for $V_3(R)$, the set of vectors in three-dimensional space, $R \times R \times R$. Thus a vector $v = [a_1, a_2, a_3]$ can be defined as the function from $R \times R \times R$ onto itself whose value at a point $P = (x_1, x_2, x_3)$ is $Q = (x_1 + a_1, x_2 + a_2, x_3 + a_3)$. As in the case of vectors in a plane, the vector v can be represented geometrically by the directed segment $\overrightarrow{PQ}$. However, we do not propose to develop here the theory of vectors in $V_3(R)$ from this geometric point of view as we did with vectors in a plane. We shall use a different approach in Section 1.6.

Quiz

Answer *true* or *false*:

(u, v, and w denote vectors; α, β, γ, and δ denote real numbers.)

1. If $(u, v) = 0$, then either $u = 0$ or $v = 0$.
2. $(u + v, u - v) = \|u\|^2 - \|v\|^2$.
3. $\|u + v + w\| \leq \|u\| + \|v\| + \|w\|$.

4. $\|u + v - w\| \le \|u\| + \|v\| - \|w\|$.

5. $(-u, -u) = -\|u\|^2$.

6. If $\|u\| = \|v\|$, then $u + v$ and $u - v$ are orthogonal.

7. If $\alpha u + \beta v = \gamma u + \delta v$ then $\alpha = \gamma$ and $\beta = \delta$.

8. $\|u + v\| \ge \|u - v\|$.

9. If $u = [2, 1]$ and $v = [1, -1]$, then $u + 2v$ and $5u - 7v$ are orthogonal.

10. If $(u, v) = (v, w) = (w, u) = 0$, then at least one of u, v, and w must be the zero vector.

Exercises

1. Let $u = [-2, 3]$. Find a vector v satisfying

$$(u, v) = \|v\| = 1.$$

2. Prove parts (a), (b), (c), (d), and (e) of Theorem 5.1.

3. Let u be a nonzero vector and let $v = (1/\|u\|)u$. Show that v is a unit vector.

4. Let $x = [2, 0]$, $y = [1, -1]$, $z = (1/\|x\|)x$, and $w = (1/\|y\|)y$. If $u = -2x + 2y$, find the real numbers α and β such that $u = \alpha z + \beta w$.

5. Let u and v be orthogonal unit vectors and let w be any vector. Show that

$$w = (w, u)u + (w, v)v.$$

6. Let x and y be orthogonal unit vectors. Let $u = c_1 x + c_2 y$ and $v = d_1 x + d_2 y$, where c_1, c_2, d_1, and d_2 are real numbers. Show that

$$(u, v) = c_1 d_1 + c_2 d_2.$$

1.6. VECTOR SPACES

Although we introduced vectors in a plane as functions on the plane and we defined their addition, scalar multiplication, inner product, etc., from this point of view, the algebraic structure of $V_2(R)$ does not really depend on these geometric concepts or on any imagery. That is to say, we can regard the elements of $V_2(R)$ as ordered pairs of numbers and define (as we have done!) their addition, scalar multiplication, inner product, etc., by means of their coordinates. There is not even a need to distinguish notationally between $[a_1, a_2]$ and (a_1, a_2). In fact, henceforth we shall use the latter notation, since it is generally adopted in the literature. The main advantage of the abstract approach to vectors in $V_2(R)$ is that it is easy to generalize these concepts not only to vectors in $V_3(R)$ but beyond. In the first place, instead of limiting ourselves to pairs or triples of numbers, we may consider *n*-tuples of numbers and define vector addition, etc., for them. Second, if we do not insist on a direct geometric interpretation, we may use number systems other than the real numbers. Actually, in defining a generalization of $V_2(R)$ we shall find it advantageous to use the complex numbers as our basic number system and to specialize to real numbers wherever it is of interest. We denote the set of complex numbers by C and the set of real numbers by R. In many instances elements of either C or R are called *scalars*. Complex *n*-tuples are just sequences of length *n* of complex numbers. Two complex *n*-tuples $(a_1, a_2, \ldots, a_n)$ and $(b_1, b_2, \ldots, b_n)$ are equal if their *coordinates* are equal, i.e., if $a_i = b_i$, $i = 1, \ldots, n$.

Definition 6.1. (*Vector space of n-tuples*). *The **vector space** $V_n(C)$ is the set of complex n-tuples with addition and scalar multiplication defined as follows. Let* $u = (a_1, a_2, \ldots, a_n)$, $v = (b_1, b_2, \ldots, b_n)$, *and let c be any complex number. Then we define*

$$u + v = (a_1 + b_1, a_2 + b_2, \ldots, a_n + b_n),$$

and

$$cu = (ca_1, ca_2, \ldots, ca_n).$$

For example, if $u = (3 + i, 2, 1 - i, -1 + 2i)$, $v = (1 + i, -2 + 3i, 4i, -1 - i)$, and $c = 2i$, then

$$u + v = (4 + 2i, 3i, 1 + 3i, -2 + i),$$

and

$$cv = (-2 + 2i, -6 - 4i, -8, 2 - 2i).$$

The space $V_n(R)$ is defined in precisely the same way, except that $a_1, \ldots, a_n, b_1, \ldots, b_n$, and c are taken to be real numbers. The real numbers in the case of $V_n(R)$, and the complex numbers in the case of $V_n(C)$, are called *scalars*; the *n*-tuples are called *vectors*.

The following properties of vectors in $V_n(C)$ are immediate consequences of the definition.

Theorem 6.1. *Let u, v, and w be any vectors in $V_n(C)$ and let c and d be any scalars. Let 0_n be the n-tuple all of whose coordinates are 0. For any vector u let $-u$ denote the vector $(-1)u$. Then*

  (i) $u + v \in V_n(C)$;
 (ii) $cu \in V_n(C)$;
 (iii) $(u + v) + w = u + (v + w)$;
 (iv) $u + v = v + u$;
  (v) $u + (-u) = 0_n$;
 (vi) $1u = u$;
(vii) $0u = 0_n$;
(viii) $(c + d)u = cu + du$;
 (ix) $c(u + v) = cu + cv$;
  (x) $(cd)u = c(du)$.

For simplicity we usually write 0 instead of 0_n. We also write $u - v$ instead of $u + (-v)$.

We shall state our definitions and theorems for $V_n(C)$. Analogous definitions and theorems are valid for $V_n(R)$.

Definition 6.2.   (Subspace). *A nonempty set X of vectors in $V_n(C)$ is said to form a **subspace** of $V_n(C)$ if, for any vectors u and v in X and any complex number c, the vectors $u + v$ and cu are also in X. We say that X is **closed** under addition and under scalar multiplication. If X and Y are subspaces of $V_n(C)$ and $Y \subset X$, then Y is said to be a subspace of X; if $Y \neq X$, then Y is said to be a **proper subspace** of X.*

Observe that the intersection of two subspaces of $V_n(C)$, U and V, is a subspace of $V_n(C)$ also. For, clearly $U \cap V$ is closed under addition and scalar multiplication (see Exercise 4).

Example 6.1.
  (a) Let

$$X = \{(a_1, a_2, a_3) \in V_3(C) \,|\, 2a_1 + 3a_2 - 4a_3 = 0\},$$

i.e., let X consist of all vectors in $V_3(C)$ whose coordinates a_1, a_2, a_3 satisfy equation $2a_1 + 3a_2 - 4a_3 = 0$. We prove that X forms a subspace of $V_3(C)$. We do it by showing that X is closed under addition and scalar multiplication. That is to say, we show that if $u = (a_1, a_2, a_3)$ and $v = (b_1, b_2, b_3)$ are any elements of the set X, i.e., any triples such that

$2a_1 + 3a_2 - 4a_3 = 0$ and $2b_1 + 3b_2 - 4b_3 = 0$, then their sum $u + v$ and any scalar multiple cu are also in X. Now

$$u + v = (a_1 + b_1, a_2 + b_2, a_3 + b_3),$$

$$cu = (ca_1, ca_2, ca_3).$$

The question is: do $u + v$ and cu belong to X? The criterion of membership in X is that twice the first coordinate plus three times the second coordinate minus four times the third coordinate is 0. We check that

$$2(a_1 + b_1) + 3(a_2 + b_2) - 4(a_3 + b_3) = (2a_1 + 3a_2 - 4a_3)$$
$$+ (2b_1 + 3b_2 - 4b_3)$$

$$= 0 + 0$$

$$= 0,$$

$$2(ca_1) + 3(ca_2) - 4(ca_3) = c(2a_1 + 3a_2 - 4a_3)$$

$$= c0$$

$$= 0.$$

Hence X is a subspace.

(b) Let

$$Y = \{(a_1, a_2, a_3) \in V_3(R) \mid 2a_1 + 3a_2 - 4a_3 = 5\}.$$

Then Y is not a subspace. For example, the vector $(1, 1, 0)$ belongs to Y but $2(1, 1, 0) = (2, 2, 0)$ does not. For

$$2 \times 2 + 3 \times 2 - 4 \times 0 = 10 \neq 5.$$

Thus Y is not closed under scalar multiplication.

It should be noted that in order to prove that a set X forms a subspace we have to show that the sum of *any* two vectors in X belongs to X and that *any* scalar multiple of *any* vector in X belongs to X. On the other hand, to prove that a set Y is not a subspace, all we have to do is to produce either two specific vectors in Y whose sum is not in Y or a particular vector in Y some scalar multiple of which does not belong to Y.

Definition 6.3. (**Linear combination**). *Let* $v_1, \ldots, v_k$ *be vectors in* $V_n(C)$ *and let* $c_1, \ldots, c_k$ *be scalars. The vector*

$$\sum_{j=1}^{k} c_j v_j = c_1 v_1 + c_2 v_2 + \cdots + c_k v_k$$

is called a **linear combination** *of* $v_1, \ldots, v_k$ *with* **coefficients** $c_1, \ldots, c_k$.

Theorem 6.2. *Let* $X = \{v_1, \ldots, v_k\}$ *be a set of vectors in* $V_n(C)$. *The set of all linear combinations of* $v_1, \ldots, v_k$ *forms a subspace of* $V_n(C)$. *[This subspace is denoted by* $\langle v_1, \ldots, v_k \rangle$ *or by* $\langle X \rangle$ *and it is said to be spanned (or generated) by* $v_1, \ldots, v_k$.]

Proof. Let $u_1 = \sum_{j=1}^{k} c_j v_j$ and $u_2 = \sum_{j=1}^{k} d_j v_j$ be elements of $\langle v_1, \ldots, v_k \rangle$ and let a be any scalar; then

$$u_1 + u_2 = \sum_{j=1}^{k} c_j v_j + \sum_{j=1}^{k} d_j v_j$$

$$= \sum_{j=1}^{k} (c_j + d_j) v_j \in \langle v_1, \ldots, v_k \rangle,$$

and

$$au_1 = a \sum_{j=1}^{k} c_j v_j$$

$$= \sum_{j=1}^{k} (ac_j) v_j \in \langle v_1, \ldots, v_k \rangle.$$

Thus $\langle v_1, \ldots, v_k \rangle$ is closed under both addition and scalar multiplication.

Example 6.2 Let $v_1 = (2, 1, 0)$, $v_2 = (-2, -1, 3)$, and $v_3 = (4, 2, 1)$. Then

$$c_1 v_1 + c_2 v_2 + c_3 v_3 = (2c_1 - 2c_2 + 4c_3, c_1 - c_2 + 2c_3, 3c_2 + c_3)$$

and it is easy to see that

$$\langle v_1, v_2, v_3 \rangle = \{(a_1, a_2, a_3) \in V_3(C) \,|\, a_1 = 2a_2\}.$$

Indeed, if (a_1, a_2, a_3) is any vector with $a_1 = 2a_2$, then

$$(a_1, a_2, a_3) = (a_2 + \tfrac{1}{3}a_3)v_1 + \tfrac{1}{3}a_3 v_2 + 0v_3. \tag{1}$$

Note that (1) proves not only that $(a_1, a_2, a_3) \in \langle v_1, v_2, v_3 \rangle$ but that actually $(a_1, a_2, a_3) \in \langle v_1, v_2 \rangle$. Since this is true for any vector in $\langle v_1, v_2, v_3 \rangle$, we have $\langle v_1, v_2, v_3 \rangle = \langle v_1, v_2 \rangle$. This shows that as far as spanning the subspace $\langle v_1, v_2, v_3 \rangle$ is concerned, the vector v_3 is superfluous. Clearly neither $\langle v_1, v_2 \rangle = \langle v_1 \rangle$ nor $\langle v_1, v_2 \rangle = \langle v_2 \rangle$, and thus $\{v_1, v_2\}$ is a minimal spanning set for $\langle v_1, v_2 \rangle$.

We are now going to develop these ideas in a general situation.

Definition 6.4. (Linear dependence). *The vectors* $v_1, \ldots, v_k$ *are said to be* **linearly dependent** *if there exist scalars* $c_1, \ldots, c_k$, *not all* 0, *such that*

$$\sum_{j=1}^{k} c_j v_j = 0. \tag{2}$$

Otherwise the vectors $v_1, \ldots, v_k$ *are* **linearly independent;** *that is,* $v_1, \ldots, v_k$ *are linearly independent if* $\sum_{j=1}^{k} c_j v_j = 0$ *implies* $c_1 = \cdots = c_k = 0$. *If* (2) *holds and not all* c_j *are* 0, *we say that* $v_1, \ldots, v_k$ *satisfy a* **nontrivial linear relation.**

To prove that a particular set of vectors $v_1, \ldots, v_k$ is linearly dependent, all we have to do is to find one set of numbers $c_1, \ldots, c_k$, not all zero, such that (2) holds. On the other hand, if we wish to show that vectors $v_1, \ldots, v_k$ are linearly independent, we must prove that no such set of scalars can exist, i.e., we must show that the assumption

$$\sum_{j=1}^{k} c_j v_j = 0$$

leads inevitably to the conclusion that $c_1 = \cdots = c_k = 0$.

Examples 6.3.

(a) Let $v_1 = (2, 1, 1)$, $v_2 = (-2, 1, 2)$, $v_3 = (8, 2, 1)$, and $v_4 = (4, 4, 5)$. Then v_1, v_2, v_3, and v_4 are linearly dependent, since $3v_1 + 3v_2 + v_3 - 2v_4 = 0$. The scalars 3, 3, 1, and -2 are in no way unique. For example, we also have $3v_1 - 5v_2 - 3v_3 + 2v_4 = 0$.

(b) Let $u_1 = (2, 1, 1)$, $u_2 = (-2, 1, 2)$, and $u_3 = (0, 0, 1)$. We show that u_1, u_2, and u_3 are linearly independent. Indeed, assume that

$$c_1 u_1 + c_2 u_2 + c_3 u_3 = 0,$$

i.e., that

$$2c_1 - 2c_2 = 0,$$

$$c_1 + c_2 = 0,$$

$$c_1 + 2c_2 + c_3 = 0.$$

The first two equations hold only if $c_1 = c_2 = 0$, and hence from the third equation, c_3 must be 0 as well. Thus u_1, u_2, and u_3 are linearly independent.

Theorem 6.3. *The vectors $v_1, \ldots, v_k$ are linearly dependent if and only if one of them is a linear combination of the others.*

Proof. Suppose that one of $v_1, \ldots, v_k$ is a linear combination of the others:

$$v_t = c_1 v_1 + \cdots + c_{t-1} v_{t-1} + c_{t+1} v_{t+1} + \cdots + c_k v_k.$$

Then

$$c_1 v_1 + \cdots + c_{t-1} v_{t-1} + (-1)v_t + c_{t+1} v_{t+1} + \cdots + c_k v_k = 0,$$

and, since the coefficient of v_t is certainly nonzero, the vectors $v_1, \ldots, v_k$ are linearly dependent. Conversely, suppose that $v_1, \ldots, v_k$ are linearly dependent, i.e., that there exist scalars $c_1, \ldots, c_k$, not all zero, such that $\sum_{i=1}^{k} c_i v_i = 0$. Suppose that $c_r \neq 0$. Then

$$v_r = -\frac{c_1}{c_r} v_1 - \cdots - \frac{c_{r-1}}{c_r} v_{r-1} - \frac{c_{r+1}}{c_r} v_{r+1} - \cdots - \frac{c_k}{c_r} v_k.$$

For example, if $3v_1 + 3v_2 + v_3 - 2v_4 = 0$ [see Example 6.3(a)], then

$$v_1 = -v_2 - \tfrac{1}{3} v_3 + \tfrac{2}{3} v_4.$$

Suppose now that $v = \sum_{j=1}^{k} c_j v_j$ and that the vectors $v_1, \ldots, v_k$ belong to a subspace $\langle u_1, \ldots, u_m \rangle$, i.e.,

$$v_j = \sum_{i=1}^{m} a_{ij} u_i, \qquad j = 1, \ldots, k$$

for some scalars a_{ij}, $i = 1, \ldots, m$, $j = 1, \ldots, k$. Then

$$v = \sum_{j=1}^{k} c_j \sum_{i=1}^{m} a_{ij} u_i$$

$$= \sum_{i=1}^{m} \left(\sum_{j=1}^{k} c_j a_{ij} \right) u_i \in \langle u_1, \ldots, u_m \rangle.$$

In other words, a linear combination of vectors that are themselves linear combinations of $u_1, \ldots, u_m$ is a linear combination of $u_1, \ldots, u_m$. In particular, if $v \in \langle v_1, v_2, \ldots, v_k \rangle$, where not all the v_j are 0, and v_1 is a linear combination of $v_2, \ldots, v_k$, then $v \in \langle v_2, \ldots, v_k \rangle$. Since this is true for any v in $\langle v_1, \ldots, v_k \rangle$, we have in this case: $\langle v_1, \ldots, v_k \rangle = \langle v_2, \ldots, v_k \rangle$. We can continue the elimination of superfluous v_j until all the remaining v_j are linearly independent. That is to say, we can find a linearly independent subset $\{v_{i_1}, \ldots, v_{i_r}\}$ of $\{v_1, \ldots, v_k\}$ such that

$$\langle v_{i_1}, \ldots, v_{i_r} \rangle = \langle v_1, \ldots, v_k \rangle.$$

Definition 6.5. (Basis). *If $v_1, \ldots, v_r$ span a subspace V of $V_n(C)$ and $v_1, \ldots, v_r$ are linearly independent, then they are said to form a **basis** of V.*

Example 6.4. Let e_j denote the n-tuple in which the jth coordinate is 1 and all the other coordinates are 0. Then $e_1, \ldots, e_n$ form a basis of $V_n(C)$. For, if $(a_1, \ldots, a_n)$ is any n-tuple in $V_n(C)$, then

$$(a_1, \ldots, a_n) = \sum_{j=1}^{n} a_j e_j$$

and therefore

$$\langle e_1, \ldots, e_n \rangle = V_n(C).$$

It is easy to see that $e_1, \ldots, e_n$ are linearly independent. In fact, suppose that

$$\sum_{j=1}^{n} c_j e_j = 0.$$

Then

$$(c_1, c_2, \ldots, c_n) = (0, \ldots, 0),$$

and

$$c_1 = c_2 = \cdots = c_n = 0.$$

Thus $e_1, \ldots, e_n$ are linearly independent and form a basis of $V_n(C)$. This basis is called the *standard basis of $V_n(C)$*.

Theorem 6.4. *Let $v_1, \ldots, v_k$ be a basis of V.*

  (a) *If*

$$\sum_{i=1}^{k} a_i v_i = \sum_{i=1}^{k} b_i v_i,$$

  then $a_i = b_i$, $i = 1, \ldots, k$.

  (b) *If $u_1, \ldots, u_r$ are linearly independent vectors in V, then $r \leq k$ and for some set of $k - r$ of the v_i, say $v_{r+1}, \ldots, v_k$, the set $u_1, \ldots, u_r$, $v_{r+1}, \ldots, v_k$ is a basis of V.*

  (c) *Any two bases of V contain the same number of elements.*

  Proof.
  (a) If

$$\sum_{i=1}^{k} a_i v_i = \sum_{i=1}^{k} b_i v_i,$$

then

$$\sum_{i=1}^{k} (a_i - b_i)v_i = 0,$$

and since $v_1, \ldots, v_k$ are linearly independent, all the coefficients must be 0, i.e., $a_i = b_i$, $i = 1, \ldots, k$.

  (b) We use induction on r. First suppose that $r = 1$. Now, V is assumed to have a basis $v_1, \ldots, v_k$. Therefore $k \geq 1 = r$. Also, $u_1 \in \langle v_1, \ldots, v_k \rangle$, i.e.,

$$u_1 = a_1 v_1 + \cdots + a_k v_k \tag{3}$$

for some scalars $a_1, \ldots, a_k$. Moreover, these scalars cannot all be 0, because $u_1 \neq 0$, by our hypothesis (see Exercise 3). Thus we can assume without loss of generality that $a_1 \neq 0$ (the a_i can be relabeled, if necessary, so that $a_1 \neq 0$) and obtain

$$v_1 = a_1^{-1} u_1 - (a_1^{-1} a_2)v_2 - \cdots - (a_1^{-1} a_k)v_k \in \langle u_1, v_2, \ldots, v_k \rangle.$$

Therefore,

$$V = \langle u_1, v_2, \ldots, v_k \rangle.$$

We prove that $u_1, v_2, \ldots, v_k$ are linearly independent and therefore form a basis of V. Suppose $u_1, v_2, \ldots, v_k$ are linearly dependent, so that

$$c_1 u_1 + c_2 v_2 + \cdots + c_k v_k = 0 \tag{4}$$

for some scalars $c_1, \ldots, c_k$, not all 0. Note that c_1 cannot be 0; otherwise $v_2, \ldots, v_k$ would satisfy a nontrivial linear relation. Eliminate u_1 between (3) and (4) to obtain

$$c_1 a_1 v_1 + (c_2 + c_1 a_2)v_2 + \cdots + (c_k + c_1 a_k)v_k = 0. \tag{5}$$

Since $v_1, \ldots, v_k$ are linearly independent, all the coefficients in (5) must be 0. In particular, we must have $c_1 a_1 = 0$. But this is impossible, because $a_1 \neq 0$ and $c_1 \neq 0$. This contradiction shows that our original supposition, that $u_1, v_2, \ldots, v_k$ satisfy a nontrivial linear relation, cannot hold. Therefore $u_1, v_2, \ldots, v_k$ must be linearly independent and they form a basis of V.

Now, we continue our proof by induction and assume that the theorem holds for $r - 1$ vectors $u_1, \ldots, u_{r-1}$, i.e., that either $r - 1 < k$ and

$$u_1, \ldots, u_{r-1}, v_r, \ldots, v_k \tag{6}$$

is a basis of V or $r - 1 = k$ and

$$u_1, \ldots, u_{r-1}$$

is a basis for V. Clearly the second alternative is impossible. For, if $u_1, \ldots, u_{r-1}$ were a basis, then $u_r \in \langle u_1, \ldots, u_{r-1} \rangle$ and $u_1, \ldots, u_{r-1}, u_r$ would be linearly dependent by Theorem 6.3. Thus it suffices to assume that $r - 1 < k$ and that (6) is a basis of V. Then

$$u_r = \sum_{j=1}^{r-1} a_j u_j + \sum_{j=r}^{k} b_j v_j \tag{7}$$

for some scalars $a_1, \ldots, a_{r-1}, b_r, \ldots, b_k$. Now, not all b_j can be 0; otherwise $u_r, u_1, \ldots, u_{r-1}$ would satisfy a nontrivial linear relation. Assume without loss of generality that $b_r \neq 0$. Then we can solve (7) for v_r:

$$v_r = -\sum_{j=1}^{r-1} (b_r^{-1} a_j)u_j + b_r^{-1} u_r$$

$$-\sum_{j=r+1}^{k} (b_r^{-1} b_j)v_j \in \langle u_1, \ldots, u_{r-1}, u_r, v_{r+1}, \ldots, v_k \rangle.$$

Since every vector in the basis (6) is in the subspace $\langle u_1, \ldots, u_r, v_{r+1}, \ldots, v_k \rangle$ it is clear that

$$\langle u_1, \ldots, u_r, v_{r+1}, \ldots, v_k \rangle = V.$$

It remains to prove that the vectors $u_1, \ldots, u_r, v_{r+1}, \ldots, v_k$ are linearly independent. Suppose that they are not, i.e., that

$$\sum_{j=1}^{r} c_j u_j + \sum_{j=r+1}^{k} c_j v_j = 0, \tag{8}$$

where not all the scalars $c_1, \ldots, c_k$ are 0. Note that in this case we must have $c_r \neq 0$, for otherwise vectors $u_1, \ldots, u_{r-1}, v_{r+1}, \ldots, v_k$ of the basis (6) would be linearly dependent. We can, therefore, eliminate u_r between (7) and (8):

$$\sum_{j=1}^{r-1} (c_j + c_r a_j) u_j + c_r b_r v_r + \sum_{j=r+1}^{k} (c_j + c_r b_j) v_j = 0. \tag{9}$$

But $u_1, \ldots, u_{r-1}, v_r, v_{r+1}, \ldots, v_k$ form a basis of V and therefore every coefficient in (9) must be 0. In particular, $c_r b_r$ must be 0. This, however, is impossible, since neither c_r nor b_r is 0. Hence our assumption that the vectors $u_1, \ldots, u_r, v_{r+1}, \ldots, v_k$ were linearly dependent is false.

(c) Suppose that $u_1, \ldots, u_r$ and $v_1, \ldots, v_k$ are two bases of V. Then, according to (b), $r \leq k$ and, by reversing the roles of the u_j and the v_j, we must also have $k \leq r$. Hence $k = r$. This completes the proof of Theorem 6.4(c), which states essentially that for a given subspace the number of vectors in any basis is the same.

Definition 6.6. (**Dimension**). *Let V be a subspace of $V_n(C)$. The **dimension** of V, denoted by dim V, is the number of vectors in a basis of V. If V consists of the zero vector only, we set dim $V = 0$.*

Theorem 6.5.

   (a) *Let $V = \langle v_1, \ldots, v_k \rangle$ be a subspace of $V_n(C)$. Suppose that $v_1, \ldots, v_r$ are linearly independent and that no other linearly independent subset of $X \{v_1, \ldots, v_k\}$ contains more than r vectors. Then $v_1, \ldots, v_r$ form a basis of V.*

   (b) *If U is a proper subspace of V, then dim $U <$ dim V.*

   (c) *If U and W are subspaces of $V_n(C)$ and dim $U +$ dim $W > n$, then dim$(W \cap U) > 0$.*

Proof.

(a) Let v be any vector in X. Since no set of linearly independent vectors in X can have more than r vectors, the vectors $v, v_1, \ldots, v_r$ must be linearly dependent. There exist, therefore, scalars $c_0, c_1, \ldots, c_r$, not all 0, satisfying $c_0 v + c_1 v_1 + \ldots + c_r v_r = 0$. Now $c_0 = 0$; otherwise $v_1, \ldots, v_r$ would satisfy a nontrivial linear relation. Therefore

$$v = (-c_0^{-1} c_1) v_1 + \ldots + (-c_0^{-1} c_r) v_r \, \epsilon \, <v_1, \ldots, v_r>.$$

This is true of any vector v in X. Therefore v is spanned by $v_1, \ldots, v_r$, and since these vectors are linearly independent, they form a basis. Note that since no linearly independent set of vectors in $V_n(C)$ can contain more than n vectors by Theorem 6.4(b), it follows that every subspace of $V_n(C)$ has a basis, by the argument just given. (See proof of Theorem 1.1(a), p. 151.)

(b) Let dim $V = r$. By Theorem 6.4(b) no set of linearly independent vectors in U can contain more than r vectors. Let $u_1, \ldots, u_s$ be a linearly independent set of vectors in U that contains as many vectors as any linearly independent set in U. Then $s \leq r$, and, by part (a), $u_1, \ldots, u_s$ form a basis of U. Moreover, $s = r$; otherwise $u_1, \ldots, u_s$, by Theorem 6.4(b), would form a basis of V and we would have $U = V$.

(c) Let $u_1, \ldots, u_r$ and $w_1, \ldots, w_s$ be bases of U and W, respectively. Then $r + s = \dim U + \dim W > n$, and by Theorem 6.4(b) the set $\{u_1, \ldots, u_r, w_1, \ldots, w_s\}$ must be linearly dependent. Thus there exist scalars $a_1, \ldots, a_r, b_1, \ldots, b_s$, not all zero, such that

$$\sum_{i=1}^{r} a_i u_i + \sum_{i=1}^{s} b_i w_i = 0. \tag{10}$$

Let

$$v = \sum_{i=1}^{r} a_i u_i = -\sum_{i=1}^{s} b_i w_i. \tag{11}$$

Then $v \neq 0$. For $v = 0$ would mean that

$$\sum_{i=1}^{r} a_i u_i = \sum_{i=1}^{s} b_i w_i = 0,$$

and since not all the scalars $a_1, \ldots, a_r, b_1, \ldots, b_s$ can be zero, that either $u_1, \ldots, u_r$ or $w_1, \ldots, w_s$ are linearly dependent. Also, (11) implies that $v \in \langle u_1, \ldots, u_r \rangle = U$ and $v \in \langle w_1, \ldots, w_s \rangle = W$. Hence $U \cap W$ contains a nonzero vector and dim $U \cap W > 0$.

Quiz

Answer *true* or *false*:

1. If $u_1, \ldots, u_r$ are linearly dependent, then $u_1, \ldots, u_r, u_{r+1}, \ldots, u_k$ are linearly dependent.

2. If $u_1, \ldots, u_r$ are linearly independent, then $u_1, \ldots, u_r, u_{r+1}, \ldots, u_k$ are linearly independent.

3. If $u_1, \ldots, u_r, u_{r+1}, \ldots, u_k$ are linearly dependent, then $u_1, \ldots, u_r$ are linearly dependent.

4. If $u_1, \ldots, u_r, u_{r+1}, \ldots, u_k$ are linearly independent, then $u_1, \ldots, u_r$ are linearly independent.

5. A subspace of $V_n(R)$ must always contain the zero vector.

6. If X and Y are disjoint subsets of $V_n(C)$ (i.e., $X \cap Y = \varnothing$), then $\langle X \rangle \neq \langle Y \rangle$.

   In the next four questions let $u = (a_1, a_2, a_3, a_4, a_5)$, $v = (b_1, b_2, b_3, b_4, b_5)$, and $w = (c_1, c_2, c_3, c_4, c_5)$ be vectors in $V_5(C)$, and let $u' = (a_1, a_2, a_3)$, $v' = (b_1, b_2, b_3)$, and $w' = (c_1, c_2, c_3)$ be in $V_3(C)$.

7. If u, v, and w are linearly dependent then u', v', and w' are linearly dependent.

8. If u', v', and w' are linearly dependent, then u, v, and w are linearly dependent.

9. If u, v, and w are linearly independent, then u', v', and w' are linearly independent.

10. If u', v', and w' are linearly independent, then u, v, and w are linearly independent.

Exercises

1. Prove that any $k + 1$ vectors in a k-dimensional subspace are linearly dependent.

2. Show that

$$X = \{(x_1, x_2, x_3, x_4) \in V_4(C) \mid x_1 + x_2 + x_3 + x_4 = 0\}$$

is a subspace of $V_4(C)$. <u>Find a basis of X.</u>

3. Show that any set of vectors in $V_n(C)$ containing the zero vector is linearly dependent.

4. Let U and V be subspaces of $V_n(C)$. Show that $U \cap V$ forms a subspace of $V_n(C)$.

5. Let U and V be subspaces of $V_n(C)$. The *linear sum* of U and V, denoted by $U + V$, is the set consisting of all vectors in $V_n(C)$ of the form $u + v$, $u \in U$, $v \in V$. Show that $U + V$ is a subspace of $V_n(C)$.

6. Let U and V be subspaces of $V_n(C)$. Prove that $\dim (U + V) = \dim U + \dim V - \dim (U \cap V)$. (*Hint:* Let $w_1, \ldots, w_r$ be a basis of $U \cap V$. Complete $w_1, \ldots, w_r$ first to a basis of U and then to a basis of V; show that the union of these bases is linearly independent.)

7. Let $a = (1, 2, -1, 1)$, $b = (1, -2, -1, 3)$, $c = (1, 2, 3, 0)$, and $d = (2, 2, 2, 2)$. Find a basis of $\langle a, b \rangle \cap \langle c, d \rangle$ and a basis of $\langle a, b \rangle + \langle c, d \rangle$.

2

Matrices

2.1. MATRIX MULTIPLICATION

In Section 1.3 we discussed linear transformations of the plane into itself and we saw there that such transformations could be defined in the following way. Let a_{11}, a_{12}, a_{21}, and a_{22} be four numbers and to each point $P = (x_1, x_2)$ correspond the point $T(P) = Q = (y_1, y_2)$, where

$$y_1 = a_{11}x_1 + a_{12}x_2,$$

$$y_2 = a_{21}x_1 + a_{22}x_2.$$

$$(1)$$

As we observed before, the first subscript on the numbers a indicates with which coordinate of $T(P)$ we are dealing, and the second subscript on the a tells us on which coordinate of the point $P = (x_1, x_2)$ we are operating. It will be observed in (1) that the only thing that really matters are the numbers a_{ij}, $i = 1, 2, j = 1, 2$, in the definition of T. Thus in considering the linear transformation T, we are led to the array or *matrix* of numbers

$$\begin{bmatrix} a_{11} & a_{12} \\ a_{21} & a_{22} \end{bmatrix}. \tag{2}$$

It is this central idea of abstracting the matrix of coefficients from the formulas defining the linear transformation (1) and performing certain algebraic operations on these matrices that has been so productive in the analysis of linear functions. Thus if we denote the array or matrix (2) by the single symbol A and the points P and Q by x and y, respectively, it would be very suggestive of (1) to write

$$y = Ax. \tag{3}$$

As a matter of fact, a linear transformation of the real line into itself has precisely the form (3), in which x is a number, A is a fixed number, and the juxtaposition of A and x simply means multiplication.

We now extend this idea of writing the system of equations (1) in the form of a single equation (3) to the general case of linear transformations:

$$T: V_n(R) \to V_m(R). \tag{4}$$

Hereafter in this chapter R will be the set of real numbers or the set of complex numbers. In most instances it will not matter which set we are using. Thus suppose T is given by

$$
\begin{aligned}
y_1 &= a_{11}x_1 + a_{12}x_2 + \cdots + a_{1n}x_n \\
y_2 &= a_{21}x_1 + a_{22}x_2 + \cdots + a_{2n}x_n \\
&\;\vdots \qquad\qquad\qquad\quad \vdots \\
y_m &= a_{m1}x_1 + a_{m2}x_2 + \cdots + a_{mn}x_n,
\end{aligned}
\tag{5}
$$

in which once again the first subscript on the number a_{ij} tells us which coordinate of the function value we have and the second subscript indicates with which coordinate of the point $x = (x_1, \ldots, x_n)$ we are dealing. In analogy with the relation between (1) and (3), we write

$$y = Ax, \tag{6}$$

where $y = (y_1, \ldots, y_m) \in V_m(R)$, $x = (x_1, \ldots, x_n) \in V_n(R)$, and

$$
A = \quad
\begin{matrix}
 & j \\
i & \begin{bmatrix} a_{11} & \cdots & a_{1n} \\ \vdots & -a_{ij} & \vdots \\ a_{m1} & \cdots & a_{mn} \end{bmatrix}
\end{matrix}.
\tag{7}
$$

The array (7) is called an $m \times n$ *matrix*; the numbers a_{ij} are called the *entries* of the matrix A; the sequence of numbers

$$(a_{i1}, a_{i2}, \ldots, a_{in}) \tag{8}$$

is called the *i*th *row* of A. The sequence of numbers

$$(a_{1j}, a_{2j}, \ldots, a_{mj}) \tag{9}$$

is called the *j*th *column* of A. (We have not written the *j*th column of A vertically as a column because it takes too much space; besides a sequence is, after all, completely known once one knows the order in which the numbers occur.)

Definition 1.1. (**Matrix notation**). *Let* a_{ij}, $i = 1, \ldots, m$, $j = 1, \ldots, n$, *be mn numbers. The* $m \times n$ *array*

$$A = \begin{bmatrix} a_{11} & a_{12} & \cdots & a_{1n} \\ a_{21} & a_{22} & & a_{2n} \\ \vdots & \vdots & & \vdots \\ a_{m1} & a_{m2} & \cdots & a_{mn} \end{bmatrix}$$

is called an $m \times n$ **matrix** *and the numbers* a_{ij} *are called the* **elements** *or* **entries** *of* A. *The ith* **row** *of* A *is the n-tuple*

$$(a_{i1}, \ldots, a_{in}) \tag{10}$$

and is denoted by $A_{(i)}$; *the jth* **column** *of* A *is the m-tuple*

$$(a_{1j}, \ldots, a_{mj}) \tag{11}$$

and is denoted by $A^{(j)}$. *The set of all* $m \times n$ *matrices with entries from the set* R *will be systematically denoted by* $M_{m,n}(R)$. *In case* $m = n$, *i.e., the matrices under consideration have the same number of rows and columns, we shall shorten the notation for* $M_{m,n}(R)$ *to* $M_n(R)$. *A matrix* A *in* $M_n(R)$ *is said to be* **square**; *in case we want to designate the size of the matrix, i.e., the number of rows and columns, we say that it is n-square. We shall also write*

$$A = (a_{ij}), \tag{12}$$

in which we omit the range in which i and j vary only in case this is previously understood in the context. We shall also sometimes designate a_{ij}, *the* (i, j) *entry of the matrix* A, *by* A_{ij}. *Two matrices will be equal if they have the same number of rows, the same number of columns, and the corresponding entries are equal.*

For example, if $m = 2$ and $n = 3$, consider the matrix

$$A = \begin{bmatrix} 2 & 1 & 4 \\ -5 & 0 & 3 \end{bmatrix} \in M_{2,3}(R).$$

Then $a_{23} = 3$, $a_{22} = 0$, and

$$A_{(1)} = (2, 1, 4),$$
$$A_{(2)} = (-5, 0, 3),$$
$$A^{(1)} = (2, -5),$$
$$A^{(2)} = (1, 0),$$
$$A^{(3)} = (4, 3).$$

If

$$B = \begin{bmatrix} 2 & 1 & 4 & 0 \\ -5 & 0 & 3 & 0 \end{bmatrix},$$

it is *not* true that $A = B$, because the two matrices do not have the same number of columns.

Equation (6),

$$y = Ax,$$

represents the linear transformation

$$T : V_n(R) \to V_m(R)$$

given by equations (5). Now, suppose $V_p(R)$ is a third space of p-tuples and S is a linear transformation from $V_m(R)$ to $V_p(R)$, i.e., $S : V_m(R) \to V_p(R)$. Now T goes from $V_n(R)$ to $V_m(R)$ and S goes from $V_m(R)$ to $V_p(R)$. Hence we can compose these two linear functions in the same way in which we compose arbitrary functions. In other words, we can define a function P whose domain is $V_n(R)$ and whose function values in $V_p(R)$ are given by

$$P(x) = S(T(x)). \tag{13}$$

We stated that S was a linear transformation from $V_m(R)$ to $V_p(R)$ and hence there exists a matrix $B \in M_{p,m}(R)$, i.e., a $p \times m$ matrix $B = (b_{ij})$ such that if $z = (z_1, \ldots, z_p)$ and $z = S(y)$, then a system of equations analogous to (5) must hold for S:

$$
\begin{aligned}
z_1 &= b_{11}y_1 + b_{12}y_2 + \cdots + b_{1m}y_m \\
z_2 &= b_{21}y_1 + b_{22}y_2 + \cdots + b_{2m}y_m \\
& \vdots \qquad\qquad\qquad\qquad \vdots \\
z_p &= b_{p1}y_1 + b_{p2}y_2 + \cdots + b_{pm}y_m .
\end{aligned}
\tag{14}
$$

We can express the system of equations (14), precisely as we did for the system of equations (5), by

$$ z = By. $$

We see then from (5) and (14) that we can express the coordinates of the point z in terms of the coordinates of the point x. Thus for each s, $s = 1, \ldots, p$, we have

$$
\begin{aligned}
z_s &= b_{s1}y_1 + \cdots + b_{sm}y_m \\
&= b_{s1}\left(\sum_{j=1}^{n} a_{1j}x_j \right) + b_{s2}\left(\sum_{j=1}^{n} a_{2j}x_j \right) + \cdots + b_{sm}\left(\sum_{j=1}^{n} a_{mj}x_j \right).
\end{aligned}
\tag{15}
$$

We want to collect together all the coefficients of each of the x_j in (15). Thus from (15) we see that for a fixed x_j the kth term in the sum contributes the coefficient $b_{sk}a_{kj}$, $k = 1, \ldots, m$. Hence the total coefficient of x_j is

$$ b_{s1}a_{1j} + b_{s2}a_{2j} + \cdots + b_{sm}a_{mj} = \sum_{k=1}^{m} b_{sk}a_{kj}. \tag{16} $$

If we set

$$ c_{sj} = \sum_{k=1}^{m} b_{sk}a_{kj}, \qquad j = 1, \ldots, n, \quad s = 1, \ldots, p, \tag{17} $$

we see that the composed function P in (13) for which $z = P(x)$ is also described by a system of equations of the type (5), i.e.,

$$z_1 = \sum_{j=1}^{n} c_{1j} x_j,$$

$$z_2 = \sum_{j=1}^{n} c_{2j} x_j, \tag{18}$$

$$\vdots$$

$$z_p = \sum_{j=1}^{n} c_{pj} x_j,$$

in which the c_{sj} are given by (17).

Let us summarize what we have done. We have two linear transformations, $T : V_n(R) \to V_m(R)$ and $S : V_m(R) \to V_p(R)$; we have defined the composite function $P = ST$, $P : V_n(R) \to V_p(R)$. Next, T is given by

$$y = Ax, \tag{19}$$

and S is given by

$$z = By, \tag{20}$$

and if we formally substitute (19) in (20), we get

$$z = By$$
$$= BAx. \tag{21}$$

If we look at (21) and (18), it would make perfect sense to define the matrix C in $M_{p,n}(R)$ by the equation (17), to call it the product of B and A, and to write

$$C = BA.$$

This is precisely what leads us to the definition of the product of two matrices.

Definition 1.2. **(Matrix product).** *If $A = (a_{ij}) \in M_{m,n}(R)$ and $B = (b_{ij}) \in M_{p,m}(R)$, we define a matrix $C = (c_{ij}) \in M_{p,n}(R)$, called the product of B and A and written*

$$C = BA, \tag{22}$$

by

$$c_{ij} = \sum_{k=1}^{m} b_{ik} a_{kj}, \qquad i = 1, \ldots, p, \quad j = 1, \ldots, n. \qquad (23)$$

We can summarize the computation that motivated our definition of matrix product in the following theorem.

Theorem 1.1. *If $T : V_n(R) \to V_m(R)$ and $S : V_m(R) \to V_p(R)$ are linear transformations given by*

$$y = Ax$$

and

$$z = By,$$

respectively, where $A \in M_{m,n}(R)$ and $B \in M_{p,m}(R)$, then the composite function $P = ST : V_n(R) \to V_p(R)$ is given by

$$z = Cx, \qquad (24)$$

where $C = BA \in M_{p,n}(R)$ is the product of the matrices B and A. Moreover, it follows from (24) that the composite P of two linear transformations is once again a linear transformation.

We recall that, in general, function composition is associative [see Section 1.2, formula (8)]. In other words, suppose $T : V_n(R) \to V_m(R)$, $S : V_m(R) \to V_p(R)$, and $L : V_p(R) \to V_q(R)$ are three linear transformations given by

$$y = Ax,$$
$$z = By, \qquad (25)$$
$$w = Dz,$$

respectively, where A is an $m \times n$ matrix, B is a $p \times m$ matrix, and D is a $q \times p$ matrix. There are two ways, of course, in which we can compose these three functions to produce the composite linear transformation $H : V_n(R) \to V_q(R)$, namely, $L(ST)$ and $(LS)T$. We know from the associativity of function composition in general that

$$H = L(ST)$$
$$= (LS)T. \qquad (26)$$

Now according to Theorem 1.1 applied first to $L(ST)$ and then to $(LS)T$, we know that H is given by both

$$w = D(BA)x \tag{27}$$

and

$$w = (DB)Ax. \tag{28}$$

Thus it will follow that matrix multiplication is associative if we know the following fact, which we state as a theorem and proceed to prove.

Theorem 1.2. *If $H : V_n(R) \to V_q(R)$ is given by both*

$$w = Ex \tag{29}$$

and

$$w = Fx, \tag{30}$$

where $w = (w_1, \ldots, w_q) \in V_q(R)$, $x = (x_1, \ldots, x_n) \in V_n(R)$, and E and F are matrices in $M_{q,n}(R)$, then

$$E = F. \tag{31}$$

Proof. Let $E = (e_{ij})$ and $F = (f_{ij})$. Now in (29) and (30) let x be the n-tuple with 1 as jth coordinate and 0 for the remaining coordinates, i.e.,

$$x = (0, \ldots, 0, \overset{j}{1}, 0, \ldots, 0).$$

We find that for this x,

$$w_k = \sum_{t=1}^{n} e_{kt} x_t = e_{kj}$$

and

$$w_k = \sum_{t=1}^{n} f_{kt} x_t = f_{kj}.$$

Hence $e_{kj} = f_{kj}, j = 1, \ldots, n, k = 1, \ldots, q$. In other words, corresponding elements of E and F are equal.

Now if we look back at (27) and (28), we see that H is given by both

$$w = [D(BA)]x$$

and

$$w = [(DB)A]x,$$

with E playing the role of $[D(BA)]$ and F playing the role of $[(DB)A]$. Hence (31) immediately implies the following theorem.

Theorem 1.3. *If A, B, and D are matrices for which the products $D(BA)$ and $(DB)A$ are defined, then*

$$D(BA) = (DB)A. \tag{32}$$

The common value of $D(BA)$ and $(DB)A$ will be denoted by DBA.

In other words, matrix multiplication is *associative*.

We continue with some examples of matrix multiplication. Suppose

$$D = \begin{bmatrix} 2 & 1 & 3 \\ 0 & 1 & -1 \end{bmatrix},$$

$$B = \begin{bmatrix} 3 & 1 & 0 \\ -5 & 1 & 0 \\ 1 & 4 & 2 \end{bmatrix},$$

and

$$A = \begin{bmatrix} 0 & 0 & 1 & 0 \\ 0 & 0 & -1 & 0 \\ 0 & 0 & 2 & 0 \end{bmatrix}.$$

Then we know that the product DBA can be computed in two ways: $(DB)A$ or $D(BA)$. It is clearly more sensible to take the latter alternative because looking at A one sees that BA is going to have many zeros in it, whereas if DB were computed first, we would have a lot of arithmetic to do. Now according to Definition 1.2 of matrix multiplication, we immediately see that

$$BA = \begin{bmatrix} 0 & 0 & 2 & 0 \\ 0 & 0 & -6 & 0 \\ 0 & 0 & 1 & 0 \end{bmatrix}.$$

Next we can compute $D(BA)$ to obtain

$$D(BA) = \begin{bmatrix} 0 & 0 & 1 & 0 \\ 0 & 0 & -7 & 0 \end{bmatrix}.$$

Many rather unexpected things happen in multiplying matrices that never occur in the multiplication of numbers. For example, if

$$A = \begin{bmatrix} 0 & 1 & 0 & 0 \\ 0 & 0 & 1 & 0 \\ 0 & 0 & 0 & 1 \\ 0 & 0 & 0 & 0 \end{bmatrix},$$

then we compute directly from Definition 1.2 that

$$AA = \begin{bmatrix} 0 & 0 & 1 & 0 \\ 0 & 0 & 0 & 1 \\ 0 & 0 & 0 & 0 \\ 0 & 0 & 0 & 0 \end{bmatrix},$$

$$AAA = \begin{bmatrix} 0 & 0 & 0 & 1 \\ 0 & 0 & 0 & 0 \\ 0 & 0 & 0 & 0 \\ 0 & 0 & 0 & 0 \end{bmatrix},$$

and finally

$$AAAA = \begin{bmatrix} 0 & 0 & 0 & 0 \\ 0 & 0 & 0 & 0 \\ 0 & 0 & 0 & 0 \\ 0 & 0 & 0 & 0 \end{bmatrix}.$$

Thus we see that a product of matrices (in this case every factor is the same!) can have every entry zero and yet each of the factors has nonzero entries. Another surprising aspect of matrix multiplication is that in general the product is not *commutative*. That is, it is not usually the case that

$$AB = BA. \tag{33}$$

Considerations of size alone tell us that (33) cannot be expected to hold in general, e.g., if A is 2×3 and B is 3×2, then AB is 2×2, whereas BA is 3×3. But even in the case that A and B are both n-square matrices, it nevertheless makes a difference in which order the product is computed.

Thus if

$$A = \begin{bmatrix} 1 & 1 \\ 0 & 1 \end{bmatrix},$$

and

$$B = \begin{bmatrix} 1 & 1 \\ -1 & 1 \end{bmatrix},$$

then

$$AB = \begin{bmatrix} 0 & 2 \\ -1 & 1 \end{bmatrix}$$

while

$$BA = \begin{bmatrix} 1 & 2 \\ -1 & 0 \end{bmatrix}.$$

On the other hand, matrix multiplication does share some of the properties of ordinary number multiplication. Suppose that A is an $m \times n$ matrix and let I_m be the m-square matrix whose (i, j) entry is 1 if $i = j$ and is zero otherwise. Thus

$$I_m = \begin{bmatrix} 1 & 0 & \cdots & & 0 \\ 0 & & & & \vdots \\ \vdots & & \ddots & & \\ \vdots & & & & 0 \\ 0 & & \cdots & 0 & 1 \end{bmatrix}.$$

We immediately see that

$$I_m A = A,$$

and, by a similar computation,

$$A I_n = A.$$

Thus the matrices I_m and I_n act in the same way as the number 1 does in ordinary multiplication.

In one of the immediately preceding examples we had occasion to use the matrix A as a factor in a product several times. We introduce the notation of exponents for matrix multiplication, and because of the associative law we can operate with powers of a matrix in much the same way as we operate with powers of a number.

Definition 1.3. **(Notation).** *If A is an n-square matrix and p is a positive integer, then A^p is the n-square matrix obtained by multiplying A by itself p times. The n-square matrix I_n whose (i,j) entry is 1 if $i = j$, and zero otherwise, is called the n-square* **identity** *matrix. As we have seen,*

$$AI_n = A,$$

and

$$I_nA = A.$$

The matrix

$$A^0$$

is by definition equal to I_n. If the (i,j) entry of A is zero for $i \neq j$, we say that A is a **diagonal** *matrix. Thus a diagonal matrix has the following appearance:*

$$A = \begin{bmatrix} a_{11} & 0 & \cdots & & 0 \\ & 0 & & 0 & \cdot \\ \vdots & & 0 & \cdot & \vdots \\ & & & \cdot & 0 \\ 0 & & \cdots & 0 & a_{nn} \end{bmatrix}.$$

We sometimes write

$$A = \text{diag}\,(a_{11}, \ldots, a_{nn}).$$

In general the **main diagonal** *of A is just the n-tuple of numbers*

$$(a_{11}, \ldots, a_{nn}).$$

If $a_{ij} = 0$ whenever $i > j$, we say that A is an **upper triangular** *matrix and then A has the appearance*

$$A = \begin{bmatrix} a_{11} & a_{12} & & \cdots & & a_{1n} \\ 0 & a_{22} & & & & a_{2n} \\ 0 & & a_{33} & & & a_{3n} \\ \vdots & & & \cdot & \cdot & \vdots \\ & & & & \cdot & \\ 0 & & \cdots & & 0 & a_{nn} \end{bmatrix}.$$

If $a_{ij} = 0$ *whenever* $i < j$, *then A is called a* **lower triangular** *matrix and has the following appearance:*

$$A = \begin{bmatrix} a_{11} & 0 & & \cdots & & 0 \\ a_{21} & a_{22} & 0 & & & 0 \\ a_{31} & a_{32} & a_{33} & 0 & & 0 \\ \vdots & & & \ddots & & \vdots \\ & & & & \ddots & 0 \\ a_{n1} & a_{n2} & & \cdots & & a_{nn} \end{bmatrix}.$$

Finally, the $m \times n$ *matrix, every one of whose entries is zero, is called the zero matrix and is denoted by* $0_{m,n}$. *If* $m = n$, *we write* 0_n *(and sometimes just* 0) *for* $0_{n,n}$.

Let us observe that the associative law does indeed allow us to compute with powers of a square matrix in much the same way that one computes with powers of a real number. To begin with, consider

$$A^3 = AAA.$$

It is permissible for us to write AAA in view of Theorem 1.3. Similarly, $(AAA)A$ is the same as $(AA)(AA)$, etc., in which the "etc." means that any way we care to insert parentheses in the product of the four A's will produce precisely the same result. Once again this is simply an application of Theorem 1.3.

Observe that

$$A^p A^q = \overbrace{A \cdots A}^{p} \overbrace{A \cdots A}^{q}$$

$$= A^{p+q} \tag{34}$$

$$= A^q A^p.$$

It is clear that if A is an $m \times n$ matrix, then

$$A 0_{n,k} = 0_{m,k},$$
$$0_{k,m} A = 0_{k,n}. \tag{35}$$

Quiz

Answer *true* or *false*:

1. If

$$A = \begin{bmatrix} 0 & 0 & 0 \\ 1 & 0 & 0 \\ -1 & -1 & -1 \end{bmatrix},$$

then $A_{(1)} = (0, 0, 1)$.

2. If

$$A = \begin{bmatrix} 0 \\ 0 \\ 1 \end{bmatrix},$$

then $A_{(2)} = (0)$.

3. If

$$A = \begin{bmatrix} 0 & 1 \\ 0 & 0 \end{bmatrix},$$

then $A^2 = 0_2$.

4. If

$$A = \begin{bmatrix} 1 & 0 \\ -1 & -1 \end{bmatrix} \quad \text{and} \quad B = \begin{bmatrix} 1 & 0 \\ 0 & 2 \end{bmatrix},$$

then $AB = BA$.

5. If A and B are matrices for which the product AB is defined and $AB = 0_{p,q}$, then either A or B must be a zero matrix; i.e., all entries must be zero.

6. If A is a nonzero $n \times n$ matrix and $AB = A$, then B must be the $n \times n$ identity matrix I_n. (*Hint:* Suppose

$$A = \begin{bmatrix} 1 & 0 \\ 0 & 0 \end{bmatrix}.)$$

7. If A is a $1 \times m$ matrix, B is an $m \times 1$ matrix, and C is a $1 \times p$ matrix, then ABC is a $1 \times p$ matrix.

8. Let $T: V_2(R) \to V_2(R)$ be the linear transformation which sends each point P into its mirror image Q across the horizontal axis. Then T is represented by the equation $y = Ax$, where (x_1, x_2) are the coordinates of P, (y_1, y_2) are the coordinates of Q, and

$$A = \begin{bmatrix} 1 & 0 \\ 0 & -1 \end{bmatrix}.$$

9. Using the same notation as in the preceding example, suppose T is the linear transformation which sends P into its mirror image through the origin. Then

$y = Ax$ represents T, where

$$A = \begin{bmatrix} -1 & 0 \\ 0 & -1 \end{bmatrix}.$$

10. The matrix

$$A = \begin{bmatrix} 1 & 2 & 3 & 4 \\ 0 & 1 & 4 & 2 \\ 0 & 0 & 0 & 1 \end{bmatrix}$$

is upper triangular.

Exercises

1. If $T: V_2(R) \to V_3(R)$ is given by $y = Ax$,

$$A = \begin{bmatrix} 1 & 0 \\ 0 & 2 \\ -3 & 5 \end{bmatrix},$$

and $S: V_3(R) \to V_1(R)$ [i.e., $V_1(R) = R$] is given by $z = By$,

$$B = [2 \quad 5 \quad 0],$$

then find the matrix C such that the composed transformation $ST: V_2(R) \to V_1(R)$ is given by the equation $z = Cx$.

2. Compute the product ABC by associating the factors in two different ways:

$$A = \begin{bmatrix} 1 & 2 & 3 \\ 4 & 5 & 6 \end{bmatrix},$$

$$B = \begin{bmatrix} 4 \\ 6 \\ -1 \end{bmatrix},$$

$$C = [1 \quad 2 \quad -5 \quad 6].$$

Which of the two is easier?

3. Can two rectangular matrices commute if at least one of them is not square? Why?

4. Find A^4, where A is the matrix

$$\begin{bmatrix} 0 & 0 & 1 \\ 0 & 0 & 0 \\ 1 & 0 & 0 \end{bmatrix}.$$

5. Find a matrix B such that $AB = I_2$, where

$$A = \begin{bmatrix} 1 & -1 \\ 1 & 0 \end{bmatrix}.$$

6. Find a matrix C such that $CA = I_2$, where A is the matrix in the preceding exercise. Compare the two answers.

7. If

$$A = \begin{bmatrix} 1 & 1 \\ 1 & 1 \end{bmatrix},$$

then, if possible, find a matrix B such that $AB = I_2$. What goes wrong?

8. Using the matrix A in the preceding exercise, find a matrix B such that $AB = 0_2$. Is there more than one such matrix B?

9. If $A \in M_{m,n}(R)$ and $B \in M_{n,p}(R)$, show that

$$(AB)_{(i)} = A_{(i)}B,$$

and

$$(AB)^{(j)} = AB^{(j)}.$$

2.2. ADDITION AND SCALAR MULTIPLICATION OF MATRICES

The two fundamental operations in the vector space $V_n(R)$ are addition of vectors and scalar multiplication of vectors [see Chapter 1, Definition 6.1]:

$$(a_1, \ldots, a_n) + (b_1, \ldots, b_n) = (a_1 + b_1, \ldots, a_n + b_n), \tag{1}$$

$$c(a_1, \ldots, a_n) = (ca_1, \ldots, ca_n). \tag{2}$$

The problem that we wish to study now is this: suppose that $T: V_n(R) \rightarrow V_m(R)$ and $S: V_n(R) \rightarrow V_m(R)$ are two linear transformations given by the equations

$$y = Ax,$$

and

$$y = Bx, \tag{3}$$

respectively, in which $y = (y_1, \ldots, y_m)$, $x = (x_1, \ldots, x_n)$, $A = (a_{ij}) \in M_{m,n}(R)$, and $B = (b_{ij}) \in M_{m,n}(R)$. Suppose we consider the function whose value at each vector P in $V_n(R)$ is given by

$$Q = T(P) + S(P). \tag{4}$$

Question: Is this function linear and, if so, what is its matrix representation? Similarly, if c is a fixed number and we define a function whose value at each vector P in $V_n(R)$ is given by

$$Q = cT(P), \tag{5}$$

then is this function linear and, if so, what is its matrix representation? These two geometric questions are easy to answer and lead us to the definition of matrix addition and scalar multiplication of a matrix. Before considering the general case. we shall work out an example which makes the situation transparent. Thus suppose $T: V_2(R) \to V_3(R)$ is given by the first equation of (3) in which $y = (y_1, y_2, y_3)$, $x = (x_1, x_2)$, and

$$A = \begin{bmatrix} 2 & 0 \\ -1 & 3 \\ 1 & 5 \end{bmatrix},$$

and $S: V_2(R) \to V_3(R)$ is given by the second equation in (3), in which

$$B = \begin{bmatrix} 5 & 7 \\ 2 & 10 \\ -1 & 8 \end{bmatrix}.$$

If we write out the equations (3) we have

$$\begin{aligned} y_1 &= 2x_1, \\ y_2 &= -x_1 + 3x_2, \\ y_3 &= x_1 + 5x_2, \end{aligned} \tag{6}$$

and

$$\begin{aligned} y_1' &= 5x_1 + 7x_2, \\ y_2' &= 2x_1 + 10x_2, \\ y_3' &= -x_1 + 8x_2. \end{aligned} \tag{7}$$

We have used primes on the y's in (7) to distinguish the values of $T(P) = (y_1, y_2, y_3)$ and $S(P) = (y_1', y_2', y_3')$. Now, we are trying to compute the function L whose value at any P is given by

$$L(P) = T(P) + S(P). \tag{8}$$

By the definition of addition in $V_3(R)$ we see that the components of $L(P)$ are $y_1 + y_1'$, $y_2 + y_2'$, and $y_3 + y_3'$, i.e., $L(P)$ is the point $(y_1 + y_1', y_2 + y_2', y_3 + y_3') = y + y'$. If we add together corresponding equations in (6) and (7), we obtain

$$y_1 + y_1' = 2x_1 + (5x_1 + 7x_2)$$
$$= 7x_1 + 7x_2,$$
$$y_2 + y_2' = (-x_1 + 3x_2) + (2x_1 + 10x_2)$$
$$= x_1 + 13x_2,$$

and

$$y_3 + y_3' = (x_1 + 5x_2) + (-x_1 + 8x_2)$$
$$= 13x_2.$$

In other words, if we set

$$y'' = y + y',$$

then y'' is given by the equation

$$y'' = Cx, \tag{9}$$

where

$$C = \begin{bmatrix} 2+5 & 0+7 \\ -1+2 & 3+10 \\ 1+(-1) & 5+8 \end{bmatrix}$$

$$= \begin{bmatrix} 7 & 7 \\ 1 & 13 \\ 0 & 13 \end{bmatrix}.$$

Thus we see that the function L is indeed linear and moreover it is given by equation (9), in which C is the matrix obtained by adding corresponding entries of A and B.

Suppose now that we consider the function which associates with each P the vector

$$Q = cT(P),$$

as in (5). Suppose, moreover, that $T: V_2(R) \to V_3(R)$ is given by the first equation in (3), in which, as before,

$$y = (y_1, y_2, y_3),$$
$$x = (x_1, x_2),$$

and

$$A = \begin{bmatrix} 2 & 0 \\ -1 & 3 \\ 1 & 5 \end{bmatrix}.$$

Suppose, to be definite, that $c = -8$. Set $Q = cT(P) = -8T(P) = (z_1, z_2, z_3)$, so that $z_i = -8y_i$, $i = 1, 2, 3$; i.e.,

$$z_1 = -8(2x_1 + 0x_2),$$
$$z_2 = -8(-x_1 + 3x_2), \tag{10}$$
$$z_3 = -8(x_1 + 5x_2).$$

Thus $z = (z_1, z_2, z_3)$ is obtained from $x = (x_1, x_2)$ by an equation of the form

$$z = Dx, \tag{11}$$

in which

$$D = \begin{bmatrix} -16 & 0 \\ 8 & -24 \\ -8 & -40 \end{bmatrix}.$$

Hence the function given by (5) is indeed linear, and the matrix D in (11) is obtained from the original matrix A by multiplying each one of the entries of A by $c = -8$. We are therefore led to the following definitions.

Definition 2.1. (*Addition and scalar multiplication of matrices*). *Let A and B be two $m \times n$ matrices, i.e., A and B are in $M_{m,n}(R)$, where R is some set of numbers. The **sum** of A and B, written*

$$A + B,$$

is the $m \times n$ matrix obtained by adding corresponding entries of A and B.

That is, the (i, j) entry of $A + B$ is $a_{ij} + b_{ij}$, $i = 1, \ldots, m$, $j = 1, \ldots, n$. If c is a number, then the **scalar product** *of c and A, denoted by*

$$cA,$$

is the $m \times n$ matrix obtained by multiplying each of the entries of A by c. That is, the (i, j) entry of cA is ca_{ij}, $i = 1, \ldots, m$, $j = 1, \ldots, n$. We shall also write Ac for the scalar product cA. If A, B, $\ldots$, C are all $m \times n$ matrices and α, β, $\ldots$, γ are numbers, then the matrix

$$\alpha A + \beta B + \cdots + \gamma C \tag{12}$$

is called a **linear combination** *of the matrices A, B, $\ldots$, C.*

In the examples preceding Definition 2.1 we saw that the following theorem seems plausible.

Theorem 2.1. *Let $T: V_n(R) \to V_m(R)$ and $S: V_n(R) \to V_m(R)$ be two linear transformations and let c be a number. Let T be given by*

$$y = Ax \tag{13}$$

and S be given by

$$y = Bx, \tag{14}$$

where $x = (x_1, \ldots, x_n)$ and $y = (y_1, \ldots, y_m)$. Let $L: V_n(R) \to V_m(R)$ be the function whose value at any $P \in V_n(R)$ is $T(P) + S(P)$ and let $M: V_n(R) \to V_m(R)$ be the function whose value at any $P \in V_n(R)$ is $cT(P)$. Then L and M are both linear transformations and they are given by

$$y = (A + B)x \tag{15}$$

and

$$y = (cA)x, \tag{16}$$

respectively.

Proof. We establish (15). If we write out systems (13) and (14), we have

$$y_i = \sum_{j=1}^{n} a_{ij} x_j, \qquad i = 1, \ldots, m, \tag{17}$$

and

$$y_i' = \sum_{j=1}^{n} b_{ij} x_j, \qquad i = 1, \ldots, m, \tag{18}$$

where the y_i are the coordinates of $T(P)$ and the y_i' are the coordinates of $S(P)$. Let the coordinates of $T(P) + S(P)$ be y_i'', $i = 1, \ldots, m$. Then by definition,

$$y_i'' = y_i + y_i'$$

$$= \sum_{j=1}^{n} a_{ij} x_j + \sum_{j=1}^{n} b_{ij} x_j$$

$$= \sum_{j=1}^{n} (a_{ij} x_j + b_{ij} x_j)$$

$$= \sum_{j=1}^{n} (a_{ij} + b_{ij}) x_j. \tag{19}$$

Thus we see that the function L is given by (19), which, using the notation of Definition 2.1, is precisely the matrix equation (15).

The proof of the second assertion concerning (16) is done in much the same way and we therefore omit it.

We quite naturally call the transformation L in Theorem 2.1 the *sum* of T and S and write

$$L = T + S.$$

Similarly, we call the transformation M the *scalar product* of T by c and write

$$M = cT.$$

There are a number of elementary but important rules governing matrix addition and scalar multiplication and the connection between these and matrix multiplication. Some of the more elementary properties follow. Let A, B, and C be $m \times n$ matrices. Then

$$A + (B + C) = (A + B) + C, \tag{20}$$

$$A + B = B + A, \tag{21}$$

$$c(A + B) = cA + cB, \tag{22}$$

$$(c + d)A = cA + dA. \tag{23}$$

Equation (20) is the statement of the *associative* law for matrix addition, (21) is the *commutative* law for matrix addition, and (22) and (23) are the *distributive* laws for scalar multiplication. These laws are all proved in virtually one step by comparing entries. Thus, for example, the (i, j) entry of the left side of (20) is

$$a_{ij} + (b_{ij} + c_{ij}),$$

and since ordinary addition of numbers is associative, this is equal to

$$(a_{ij} + b_{ij}) + c_{ij}.$$

The latter, of course, is the (i, j) entry of $(A + B) + C$. In other words, corresponding entries on the two sides of (20) are the same. The verifications of (21), (22), and (23) are done in almost the same way and will be relegated to the exercises. The distributive laws for matrix multiplication over matrix addition are a little more difficult to prove. Thus let A be an $m \times n$ matrix and B and C be $n \times p$ matrices. Then we have the *distributive* law

$$A(B + C) = AB + AC. \tag{24}$$

We can prove (24) in much the same way that we did (20) by comparing corresponding entries of each side. By definition, the (i, j) entry of $A(B + C)$ is given by

$$a_{i1}(b_{1j} + c_{1j}) + a_{i2}(b_{2j} + c_{2j}) + \cdots + a_{in}(b_{nj} + c_{nj}),$$

which is equal to

$$(a_{i1}b_{1j} + a_{i2}b_{2j} + \cdots + a_{in}b_{nj}) + (a_{i1}c_{1j} + a_{i2}c_{2j} + \cdots + a_{in}c_{nj}). \tag{25}$$

The first parenthetical expression in (25) is by definition the (i, j) entry of AB and the second is the (i, j) entry of AC. Hence (25) is by definition the (i, j) entry of $AB + AC$, and this finishes the proof of (24). There is another distributive law analogous to (24) which states the following. Suppose that A and B are $m \times n$ matrices and C is an $n \times p$ matrix. Then

$$(A + B)C = AC + BC. \tag{26}$$

This is the second distributive law and is proved in almost exactly the same way as we proved (24). Once again we relegate the verification of (26) to the exercises.

Another bit of notation is useful to have. We know from the definition of matrix addition that if A is an $m \times n$ matrix and X is the $m \times n$ matrix, each of whose entries is the negative of the corresponding entry of A, then the (i, j) entry of $A + X$ is 0. It is natural, therefore, to denote X by $-A$. Observe that

$$-A = (-1)A, \tag{27}$$

and that

$$A + (-A) = 0_{m,n}.$$

If A and B are $m \times n$ matrices, we define the *difference* between A and B, written

$$A - B,$$

to be

$$A + (-B).$$

All the rules concerning the difference of two matrices follow immediately from the rules already developed for scalar multiplication and addition.

So far we have been considering operations between pairs of items, e.g., addition of two matrices, multiplication of two matrices, and multiplication of a matrix by a scalar. However, we can perform an operation on a matrix of a somewhat different kind in which only the matrix itself is involved. One of the simplest of these is described in the following definition.

Definition 2.2. **(Transpose).** *Let A be an $m \times n$ matrix, i.e., $A \in M_{m,n}(R)$. Then let B be an $n \times m$ matrix whose (i, j) entry is the (j, i) entry of A. That is, $B \in M_{n\ m}(R)$ and*

$$b_{ij} = a_{ji}, \qquad i = 1, \ldots, n, \quad j = 1, \ldots, m.$$

*The matrix B is called the **transpose** of A and is denoted by*

$$A^{\mathsf{T}}.$$

If A is an n-square matrix and $A = A^T$, then A is said to be **symmetric.**

For example, if

$$A = \begin{bmatrix} 1 & 2 & 3 \\ 4 & 5 & 6 \end{bmatrix},$$

then

$$A^T = \begin{bmatrix} 1 & 4 \\ 2 & 5 \\ 3 & 6 \end{bmatrix}.$$

Or, if

$$A = [1 \quad 1 \quad 1],$$

then

$$A^T = \begin{bmatrix} 1 \\ 1 \\ 1 \end{bmatrix}.$$

Again, if

$$A = \begin{bmatrix} 2 & 3 & 1 \\ 3 & 2 & 0 \\ 1 & 0 & 5 \end{bmatrix},$$

then

$$A^T = A.$$

Observe that in forming A^T, the ith row of A becomes the ith column of A^T and, similarly, the jth column of A becomes the jth row of A^T.

There are several elementary rules governing the transpose operation on matrices. Let A and B be $m \times n$ matrices and let C be an $n \times p$ matrix; then

$$(A^T)^T = A, \tag{28}$$

$$(A + B)^T = A^T + B^T, \tag{29}$$

$$(AC)^T = C^T A^T. \tag{30}$$

To prove (28) just observe that the (i, j) entry of $(A^T)^T$ is by definition the (j, i) entry of A^T, which in turn is the (i, j) entry of A, i.e., $(A^T)^T$ and A have the same (i, j) entry for each i and j. To establish (29) observe that the (i, j) entry of $(A + B)^T$ is just the (j, i) entry of $A + B$, i.e., $a_{ji} + b_{ji}$. But the latter number is just the sum of the (i, j) entries of A^T and B^T. This shows that the two sides of (29) are equal. The proof of (30) is a little less direct, but quite easy. Thus the (i, j) entry of $(AC)^T$ is by definition the (j, i) entry of AC, which is given by

$$a_{j1}c_{1i} + a_{j2}c_{2i} + \cdots + a_{jn}c_{ni}. \tag{31}$$

On the other hand, the (i, j) entry of $C^T A^T$ is

$$(C^T)_{i1}(A^T)_{1j} + \cdots + (C^T)_{in}(A^T)_{nj} = c_{1i}a_{j1} + \cdots + c_{ni}a_{jn}. \tag{32}$$

Observe that (31) and (32) are the same and the equality in (30) is established.

As an example of (30), suppose

$$A = \begin{bmatrix} 2 & 0 & 3 \\ 1 & 2 & 1 \end{bmatrix},$$

$$C = \begin{bmatrix} 1 & 1 & 5 \\ 0 & 0 & 0 \\ 3 & -5 & 2 \end{bmatrix}.$$

Then

$$(AC)^T = \begin{bmatrix} 11 & -13 & 16 \\ 4 & -4 & 7 \end{bmatrix}^T$$

$$= \begin{bmatrix} 11 & 4 \\ -13 & -4 \\ 16 & 7 \end{bmatrix}.$$

On the other hand,

$$C^T = \begin{bmatrix} 1 & 0 & 3 \\ 1 & 0 & -5 \\ 5 & 0 & 2 \end{bmatrix},$$

$$A^T = \begin{bmatrix} 2 & 1 \\ 0 & 2 \\ 3 & 1 \end{bmatrix}.$$

and

$$C^T A^T = \begin{bmatrix} 11 & 4 \\ -13 & -4 \\ 16 & 7 \end{bmatrix}$$

$$= (AC)^T.$$

Suppose we want to solve an equation

$$Ax = b, \tag{33}$$

in which A and b are numbers and we are looking for the solution x satisfying (33). We simply multiply through by A^{-1}, the inverse of A, to obtain the solution

$$x = A^{-1}b. \tag{34}$$

Of course, one has to know that $A \neq 0$ in order to make this little calculation. We have purposely written (33) to look like an equation involving a matrix A and two n-tuples, x and b. As an example, suppose A is a 2×2 matrix and x and b are in $V_2(R)$. Then equation (33) becomes

$$\begin{aligned} a_{11}x_1 + a_{12}x_2 &= b_1, \\ a_{21}x_1 + a_{22}x_2 &= b_2. \end{aligned} \tag{35}$$

Even in this simple case, the situation changes dramatically from the one for numbers. For example, suppose

$$A = \begin{bmatrix} 1 & 1 \\ 1 & 1 \end{bmatrix},$$

and

$$b = (1, 2).$$

Then (35) becomes

$$\begin{aligned} x_1 + x_2 &= 1, \\ x_1 + x_2 &= 2. \end{aligned}$$

Clearly, there are no numbers x_1 and x_2 whose sum is both 1 and 2. Thus we see that equation (33) will not always have solutions when A is a matrix and x and b are n-tuples. This means that no analogy can exist in general for the equality (34). Nevertheless, what we would like to do is the following. If there exists a matrix X for which $XA = I_2$, we can multiply both sides of (33) by X on the left to obtain

$$XAx = Xb,$$
$$I_2x = Xb,$$

and finally, since $x = I_2x$,

$$x = Xb.$$

In other words, we can solve (33) if we can find the matrix X.

Let us work out an example. Suppose

$$A = \begin{bmatrix} 1 & 1 \\ 0 & 2 \end{bmatrix},$$
$$b = (1, 1).$$

Observe that if

$$X = \begin{bmatrix} 1 & -\frac{1}{2} \\ 0 & \frac{1}{2} \end{bmatrix},$$

then

$$XA = \begin{bmatrix} 1 & -\frac{1}{2} \\ 0 & \frac{1}{2} \end{bmatrix} \begin{bmatrix} 1 & 1 \\ 0 & 2 \end{bmatrix}$$
$$= \begin{bmatrix} 1 & 0 \\ 0 & 1 \end{bmatrix}$$
$$= I_2.$$

Thus the equation

$$Ax = b$$

can be solved by multiplying through by X on the left to obtain

$$x = Xb.$$

Hence

$$x_1 = x_{11}b_1 + x_{12}b_2,$$
$$x_2 = x_{21}b_1 + x_{22}b_2,$$

and thus

$$x_1 = 1 - \tfrac{1}{2} = \tfrac{1}{2},$$
$$x_2 = 0 + \tfrac{1}{2} = \tfrac{1}{2}.$$

In other words, the solution to the system of equations

$$x_1 + x_2 = 1,$$
$$2x_2 = 1$$

is

$$x_1 = \tfrac{1}{2},$$
$$x_2 = \tfrac{1}{2}.$$

Of course, we can solve this system of equations without recourse to such indirect techniques. But we made the example easy so that we could immediately verify that the method produces the correct answer.

The matrix X (when it exists) has some of the properties of the inverse of a number. Namely, multiplication of A by X produces the identity in the same way that multiplication of a nonzero number by its inverse produces the identity, i.e., 1. We are led to the following definition.

Definition 2.3. (*Inverse of a matrix*). *Let A be an n-square matrix. If X is such a matrix that*

$$AX = XA$$
$$= I_n,$$

(36)

*then X is called an **inverse** of A.*

Observe that we have used the indefinite article "an" in this definition which makes it sound rather as if there is more than one possibility for the inverse of a matrix. Happily this is not the case. For, suppose that Y were an inverse of A also:

$$YA = AY$$
$$= I_n.$$
(37)

Then we have from (36) and (37),

$$X = XI_n$$
$$= X(AY)$$
$$= (XA)Y$$
$$= I_nY$$
$$= Y.$$

In other words, any two inverses of A must be the same. We denote the inverse of A, when it exists, by

$$A^{-1}.$$

Suppose that A and B are two n-square matrices both of which have inverses and let C be the product AB. Set

$$X = B^{-1}A^{-1}.$$
(38)

Then we can compute that

$$X(AB) = (B^{-1}A^{-1})(AB)$$
$$= B^{-1}(A^{-1}A)B$$
$$= B^{-1}(I_nB)$$
$$= B^{-1}B$$
$$= I_n,$$

and

$$(AB)X = (AB)(B^{-1}A^{-1})$$
$$= A(BB^{-1})A^{-1}$$
$$= (AI_n)(A^{-1})$$
$$= (AA^{-1})$$
$$= I_n.$$

Thus we see that we have proved the following formula:

$$(AB)^{-1} = B^{-1}A^{-1} \tag{39}$$

whenever A and B are two n-square matrices, both possessing inverses.

Now suppose that A is an n-square matrix which has an inverse. Then consider the product $(A^{-1})^T A^T$. By (30) we have

$$(A^{-1})^T A^T = (AA^{-1})^T$$
$$= I_n^T$$
$$= I_n,$$

and

$$A^T(A^{-1})^T = (A^{-1}A)^T$$
$$= I_n^T$$
$$= I_n.$$

Hence, if A has an inverse, so does A^T, and the inverse of A^T is the transpose of A^{-1}:

$$(A^T)^{-1} = (A^{-1})^T. \tag{40}$$

An $n \times n$ matrix A which has an inverse is sometimes called *nonsingular*, or *regular*, or a *unit* matrix. Thus (39) shows that the product of two nonsingular matrices is nonsingular. A matrix A which does not have an inverse is called a *singular* matrix.

For example, the matrix

$$A = \begin{bmatrix} 1 & 2 \\ 0 & 0 \end{bmatrix}$$

is singular, for if X is any 2×2 matrix, then AX must have $(0 \quad 0)$ as its second row and could not be the identity matrix I_2. However, matrices all of whose entries are different from zero can also be singular. For example, suppose

$$A = \begin{bmatrix} 1 & 1 \\ 1 & 1 \end{bmatrix},$$

and let

$$X = \begin{bmatrix} x_{11} & x_{12} \\ x_{21} & x_{22} \end{bmatrix}$$

be an arbitrary matrix. Then

$$XA = \begin{bmatrix} x_{11} + x_{12} & x_{11} + x_{12} \\ x_{21} + x_{22} & x_{21} + x_{22} \end{bmatrix}.$$

Clearly XA can never be the identity matrix, for this would require that

$$x_{11} + x_{12} = 1,$$

and

$$x_{11} + x_{12} = 0.$$

As our next example we compute the inverse of the matrix

$$\begin{bmatrix} 2 & 1 \\ 5 & 3 \end{bmatrix}.$$

We seek a matrix

$$X = \begin{bmatrix} x_{11} & x_{12} \\ x_{21} & x_{22} \end{bmatrix}$$

such that $AX = XA = I_2$. Thus we require that

$$AX = \begin{bmatrix} 2x_{11} + x_{21} & 2x_{12} + x_{22} \\ 5x_{11} + 3x_{21} & 5x_{12} + 3x_{22} \end{bmatrix}$$

$$= \begin{bmatrix} 1 & 0 \\ 0 & 1 \end{bmatrix}.$$

This leads us to a system of four equations in the four unknowns x_{11}, x_{12}, x_{21}, and x_{22}:

$$2x_{11} + x_{21} = 1,$$
$$5x_{11} + 3x_{21} = 0,$$
$$2x_{12} + x_{22} = 0,$$
$$5x_{12} + 3x_{22} = 1.$$

The first two of these equations have the solutions $x_{11} = 3$, $x_{21} = -5$, and the second two have the solutions $x_{12} = -1$, $x_{22} = 2$. Thus

$$X = \begin{bmatrix} 3 & -1 \\ -5 & 2 \end{bmatrix}.$$

We compute that

$$XA = \begin{bmatrix} 3 & -1 \\ -5 & 2 \end{bmatrix} \begin{bmatrix} 2 & 1 \\ 5 & 3 \end{bmatrix}$$

$$= \begin{bmatrix} 1 & 0 \\ 0 & 1 \end{bmatrix},$$

and hence

$$XA = AX = I_2.$$

We remark at this point that we had to verify that $XA = I_2$ even though we already knew that $AX = I_2$. One of the important theorems that we shall subsequently prove about the inverse of a matrix is that one need only verify one of these equalities and the other follows automatically.

As our final example of an operation on matrices in this section, we discuss a slight extension of the notion of transpose. Thus, suppose A is an $m \times n$ matrix with complex entries. We define the *conjugate transpose* of A to be the $n \times m$ matrix obtained by replacing each element of A^T by its complex conjugate. This matrix is denoted by

$$A^*. \tag{41}$$

If we look back at statements (28), (29), (30), and (40), we see that it is easy to prove that

$$(A^*)^* = A, \tag{42}$$

$$(A + B)^* = A^* + B^*, \tag{43}$$

$$(AC)^* = C^*A^*, \tag{44}$$

$$(A^*)^{-1} = (A^{-1})^*. \tag{45}$$

The verifications of (42), (43), (44), and (45) are left as exercises for the student.

Quiz

Answer *true* or *false*:

1. If

$$A = \begin{bmatrix} 1 & 0 \\ 0 & 1 \end{bmatrix}, \qquad B = \begin{bmatrix} 0 & 1 \\ 1 & 0 \end{bmatrix},$$

and $\alpha A + \beta B = 0_2$, then $\alpha = \beta = 0$.

2. If A is an $m \times n$ matrix, then $(-1)(-A) = A$.

3. If A and B are $m \times n$ matrices, then $(A - B) = -(B - A)$.

4. If A and B are $m \times n$ matrices and $A + B = -A$, then $A = -\frac{1}{2}B$.

5. If A is $m \times n$ and B is $n \times p$ and α and β are numbers, then $(\alpha A)(\beta B) = (\alpha \beta) AB$.

6. If A and B are $m \times n$ matrices and C is an $n \times p$ matrix, then $(A - B)C = AC - BC$.

7. If $A + A = 0_{m,n}$, then $A = 0_{m,n}$.

8. If $AB = 0_{m,n}$ and $AC = 0_{m,n}$, then $A(B + C) = 0_{m,n}$.

9. If p is an odd positive integer and A is an $n \times n$ matrix, then $(-A)^p = -A^p$.

10. If A is an $m \times n$ matrix with integer entries, then both AA^T and $A^T A$ have integer entries.

Exercises

1. Verify equations (21), (22), and (23).

2. Verify equation (26).

3. If

$$A = \begin{bmatrix} 1 & 2 & 3 \\ 4 & 5 & 6 \end{bmatrix}, \qquad B = \begin{bmatrix} 0 & 2 \\ 1 & 2 \\ 0 & -1 \end{bmatrix}, \qquad C = \begin{bmatrix} -1 & 2 \\ 0 & 4 \\ 3 & 6 \end{bmatrix},$$

then find $AB + AC$.

4. Let A be a 2×3 matrix with real number entries:

$$A = \begin{bmatrix} a_{11} & a_{12} & a_{13} \\ a_{21} & a_{22} & a_{23} \end{bmatrix};$$

find AA^T. Show that if $AA^T = 0$ (i.e., the 2×2 zero matrix), then $A = 0_{2,3}$.

5. If A is a square matrix, is it true that $AA^T = A^T A$? If not, give an example for which the equality fails.

6. Show that if $A = A^T$, then A is a square matrix and $a_{ij} = a_{ji}$ for each i and j.

7. Show that if $A + 2A^T = 0_n$, then $a_{ii} = 0$, $i = 1, \ldots, n$.

8. Let A be an $m \times n$ matrix and suppose

$$A_{(1)} = (0, \ldots, 0).$$

Show that

$$(AA^T)_{1j} = 0, \qquad j = 1, \ldots, m.$$

9. Establish formula (42).
10. Establish formula (43).
11. Establish formula (44).
12. Establish formula (45).

2.3. INTRODUCTION TO LINEAR EQUATIONS AND RANK

In this section we shall consider two closely related problems. The first of these is concerned with the development of a systematic technique for solving the equation

$$Ax = b, \tag{1}$$

where A is an $m \times n$ matrix, b is an m-tuple, and x is an "unknown" n-tuple. The second problem is to determine the number of linearly independent rows and linearly independent columns of a given $m \times n$ matrix A. We shall see that these two questions are closely linked. We begin by analyzing an example in detail. Consider the 4×7 matrix

$$A = \begin{bmatrix} 0 & 0 & 0 & 0 & 1 & 1 & 1 \\ 0 & 2 & 6 & 2 & 0 & 0 & 4 \\ 0 & 1 & 3 & 1 & 1 & 0 & 1 \\ 0 & 1 & 3 & 1 & 2 & 1 & 2 \end{bmatrix}. \tag{2}$$

The problem that we wish to solve first is the determination of the dimension of the subspace of $V_7(R)$ spanned by the rows of A. Let us tentatively call this the *row rank* of A. The steps in solving this problem consist of constructing some simplifying operations that can be performed on $A_{(1)}$, $A_{(2)}$, $A_{(3)}$, and $A_{(4)}$, the rows of A, such that the subspace of $V_7(R)$ spanned by these rows is not altered. One such operation consists of simply arranging the vectors in some other order, e.g., the dimension of the space spanned by $A_{(2)}$, $A_{(3)}$, $A_{(1)}$, and $A_{(4)}$ is also obviously the row rank of A. Another way of saying the same thing is that if we permute the rows of A in some way to obtain another matrix B, then A and B clearly have the same row rank. Another operation that we can perform on the rows of A

is to add to a given row a multiple of some other row. Suppose, for example, that we consider the subspace spanned by

$$A_{(1)}, \quad A_{(2)} + 11A_{(4)}, \quad A_{(3)}, \quad A_{(4)}. \tag{3}$$

Clearly, any linear combination of the four items in (3) is a linear combination of the original rows $A_{(1)}$, $A_{(2)}$, $A_{(3)}$, and $A_{(4)}$, so that the subspace spanned by the rows (3) is contained in the subspace spanned by $A_{(1)}$, $A_{(2)}$, $A_{(3)}$, and $A_{(4)}$. On the other hand, $A_{(1)}$, $A_{(3)}$, and $A_{(4)}$ are already in the subspace spanned by the rows (3) and

$$(A_{(2)} + 11A_{(4)}) - 11A_{(4)} = A_{(2)},$$

i.e., $A_{(2)}$ is in the subspace spanned by the rows (3) also. It follows that the subspace spanned by the rows (3) and the subspace spanned by $A_{(1)}$, $A_{(2)}$, $A_{(3)}$, and $A_{(4)}$ are the same. It thus seems reasonable to conclude that if B is a matrix obtained from A by adding to a given row of A a multiple of another row of A, then A and B have the same row rank. Finally, a third operation, which is perhaps simpler than either of the two we have discussed so far, consists of multiplying a given row by a nonzero constant. Thus it is obvious, for example, that

$$A_{(1)}, \quad -5A_{(2)}, \quad A_{(3)}, \quad A_{(4)} \tag{4}$$

span the same subspace of $V_7(R)$ as do the original rows of A. In other words, if B is a matrix obtained from A by multiplying a given row of A by a nonzero constant, then A and B have the same row rank.

We have seen in the above discussion that it is plausible to conclude that if B is any matrix obtained from A by one of the following operations, then the rows of B span the same subspace as the rows of A:

Type I operation—permute the rows;

Type II operation—add to a given row a multiple of another row;

Type III operation—multiply a given row by a non-zero number.

To abbreviate the verbiage further, we call the subspace spanned by the rows of A the *row space* of A. Our arguments to date show that if B is obtained from A by any of the above operations, then the row space of B is the same as the row space of A. Thus the procedure for finding the row space of A and its dimension, i.e., the row rank of A, is to perform a sequence of these elementary type I, II, and III operations starting with A, each time obtaining a matrix whose row space is the same as the row space of the matrix at the immediately preceding step, and hence the same as the row space of A. The goal, then, is to reduce A by a sequence of such operations to a matrix in which the row space and its dimension are easy to discern.

We work this out explicitly for the matrix A in (2). We begin by scanning the matrix A to find the first column which contains a nonzero element. In this case it is column two. By a type I operation (i.e., permuting the rows) we can bring this entry to the first row position. Thus in A we can exchange the positions of the first and third rows, which results in the matrix

$$\begin{bmatrix} 0 & 1 & 3 & 1 & 1 & 0 & 1 \\ 0 & 2 & 6 & 2 & 0 & 0 & 4 \\ 0 & 0 & 0 & 0 & 1 & 1 & 1 \\ 0 & 1 & 3 & 1 & 2 & 1 & 2 \end{bmatrix}. \tag{5}$$

Next, we can use type II operations on (5) to make all the entries which lie below the first row in column two equal to zero. Thus if we add -2 times row one to row two and then add -1 times row one to row four, we produce the following matrix:

$$\begin{bmatrix} 0 & 1 & 3 & 1 & 1 & 0 & 1 \\ 0 & 0 & 0 & 0 & -2 & 0 & 2 \\ 0 & 0 & 0 & 0 & 1 & 1 & 1 \\ 0 & 0 & 0 & 0 & 1 & 1 & 1 \end{bmatrix}. \tag{6}$$

Now we scan the matrix (6) for the first column which contains a nonzero entry below the first row. In this case it is clearly column five, and all three entries are nonzero. By a type I operation, bring one of these nonzero entries to the second row position and by multiplying the second row by an appropriate nonzero constant (a type III operation) make this entry equal to 1. In the present case, of course, the nonzero entry is already in the second row position and we reduce it to 1 by multiplying the second row of (6) by $-\frac{1}{2}$ to produce the matrix

$$\begin{bmatrix} 0 & 1 & 3 & 1 & 1 & 0 & 1 \\ 0 & 0 & 0 & 0 & 1 & 0 & -1 \\ 0 & 0 & 0 & 0 & 1 & 1 & 1 \\ 0 & 0 & 0 & 0 & 1 & 1 & 1 \end{bmatrix}. \tag{7}$$

By type II operations, we can now make all the entries in column five of the matrix (7) zeros, except the 1 in the second row, e.g., add -1 times row two to rows one, three, and four. This produces the matrix

$$\begin{bmatrix} 0 & 1 & 3 & 1 & 0 & 0 & 2 \\ 0 & 0 & 0 & 0 & 1 & 0 & -1 \\ 0 & 0 & 0 & 0 & 0 & 1 & 2 \\ 0 & 0 & 0 & 0 & 0 & 1 & 2 \end{bmatrix}. \tag{8}$$

We now scan the matrix (8) for the first column which contains a nonzero entry below row two and bring this entry by a type I operation, if necessary, to the third row position; then reduce it to 1 by multiplying the third row by an appropriate nonzero constant. In the present case, the matrix already has this form and we need not do anything. We now take the 1 in the third row position of column six of the matrix (8) and, by type II operations, reduce the remaining entries in column six to zero. For the matrix (8), this last step just consists of adding to row four -1 times row three, thereby producing the matrix

$$B = \begin{bmatrix} 0 & 1 & 3 & 1 & 0 & 0 & 2 \\ 0 & 0 & 0 & 0 & 1 & 0 & -1 \\ 0 & 0 & 0 & 0 & 0 & 1 & 2 \\ 0 & 0 & 0 & 0 & 0 & 0 & 0 \end{bmatrix}. \tag{9}$$

We now scan the matrix B for the first column (beyond column six) which contains a nonzero entry below row three. If all the rows below row three are zero, as is the case in (9), we are finished.

The row space of the matrix B is now very easy to see; for, the first three rows, i.e., the nonzero rows of (9) are, in fact, linearly independent. To see this, suppose that

$$c_1 B_{(1)} + c_2 B_{(2)} + c_3 B_{(3)} = 0. \tag{10}$$

If we write out the left side of (10) we obtain

$$c_1(0, \quad 1, \quad 3, \quad 1, \quad 0, \quad 0, \quad 2) + c_2(0, \quad 0, \quad 0, \quad 0, \quad 1, \quad 0, \quad -1)$$
$$+ c_3(0, \quad 0, \quad 0, \quad 0, \quad 0, \quad 1, \quad 2)$$
$$= (0, \quad c_1, \quad 3c_1, \quad c_1, \quad 0, \quad 0, \quad 2c_1) + (0, \quad 0, \quad 0, \quad 0, \quad c_2, \quad 0, \quad -c_2)$$
$$+ (0, \quad 0, \quad 0, \quad 0, \quad 0, \quad c_3, \quad 2c_3)$$
$$= (0, \quad c_1, \quad x, \quad x, \quad c_2, \quad c_3, \quad x).$$

(The entries indicated by x in the last vector do not matter.) This last 7-tuple is to be zero, and thus c_1, c_2, and c_3 must be zero. In other words, if a linear combination of $B_{(1)}$, $B_{(2)}$, and $B_{(3)}$ is zero, the coefficients must be zero. Thus these rows must be linearly independent and the rows $B_{(1)}$, $B_{(2)}$, and $B_{(3)}$ constitute a basis for the row space of B. But as we stated before, the row space of B is the same as the row space of A. For B was obtained from A by a sequence of elementary operations, each of which leaves the row space of the matrix at the preceding stage unaltered. We can then conclude that the row rank of A is 3 and the row space of A is spanned by the three 7-tuples $B_{(1)}$, $B_{(2)}$, and $B_{(3)}$.

We shall now see that precisely the operations that we used above to compute the row space of A will also allow us to solve the system of linear equations (1) for any m-tuple b. We shall work this out in detail using the matrix A in (2) and the m-tuple $b = (-4, \quad 2, \quad 2, \quad -2)$. Before going into the details of the example, however, we must note that operations of types I, II, and III can be performed on the system (1) without altering the set of solution vectors x. To be precise about this, suppose we write out the system of linear equations (1) as follows:

$$a_{11}x_1 + a_{12}x_2 + \cdots + a_{1n}x_n = b_1$$
$$\vdots \qquad\qquad\qquad \vdots \qquad\qquad (11)$$
$$a_{m1}x_1 + a_{m2}x_2 + \cdots + a_{mn}x_n = b_m.$$

To perform a type I operation on the system (11) means simply to exchange the position of two of the equations. This obviously is not going to affect the solutions $x = (x_1, \ldots, x_n)$ of (11). To perform a type II operation on (11) will mean that we add to one of the equations in (11) a multiple of another equation in (11), e.g., add to the pth equation c times the qth equation. In other words, we replace the system (11) by one in which every equation is identical to the one in (11) except the pth, which now reads:

$$(a_{p1} + ca_{q1})x_1 + (a_{p2} + ca_{q2})x_2 + \cdots + (a_{pn} + ca_{qn})x_n = b_p + cb_q. \quad (12)$$

Clearly, if x satisfies the system (11), it will satisfy equation (12). For, (12) can be written

$$\sum_{j=1}^{n} a_{pj}x_j + c\sum_{j=1}^{n} a_{qj}x_j = b_p + cb_q,$$

and when x satisfies (11), then

$$\sum_{j=1}^{n} a_{pj} x_j = b_p,$$

and

$$\sum_{j=1}^{n} a_{qj} x_j = b_q.$$

Thus each solution of the old system will be a solution of the new system. On the other hand, we can obtain the old system from the new one by adding to the pth equation of the new one, i.e. (12), $-c$ times the qth equation of the new one. That is, we can "undo" a type II operation by another type II operation. Thus any system resulting from (11) by a type II operation has the same set of solutions as (11). A type III operation on the system (11) just means that a given equation, say the pth, is multiplied on both sides by a nonzero constant c. It is clear that this will not alter the solutions of (11).

We see, then, that performing a set of elementary operations on the system (11) or (1), in the above sense, results in a new system which possesses precisely the same set of solutions. But performing an elementary operation on the system (1) can be incorporated into the theory of elementary operations on matrices by the following very simple device. We construct a new matrix by adjoining b to the matrix A, i.e., "stick" b onto A as an $(n + 1)$st column,

$$\begin{bmatrix} a_{11} \cdots a_{1n} \ b_1 \\ a_{21} \cdots a_{2n} \ b_2 \\ \vdots \qquad \vdots \\ a_{m1} \cdots a_{mn} \ b_m \end{bmatrix}. \tag{13}$$

The matrix (13) is called the *augmented matrix* for the system (1) and is denoted by

$$[A : b]. \tag{14}$$

It is clear that performing an elementary operation on the system (1) will replace (1) by a new system whose augmented matrix is obtained from (14) by performing the corresponding elementary operation on the rows of (14). If, for example, we multiply through the pth equation in (1) or (11) by a nonzero constant c, there results a system whose augmented matrix can be obtained from (14) by multiplying through the pth row of (14) by c. Similar remarks apply in the case of the other two elementary operations.

The idea, then, in solving the system of equations (1) is to perform a sequence of elementary operations on the augmented matrix $[A : b]$ that will reduce A in the way that we have discussed. In the example that we worked out in detail, the matrix A was given by (2). We are taking b to be $(-4, \ 2, \ 2, \ -2)$. Thus the augmented matrix is

$$[A : b] = \begin{bmatrix} 0 & 0 & 0 & 0 & 1 & 1 & 1 & -4 \\ 0 & 2 & 6 & 2 & 0 & 0 & 4 & 2 \\ 0 & 1 & 3 & 1 & 1 & 0 & 1 & 2 \\ 0 & 1 & 3 & 1 & 2 & 1 & 2 & -2 \end{bmatrix}. \tag{15}$$

Looking back, we see that we performed the following elementary operations on A that reduced it to the matrix (9):

 (i) exchange the first and third rows;

 (ii) add -2 times row one to row two;

 (iii) add -1 times row one to row four;

 (iv) multiply row two by $-\frac{1}{2}$;

 (v) add to rows one, three, and four, in succession, -1 times row two;

 (vi) add to row four -1 times row three.

Performing the elementary operations (i) through (vi) on (15) will result in a matrix of the form

$$[B : c],$$

in which B is given by (9) and c results from b by performing operations (i) through (vi) on

$$\begin{bmatrix} -4 \\ 2 \\ 2 \\ -2 \end{bmatrix}.$$

Carrying this out we have

$$
\begin{bmatrix} -4 \\ 2 \\ 2 \\ -2 \end{bmatrix} \xrightarrow{\text{(i)}} \begin{bmatrix} 2 \\ 2 \\ -4 \\ -2 \end{bmatrix} \xrightarrow{\text{(ii)}} \begin{bmatrix} 2 \\ -2 \\ -4 \\ -2 \end{bmatrix} \xrightarrow{\text{(iii)}} \begin{bmatrix} 2 \\ -2 \\ -4 \\ -4 \end{bmatrix} \xrightarrow{\text{(iv)}} \begin{bmatrix} 2 \\ 1 \\ -4 \\ -4 \end{bmatrix}
$$

$$
\xrightarrow{\text{(v)}} \begin{bmatrix} 1 \\ 1 \\ -4 \\ -4 \end{bmatrix} \xrightarrow{\text{(v)}} \begin{bmatrix} 1 \\ 1 \\ -5 \\ -4 \end{bmatrix} \xrightarrow{\text{(v)}} \begin{bmatrix} 1 \\ 1 \\ -5 \\ -5 \end{bmatrix} \xrightarrow{\text{(vi)}} \begin{bmatrix} 1 \\ 1 \\ -5 \\ 0 \end{bmatrix} = c.
$$

Thus the new system whose augmented matrix is $[B : c]$ is

$$
\begin{aligned}
x_2 + 3x_3 + x_4 + 2x_7 &= 1 \\
x_5 - x_7 &= 1 \\
x_6 + 2x_7 &= -5 \\
0 &= 0.
\end{aligned}
\tag{16}
$$

We solve the equations in (16) in reverse order:

$$
\begin{aligned}
x_6 &= -5 - 2x_7, \\
x_5 &= 1 + x_7, \\
x_2 &= 1 - 3x_3 - x_4 - 2x_7.
\end{aligned}
\tag{17}
$$

Now, (17) states that arbitrary values can be assigned to x_1, x_3, x_4 and x_7, and then x_2, x_5, and x_6 can be determined using (17). In other words, $x = (x_1, x_2, x_3, x_4, x_5, x_6, x_7)$ is a solution vector to (1) if and only if

$$
\begin{aligned}
x &= (x_1, x_2, x_3, x_4, x_5, x_6, x_7) \\
&= (x_1, 1 - 3x_3 - x_4 - 2x_7, x_3, x_4, 1 + x_7, -5 - 2x_7, x_7) \\
&= (0, 1, 0, 0, 1, -5, 0) + x_1(1, 0, 0, 0, 0, 0, 0) + x_3(0, -3, 1, 0, 0, 0, 0) \\
&\quad + x_4(0, -1, 0, 1, 0, 0, 0) + x_7(0, -2, 0, 0, 1, -2, 1).
\end{aligned}
\tag{18}
$$

We then see that the solutions to the systems (1) or (11) consist of the set of all vectors obtained by adding to the fixed vector $v_0 = (0, 1, 0, 0, 1, -5, 0)$ an arbitrary linear combination of

$$v_1 = (1, 0, 0, 0, 0, 0, 0),$$
$$v_2 = (0, -3, 1, 0, 0, 0, 0),$$
$$v_3 = (0, -1, 0, 1, 0, 0, 0),$$
$$v_4 = (0, -2, 0, 0, 1, -2, 1).$$

Note that the vector v_0 is a solution to the system (1), while v_1, v_2, v_3, and v_4 are solutions to the system of equations $Ax = 0$.

Definition 3.1. (**Row equivalence of two matrices**). *Let A and B be two m × n matrices and suppose that B can be obtained from A by a sequence of elementary row operations of types I, II, and III. Then we shall say that B is **row equivalent** to A.*

One should note that if B is row equivalent to A, then A is row equivalent to B. For, as we have just observed, any elementary row operation can be undone by an elementary row operation of the same type. Hence, if B is obtained from A by a sequence of such elementary row operations, then by performing "inverses" of these operations in opposite order on B, we will recover A.

We can summarize the work that we have been doing so far in the following important theorem.

Theorem 3.1. (**Hermite Normal Form**). *Let A be an m × n matrix of row rank r. Then A is row equivalent to a matrix B which has the following form:*
  (a) *The first r rows of B are nonzero, and the remaining m − r rows are zero.*
  (b) *There are r columns of B, columns numbered $n_1, \ldots, n_r$ ($1 \le n_1 < n_2 < \cdots < n_r \le n$), such that $B^{(n_i)} = e_i$, and $b_{ij} = 0$, $j = 1, \ldots, n_i - 1$, $i = 1, \ldots, r$.*
Here e_i is the m-tuple with 1 in the ith position, 0 elsewhere.

Observe that the matrix A in (2) was reduced to the matrix B in (9) by a sequence of elementary row operations. Moreover, the matrix B in (9) has precisely the form described in Theorem 3.1. In this case $r = 3$, the columns numbered n_1, n_2, and n_3 are columns two, five, and six in B; the first nonzero entry in row one is in column two, the first nonzero entry in row two is in column five, and the first nonzero entry in row three is in column six.

Matrices

The proof of Theorem 3.1 is just a repetition of the constructive procedure that we used in our example to reduce the matrix A in (2) to the matrix B in (9). We summarize the steps.

(i) Scan A for its first nonzero column; call it column n_1. (If A is the zero matrix, it is already in Hermite normal form.) By a type I operation, bring a nonzero entry in column n_1 into the first row position and reduce it to 1 by a type III operation. Next, annihilate the nonzero entries below the first row in column n_1 by a sequence of type II operations.

(ii) Scan rows numbered two through m of the matrix now on hand and look for the first column, call it column n_2, in which there appears a nonzero element below the first row. Observe that our choice of n_2 implies that in every row numbered two through m there must be zero entries in the columns before column n_2. Bring a nonzero entry in column n_2 to the $(2, n_2)$ position by a type I operation, make it a 1 by a type III operation, and by type II operations annihilate every entry in column n_2 except the 1 in the $(2, n_2)$ position.

(iii) Scan the matrix on hand at this point for the first column, call it n_3, which contains a nonzero entry in rows three through m. Bring a nonzero entry to the $(3, n_3)$ position, etc.

As we noted in our discussion of the example, elementary row operations on a matrix do not alter its row rank. Therefore, the matrix B obtained at the end of this reduction process must have the same row rank as the matrix A. Suppose then that the matrix B has p nonzero rows. Now, we assert that these rows must in fact be linearly independent, for if

$$\sum_{j=1}^{p} c_j B_{(j)} \tag{19}$$

were zero, then looking at position n_1 (i.e., the coordinate numbered n_1) in (19) we could conclude that $c_1 = 0$; looking at the n_2 position we could conclude that $c_2 = 0$; etc. In other words, the nonzero rows of the matrix B are linearly independent. But, since B is row equivalent to A, its row rank is r and hence $p = r$. This completes the proof.

It will be useful to us subsequently to make an observation concerning the Hermite normal form B of an $m \times m$ matrix A of row rank m. We see first from Theorem 3.1(a) that every row of B is nonzero $(m = r)$. Moreover, according to part (b) of this result, there are m columns of B which must in succession be the vectors $e_1, \ldots, e_m$, where e_i is the m-tuple with 1 in the ith position, 0 elsewhere. But after all, there are only m columns of B altogether, and so the columns of B must be $e_1, \ldots, e_m$ in succession. This is just another way of saying that B is the identity matrix I_m. We conclude then, on the basis of this discussion, the following fact:

> *If A is an m-square matrix of row rank m, then the Hermite normal form of A is I_m.*

In our next result we shall state and prove the fundamental facts concerning systems of linear equations. Almost everything we say in this result has been brought out in the discussion of the method of solution of the system of equations (1), for the special choices of A in (2) and $b = (-4, 2, 2, -2)$.

Theorem 3.2. *Let A be an $m \times n$ matrix of row rank r and let b be an m-tuple. Consider the system of equations* (1), *i.e.,*

$$Ax = b,$$

for the determination of $x = (x_1, \ldots, x_n)$.

    (a) *If b is the 0 m-tuple, then the set of solutions of $Ax = 0$ is a subspace of $V_n(R)$ of dimension $n - r$. In other words, there exist $n - r$ linearly independent vectors in $V_n(R)$, call them $v_1, \ldots, v_{n-r}$, such that any solution to $Ax = 0$ is a linear combination of these.*

    (b) *In general, the system* (1) *possesses a solution if and only if the row rank of the augmented matrix $[A : b]$ is r. The set of solutions to* (1) *(if any) can be obtained as follows: find one solution to $Ax = b$ and add to it an arbitrary linear combination of $v_1, \ldots, v_{n-r}$, the solutions to $Ax = 0$ in* (a).

Proof. Suppose that u and v are any two solutions to $Ax = 0$. Let α and β be any two elements of R and observe that

$$A(\alpha u + \beta v) = \alpha Au + \beta Av$$

$$= \alpha 0 + \beta 0$$

$$= 0.$$

In other words, an arbitrary linear combination of two solutions of the system $Ax = 0$, $\alpha u + \beta v$, is once again a solution to $Ax = 0$. Hence the set of solutions of $Ax = 0$ is a subspace of $V_n(R)$. Note also that if w and z are any two solutions to $Ax = b$, then

$$A(w - z) = Aw - Az$$

$$= b - b$$

$$= 0.$$

Thus any two solutions of $Ax = b$ differ by a solution of $Ax = 0$. Another way of saying this is as follows: if v_0 is a solution to $Ax = b$, then any other solution to the system can be obtained by adding to v_0 an arbitrary solution to $Ax = 0$; i.e., any solution to $Ax = b$ is of the form

$$v_0 + \sum_{j=1}^{n-r} k_j v_j,$$

where $v_1, \ldots, v_{n-r}$ is a basis for the set of solutions to $Ax = 0$. This proves part of (a) and (b).

We next compute the dimension of the space of solutions to $Ax = 0$ and in the process actually exhibit a basis. Moreover, if a particular solution to $Ax = b$ exists, we shall describe a method of obtaining it. Let us recall that elementary operations performed on the augmented matrix $[A : b]$ do not change the set of solutions to (1), nor do they alter the row rank of either A or $[A : b]$. Using the procedure in Theorem 3.1, perform a series of elementary row operations on the augmented matrix $[A : b]$ that reduces A to Hermite normal form B. Suppose that this produces the matrix $[B : c]$. We write out this latter matrix

$$
\begin{bmatrix}
 & n_1 & & n_2 & & n_3 & \cdots & n_r & & \\
0\cdots0 & 1 & x\cdots x & 0 & x\cdots x & 0 & x\cdots x & 0 & x\cdots x & c_1 \\
0\cdots0 & 0 & 0\cdots0 & 1 & x\cdots x & 0 & x\cdots x & 0 & x\cdots x & c_2 \\
0 & & \cdots & 0 & 0 & 0\cdots0 & 1 & x\cdots x & 0 & x\cdots x & c_3 \\
 & & & & & & 0 & & & \\
0 & & & & & & & 0 & 1 & x\cdots x & c_r \\
\hline
0 & \cdot & & & & & & & \cdot\ 0 & c_{r+1} \\
\vdots & & & & \mathbf{0} & & & & 0 & c_{r+2} \\
0 & & & & & & & & 0 & c_{m-1} \\
0 & \cdots\ 0 & \cdots & 0 & \cdots & 0 & \cdots & 0 & \cdots\ 0 & c_m \\
\end{bmatrix}
$$

$$\text{row } r \rightarrow \tag{20}$$

Concerning the Hermite normal form of A, we remind the reader that in each of the first r rows of the matrix (20) the first nonzero element we see is a 1. As we saw in our general discussion of the Hermite normal form, the r nonzero rows of B are linearly independent. The solutions to $Bx = c$ are precisely the same as the solutions to $Ax = b$, as we also saw before.

Suppose that one of $c_{r+1}, \ldots, c_m$ is not zero, say, $c_{r+1} \neq 0$. Then the $(r + 1)$st equation in the system $Bx = c$ reads

$$0x_1 + 0x_2 + \cdots + 0x_n = c_{r+1}$$
$$\neq 0. \tag{21}$$

Clearly there do not exist any $x_1, \ldots, x_n$ which satisfy (21), and thus a necessary condition for a solution to $Ax = b$ to exist is that

$$c_{r+1} = \cdots = c_m = 0. \tag{22}$$

But if (22) holds, it is obvious that the augmented matrix $[B : c]$ has row rank r, since its r nonzero rows are linearly independent. In other words, a necessary condition for the existence of a solution to $Ax = b$, or equivalently to $Bx = c$, is that the row rank of the matrix $[B : c]$ is r. But since $[B : c]$ is row equivalent to $[A : b]$, a necessary condition for the existence of a solution to $Ax = b$ is that the augmented matrix $[A : b]$ has row rank r.

Conversely, suppose the row rank of $[A : b]$, and hence of the equivalent matrix $[B : c]$, is r. Then clearly (22) would have to hold, for otherwise $[B : c]$ would have row rank at least $r + 1$. Now set

$$v_0 = (0, \ldots, 0, \overset{n_1}{c_1}, 0, \ldots, 0, \overset{n_2}{c_2}, 0, \ldots, 0, \overset{\cdots \quad n_r}{c_r}, 0, \ldots, 0) \in V_n(R),$$

in which $c_1, \ldots, c_r$ appear in positions $n_1, \ldots, n_r$ in v_0 and 0 appears in every other position. We claim that v_0 is a solution to the system $Bx = c$ and hence to (1); for, the kth equation in $Bx = c$ has the form

$$x_{n_k} + \cdots = c_k, \tag{23}$$

in which the only one of $x_{n_1}, \ldots, x_{n_r}$, which actually appears in (23) is x_{n_k}. Thus if we substitute the jth coordinate of v_0 for x_j in (23), $j = 1, \ldots, n$, the left side is precisely c_k and we have equality in (23). At this point we have seen how to obtain a solution to $Ax = b$ if one exists, namely, reduce the augmented matrix $[A : b]$ to the matrix $[B : c]$ and, using the elements of c, construct the solution vector v_0 to (1).

Our next job is to obtain a solution to the system $Ax = 0$. This amounts to setting $b = 0$ in (1). Suppose that we are looking at the system $Bx = 0$, where B is the Hermite normal form of A. We write out the system $Bx = 0$ explicitly:

$$x_{n_1} + \cdots + 0x_{n_2} + \cdots + 0x_{n_r} + \cdots = 0,$$
$$x_{n_2} + \cdots + 0x_{n_r} + \cdots = 0, \qquad (24)$$
$$x_{n_r} + \cdots = 0.$$

In the kth equation in (24), the only one of $x_{n_1}, \ldots, x_{n_r}$ which actually occurs is x_{n_k}. We emphasize that the system (24) is equivalent to $Ax = 0$, i.e., has precisely the same set of solutions as the original system $Ax = 0$. Let us examine the precise structure of a solution vector of (24):

$$x = (x_1, x_2, \ldots, \overset{n_1}{x_{n_1}}, \ldots, \overset{n_2}{x_{n_2}}, \ldots, \overset{n_r}{x_{n_r}}, \ldots, x_n) \qquad (25)$$

in which we have distinguished the components numbered $n_1, \ldots, n_r$ of x. From the first equation (24) solve for x_{n_1} in terms of the x_j, where j is none of $n_1, \ldots, n_r$; from the second equation in (24) solve for x_{n_2} in terms of the x_j, where j is again none of $n_1, \ldots, n_r$; proceed to solve for x_{n_k} in the kth equation in (24) in terms of the x_j, where j is none of $n_1, \ldots, n_r$. In (25), replace $x_{n_1}, \ldots, x_{n_r}$ by their expressions in terms of the x_j, where j is none of $n_1, \ldots, n_r$. To be specific, suppose the value of x_{n_k} obtained from the kth equation in (24) is

$$x_{n_k} = {\sum_j}' d_{kj} x_j, \qquad (26)$$

in which the prime on the summation symbol means that we are summing over only those j's different from $n_1, \ldots, n_r$. Then the solution x in (24) has the following form:

$$x = \left(x_1, x_2, \ldots, \overset{n_1}{{\sum_j}' d_{1j} x_j}, \ldots, \overset{n_2}{{\sum_j}' d_{2j} x_j}, \ldots, \overset{n_r}{{\sum_j}' d_{rj} x_j}, \ldots, x_n\right). \qquad (27)$$

In (27), the only x_j which appear are those for which j is none of $n_1, \ldots, n_r$

and we can write x in the following form:

$$
\begin{aligned}
x = &\ x_1(1, 0, \quad . \quad . \quad . \ , 0, d_{11}, 0, \ldots, 0, d_{21}, 0, \quad . \quad . \quad . \quad , 0, d_{r1}, 0, \ldots, 0) \\
&+ x_2(0, 1, 0, \ldots, 0, d_{12}, 0, \ldots, 0, d_{22}, 0, \quad . \quad . \quad . \quad , 0, d_{r2}, 0, \ldots, 0) \\
&+ \cdots \\
&+ x_k(0, \quad . \quad . \quad . \quad , 0, d_{1k}, 0, \ldots, 0, d_{2k}, 0, \ldots, 1, \ldots, 0, d_{rk}, 0, \ldots, 0) \\
&+ \cdots \\
&+ x_n(0, \quad . \quad . \quad . \quad , 0, d_{1n}, 0, \ldots, 0, d_{2n}, 0, \quad . \quad . \quad . \quad , 0, d_{rn}, 0, \ldots, 0, 1).
\end{aligned}
$$

with column markers n_1, n_2, $\cdots$, n_r.

$$
(28)
$$

Let v_k be the vector in $V_n(R)$ appearing next to x_k in (28). Observe that the kth coordinate of v_k is 1. Since there are $n - r$ scalars x_k in (28), there are, of course, $n - r$ vectors v_k. We have expressed any solution to $Ax = 0$ as a linear combination of the $n - r$ vectors v_k. Also, notice that these vectors v_k are automatically linearly independent. For, to say that a linear combination of them is zero would be to say, looking at (28) and the form of the v_k, that each x_j would have to be zero where j is none of $n_1, \ldots, n_r$. This is because the only way in which the first component in (28) can equal zero is to have $x_1 = 0$, etc. Thus we have exhibited $n - r$ linearly independent vectors in $V_n(R)$ such that the totality of solutions to $Ax = 0$ is precisely the totality of linear combinations of these vectors. This completes the proof of the theorem.

We formally define some of the ideas that have so far emerged in our discussion of linear equations. If in the system of equations (1),

$$
Ax = b,
$$

b is not the zero vector, then the system is called *nonhomogeneous*. If b is the zero vector, the system is called *homogeneous*. The set of solutions to the homogeneous system of equations

$$
Ax = 0
$$

is called the *null space* of A. The dimension of the null space is called the *nullity* of the system or the nullity of the matrix A. We can restate Theorem 3.2 as follows:

Any solution to the system of equations $Ax = b$ may be obtained as follows. Find one solution to the nonhomogeneous system $Ax = b$ and add *to it an arbitrary solution to the homogeneous system Ax = 0. The nullity of the system Ax = 0 is n − r, where r is the row rank of A and n is the number of unknowns.*

Quiz

Answer *true* or *false*:

1. Every system of two equations in three unknowns has a solution.
2. The row rank of

$$\begin{bmatrix} 0 & 1 & 2 & 3 \\ 0 & 2 & 4 & 6 \\ 0 & 0 & 0 & 0 \end{bmatrix}$$

   is 2.
3. The system of equations $Ax = b$, in which A is the matrix in Question 2 and $b = (0, 0, 1)$, has no solutions.
4. The nullity of the system of equations $Ax = 0$, where A is the matrix in Question 2, is two.
5. The nullity of the system $x_1 + x_2 + x_3 = 0$ is two.
6. The coefficient matrix in the system of equations

$$x_1 + x_3 + x_5 = 0,$$
$$x_2 + x_4 + x_6 = 0,$$
$$x_1 + x_5 + x_7 = 0$$

   is

$$\begin{bmatrix} 1 & 1 & 1 \\ 1 & 1 & 1 \\ 1 & 1 & 1 \end{bmatrix}.$$

7. The coefficient matrix in Question 6 is

$$\begin{bmatrix} 1 & 0 & 1 & 0 & 1 & 0 & 0 \\ 0 & 1 & 0 & 1 & 0 & 1 & 0 \\ 1 & 0 & 0 & 0 & 1 & 0 & 1 \end{bmatrix}.$$

8. The Hermite normal form of the matrix in Question 2 is

$$\begin{bmatrix} 0 & 1 & 2 & 3 \\ 0 & 0 & 0 & 0 \end{bmatrix}.$$

9. The Hermite normal form of the matrix

$$\begin{bmatrix} 1 & 2 & 3 \\ 2 & 1 & 0 \\ 0 & 0 & 1 \end{bmatrix}$$

is

$$\begin{bmatrix} 1 & 0 & 0 \\ 0 & 1 & 0 \\ 0 & 0 & 1 \end{bmatrix}.$$

10. The system of equations

$$\begin{aligned} x_1 + 2x_2 + 3x_3 &= b_1, \\ 2x_1 + x_2 &= b_2, \\ x_3 &= b_3 \end{aligned}$$

always has exactly one solution for any b_1, b_2, and b_3.

Exercises

1. Find the general form of all solutions to the system of equations $Ax = b$, where

$$A = \begin{bmatrix} 2 & 3 & -1 & 1 \\ 3 & 2 & -2 & 2 \\ 5 & 0 & -4 & 4 \end{bmatrix}$$

and

$$b = (-1, 1, 5).$$

2. Find the rank of the augmented matrix $[A : b]$ in Exercise 1.

3. Reduce the matrix

$$A = \begin{bmatrix} 1 & 3 & 2 \\ -1 & -1 & -1 \\ 2 & 3 & -2 \end{bmatrix}$$

to Hermite normal form.

4. What are the solutions to the system of equations $Ax = 0$, where A is the matrix in Exercise 3?

5. Find the nullity of the system $Ax = 0$, where

$$A = \begin{bmatrix} 1 & 1 & 1 \\ 1 & 1 & 1 \\ 1 & 1 & 1 \end{bmatrix}.$$

6. Find the row rank of the matrix

$$A = \begin{bmatrix} 1 & 2 & 3 & 4 \\ -1 & -2 & -3 & 5 \\ 0 & 0 & 0 & 9 \end{bmatrix}$$

by reducing it to Hermite normal form.

7. Find the inverse of the matrix

$$A = \begin{bmatrix} 1 & 3 & 2 \\ -1 & -1 & -1 \\ 2 & 3 & -2 \end{bmatrix}.$$

(See Exercise 3.)

8. Show that if A is an n-square matrix of rank n, then the system $Ax = b$ has a unique solution for any given n-tuple b.

9. Show that if A is an $m \times n$ matrix of rank n, then the system $Ax = b$ has at most one solution n-tuple.

10. Reduce the matrix

$$A = \begin{bmatrix} 2 & -1 & 3 & 0 & 1 & -2 \\ -1 & 2 & 0 & 3 & -1 & 2 \\ 1 & -1 & 1 & -1 & 2 & -4 \\ 1 & -1 & 1 & -1 & 1 & -2 \end{bmatrix}$$

to Hermite normal form.

11. Let A be the matrix in Exercise 10.
(a) What is the row rank of A?
(b) What is the nullity of A?
(c) Find a basis for the space of solutions of the system $Ax = 0$.

12. Let A be the matrix in Exercise 10 and let $b = (1, 1, 1, 0)$. Describe the set of all solutions of the system $Ax = b$.

13. Let A be the matrix in Exercise 10 and let $c = (1, -1, 2, 1)$. Describe the set of all solutions of the system $Ax = c$.

2.4. RANK AND INVERSES

In Definition 2.3 for the inverse of an n-square matrix A, we saw that if A did have an inverse, this inverse was unique, and we denoted it by A^{-1}. Also recall that a matrix with an inverse is called nonsingular. Our motivation in introducing the concept of an inverse was to solve the equation $Ax = b$ by multiplying through by the inverse of A in exactly the same way as we do for ordinary numbers. In this section we shall show how the techniques we developed in Section 2.3 for obtaining the Hermite normal form will also provide us with a method of deciding when a matrix has an inverse. Moreover, we shall develop a technique for obtaining the inverse if it exists. Recall that it is very possible for a nonzero matrix to be singular, i.e., not to have an inverse. For example, we saw near the end of Section 2.2 that the matrix

$$A = \begin{bmatrix} 1 & 1 \\ 1 & 1 \end{bmatrix}$$

is singular.

We shall begin by showing that the elementary row operations on an $m \times n$ matrix A can, in fact, be accomplished by premultiplying A by suitable nonsingular matrices. This fact is actually quite simple to see. Thus, to accomplish a type I elementary row operation, say interchanging rows s and t, let E be the matrix that one obtains from the m-square identity matrix I_m by interchanging rows s and t; e.g., if $m = 3$ and $s = 1$ and $t = 3$, then

$$E = \begin{bmatrix} 0 & 0 & 1 \\ 0 & 1 & 0 \\ 1 & 0 & 0 \end{bmatrix}.$$

If we multiply A on the left by E, then each row of EA, other than rows s and t, will be precisely the same as the corresponding row of A. However, row s of EA will be row t of A and row t of EA will be row s of A. For example,

$$EA = \begin{bmatrix} 0 & 0 & 1 \\ 0 & 1 & 0 \\ 1 & 0 & 0 \end{bmatrix} \begin{bmatrix} a_{11} & a_{12} & a_{13} & a_{14} \\ a_{21} & a_{22} & a_{23} & a_{24} \\ a_{31} & a_{32} & a_{33} & a_{34} \end{bmatrix}$$
$$= \begin{bmatrix} a_{31} & a_{32} & a_{33} & a_{34} \\ a_{21} & a_{22} & a_{23} & a_{24} \\ a_{11} & a_{12} & a_{13} & a_{14} \end{bmatrix}.$$

It is clear that premultiplying any matrix A by E will result in a matrix in which the rows s and t are interchanged. That is, E works for all matrices A. In particular, if we form the product EE, then the result will be the matrix that one obtains from E by interchanging rows s and t of E. But E itself was obtained from the identity matrix I_m by interchanging rows s and t. Hence

$$EE = I_m, \tag{1}$$

and we conclude that E is nonsingular and

$$E^{-1} = E. \tag{2}$$

Now consider a type II elementary row operation in which we add to row t a constant c times row s, $s \neq t$. Let E denote the matrix obtained from the identity matrix I_m by performing this elementary row operation on I_m. For example, if $s = 1$, $t = 3$, and $m = 3$, then E has the following form:

$$E = \begin{bmatrix} 1 & 0 & 0 \\ 0 & 1 & 0 \\ c & 0 & 1 \end{bmatrix}.$$

Suppose we now form the product EA, where A is a 3×4 matrix. Then

$$EA = \begin{bmatrix} 1 & 0 & 0 \\ 0 & 1 & 0 \\ c & 0 & 1 \end{bmatrix} \begin{bmatrix} a_{11} & a_{12} & a_{13} & a_{14} \\ a_{21} & a_{22} & a_{23} & a_{24} \\ a_{31} & a_{32} & a_{33} & a_{34} \end{bmatrix}$$

$$= \begin{bmatrix} a_{11} & a_{12} & a_{13} & a_{14} \\ a_{21} & a_{22} & a_{23} & a_{24} \\ a_{31} + ca_{11} & a_{32} + ca_{12} & a_{33} + ca_{13} & a_{34} + ca_{14} \end{bmatrix}.$$

Thus we see that premultiplying A by the matrix E replaces the third row of A by the row we obtain by adding c times the first row to the third row of A, i.e., premultiplication by E accomplishes the type II operation. Now let F be the matrix obtained from the identity matrix I_m by adding to row t of the identity matrix $-c$ times row s, where s and t are the rows indicated above. For example, in the case we just considered, F has the following form:

$$\begin{bmatrix} 1 & 0 & 0 \\ 0 & 1 & 0 \\ -c & 0 & 1 \end{bmatrix}.$$

As we just saw, premultiplying any matrix A by F will result in a matrix in which $-c$ times row one is added to row three. In particular, if we premultiply E by F, we will add $-c$ times row one of E to row three of E and it is obvious that this will result in the identity matrix. In other words, $FE = I_3$. If one now thinks of the product EF, then this will result in a matrix obtained from F by adding c times the first row of F to the third row of F. Once again this produces the identity matrix. These remarks are clearly true for m-square matrices in general, and we can therefore state that

$$FE = EF$$
$$= I_m, \tag{3}$$

and conclude that E is nonsingular and that its inverse is a matrix of the same type:

$$E^{-1} = F. \tag{4}$$

Next let E be a matrix obtained from I_m by multiplying row s of I_m by the nonzero constant c. For example, if $m = 3$ and $s = 2$, then

$$E = \begin{bmatrix} 1 & 0 & 0 \\ 0 & c & 0 \\ 0 & 0 & 1 \end{bmatrix},$$

and the student can easily verify that

$$EA = \begin{bmatrix} 1 & 0 & 0 \\ 0 & c & 0 \\ 0 & 0 & 1 \end{bmatrix} \begin{bmatrix} a_{11} & a_{12} & a_{13} & a_{14} \\ a_{21} & a_{22} & a_{23} & a_{24} \\ a_{31} & a_{32} & a_{33} & a_{34} \end{bmatrix}$$

$$= \begin{bmatrix} a_{11} & a_{12} & a_{13} & a_{14} \\ ca_{21} & ca_{22} & ca_{23} & ca_{24} \\ a_{31} & a_{32} & a_{33} & a_{34} \end{bmatrix}.$$

In other words, premultiplying the matrix A by E accomplishes the desired elementary row operation, i.e., the product EA is the matrix obtained from A by multiplying row two of A by the nonzero constant c. Now let F be the matrix obtained from I_m by multiplying row s of I_m by c^{-1}. In our present example,

$$F = \begin{bmatrix} 1 & 0 & 0 \\ 0 & c^{-1} & 0 \\ 0 & 0 & 1 \end{bmatrix}.$$

As we have just seen, premultiplying F by E will multiply row two of F by c and thus $EF = I_3$. Turning the argument around, FE is the matrix obtained from E by multiplying row two of E by c^{-1}; hence $FE = I_3$. Once again these remarks are easily seen to hold for matrices of any size.

We summarize what we have done so far in the following definition and theorem.

Definition 4.1. **(*Elementary matrices.*)** *If E is an m-square matrix obtained from the identity matrix I_m by performing an elementary row operation on I_m, then E is called an **elementary matrix**. We shall refer to the corresponding elementary matrices as being of the same types as the elementary operations used to produce them.*

Theorem 4.1. *An elementary row operation on an $m \times n$ matrix A may be accomplished by forming the product EA, where E is an m-square elementary matrix of the appropriate type. The elementary matrices are nonsingular and their inverses are given according to the following:*

(a) *If E is a type I elementary matrix, then*

$$E^{-1} = E. \tag{5}$$

(b) *If E is a type II elementary matrix obtained by adding c times row s to row t of I_m, $s \neq t$, then E^{-1} is the type II elementary matrix obtained by adding $-c$ times row s to row t of I_m.*

(c) *If E is a type III elementary matrix obtained by multiplying row s by the nonzero constant c, then E^{-1} is the type III elementary matrix obtained by multiplying row s of I_m by c^{-1}.*

Any $m \times n$ matrix A of row rank r is row equivalent to a matrix B in Hermite normal form, as we saw in Theorem 3.1. Thus, combining this with Theorem 4.1, we can state the following result.

Theorem 4.2. *If A is an $m \times n$ matrix of row rank r, then there exists a product P of m-square elementary matrices such that $PA = B$ is the Hermite normal form of A.*

Theorem 4.2 now allows us to prove the following very important fact about nonsingular matrices.

Theorem 4.3. *Let A be an m-square matrix. The following statements are all equivalent to A being nonsingular:*

(a) *A is row equivalent to the identity matrix I_m.*

(b) *The row rank of A is m.*

(c) *A is the product of elementary matrices.*

Proof. Suppose A is row equivalent to I_m. This means that by performing a sequence of elementary row operations on A we obtain I_m. According to Theorem 4.1, this implies that we can find a product of elementary matrices, $P = E_1 \cdots E_k$, such that

$$PA = (E_1 \cdots E_k)A$$
$$= I_m. \tag{6}$$

Also, by Theorem 4.1, we know that each of the matrices $E_1, \ldots, E_k$ is nonsingular. According to formula (38) in Section 2.2 we conclude that P is nonsingular and, in fact,

$$P^{-1} = E_k^{-1} \cdots E_1^{-1}. \tag{7}$$

For,

$$PP^{-1} = (E_1 \cdots E_k)(E_k^{-1} \cdots E_1^{-1})$$
$$= (E_1 \cdots E_{k-1})(E_k E_k^{-1})(E_{k-1}^{-1} \cdots E_1^{-1})$$
$$= (E_1 \cdots E_{k-1})I_m(E_{k-1}^{-1} \cdots E_1^{-1})$$
$$= (E_1 \cdots E_{k-1})(E_{k-1}^{-1} \cdots E_1^{-1})$$
$$= \cdots$$
$$= I_m.$$

Hence from (6) we see that

$$A = P^{-1}$$
$$= E_k^{-1} \cdots E_1^{-1}, \tag{8}$$

and thus

$$AP = P^{-1}P$$
$$= I_m.$$

We have proved that

$$AP = I_m,$$
$$PA = I_m,$$

and thus A is nonsingular and $A^{-1} = P$. We have now established that condition **(a)** implies that A is nonsingular. Moreover, (8) tells us that if A is nonsingular, it is row equivalent to the identity matrix, and since each of $E_1^{-1}, \ldots, E_k^{-1}$ is an elementary matrix, we can conclude from (8) that A is a product of elementary matrices. Thus if A is nonsingular, condition (a) follows. It is also obvious that if A is a product of elementary matrices, then A is nonsingular, since we have just exhibited the inverse of A under these circumstances. Hence (c) implies that A is nonsingular.

Suppose now that A is nonsingular. We reduce it to Hermite form by forming

$$(E_1 \cdots E_k)A = B, \tag{9}$$

where $E_1, \ldots, E_k$ are elementary matrices again. Since A is nonsingular, A^{-1} exists and from (9) we have

$$(E_1 \cdots E_k)AA^{-1} = BA^{-1},$$

or

$$E_1 \cdots E_k = BA^{-1}. \tag{10}$$

If we look back at the discussion immediately following Theorem 3.1, we see that B will have a zero row unless the rows of B are, in succession,

$$(1, 0, 0, \ldots, 0),$$
$$(0, 1, 0, \ldots, 0), \tag{11}$$
$$\vdots$$
$$(0, 0, \ldots, 0, 1).$$

In other words, unless B is the identity matrix I_m, its last row will be zero. But then BA^{-1} would have a zero last row also, as one sees by simply checking the matrix multiplication. Then (10) would tell us we have a nonsingular matrix, namely $E_1 \cdots E_k$, with a zero last row. But this is impossible, because for any X the product $(E_1 \cdots E_k)X$ would also have a zero last row and could never be I_m. We have proved that if A is nonsingular, then its Hermite form is I_m and hence that A is a product of elementary matrices, i.e., condition (c) holds. Moreover, it also follows that if A is nonsingular, then the row rank of A is m, i.e., A being nonsingular implies (b). Conversely, if the row rank of A is m then once again the rows of B must be (11). It follows that $B = I_m$, and hence

$$(E_1 \cdots E_k)A = I_m;$$

i.e., A is row equivalent to the identity matrix. As we have seen above, this implies that A must be nonsingular. We have proved that **(b)** implies that A is nonsingular.

As an example, let us show that the matrix

$$\begin{bmatrix} 2 & 1 & 1 \\ 1 & 2 & 1 \\ 1 & 1 & 2 \end{bmatrix}$$

is nonsingular by proving that its Hermite normal form is the identity matrix I_3. To begin with, interchange rows one and two. In succession, subtract twice the first row from the second row and then subtract the first row from the third row. This produces the matrix

$$\begin{bmatrix} 1 & 2 & 1 \\ 0 & -3 & -1 \\ 0 & -1 & 1 \end{bmatrix}. \tag{12}$$

In (12) interchange rows two and three, and multiply each of these rows by -1 to produce the matrix

$$\begin{bmatrix} 1 & 2 & 1 \\ 0 & 1 & -1 \\ 0 & 3 & 1 \end{bmatrix}. \tag{13}$$

Then by type II operations annihilate the nonzero elements in column two to obtain

$$\begin{bmatrix} 1 & 0 & 3 \\ 0 & 1 & -1 \\ 0 & 0 & 4 \end{bmatrix}. \tag{14}$$

Then, by a type III operation on row three followed by type II operations on rows one and two, it is clear that (14) is row equivalent to I_3. Hence the original matrix is nonsingular.

We remark that equation (6),

$$PA = (E_1 \cdots E_k)A$$
$$= I_m,$$

shows us how we can construct the inverse of a nonsingular matrix A. For, the preceding formula says that the product $E_1 \cdots E_k$ is A^{-1}. If we think of $E_1 \cdots E_k$ as

$$(E_1 \cdots E_k)I_m, \tag{15}$$

then (15) shows that the same sequence of elementary operations which reduces A to I_m will reduce I_m to A^{-1}.

The above remark allows us to compute the inverse of A in a purely schematic way. Write down A and immediately below it write I_m. Perform the necessary sequence of elementary operations on A to reduce it to I_m. Perform precisely the same sequence of elementary operations on I_m. When A is reduced to I_m, I_m will be reduced to A^{-1}. We illustrate by computing the inverse of the matrix A:

$$A = \begin{bmatrix} 2 & 1 & 1 \\ 1 & 2 & 1 \\ 1 & 1 & 2 \end{bmatrix},$$

$$I_3 = \begin{bmatrix} 1 & 0 & 0 \\ 0 & 1 & 0 \\ 0 & 0 & 1 \end{bmatrix}.$$

(a) Interchange rows one and three, subtract row one from row two, and then subtract twice row one from row three in both matrices. This produces the pair

$$\begin{bmatrix} 1 & 1 & 2 \\ 0 & 1 & -1 \\ 0 & -1 & -3 \end{bmatrix},$$

$$\begin{bmatrix} 0 & 0 & 1 \\ 0 & 1 & -1 \\ 1 & 0 & -2 \end{bmatrix}. \tag{16}$$

(b) In the pair (16) subtract row two from row one and add row two to row three to produce the pair

$$\begin{bmatrix} 1 & 0 & 3 \\ 0 & 1 & -1 \\ 0 & 0 & -4 \end{bmatrix},$$

$$\begin{bmatrix} 0 & -1 & 2 \\ 0 & 1 & -1 \\ 1 & 1 & -3 \end{bmatrix}. \tag{17}$$

(c) In each of the matrices (17) multiply row three by $-\frac{1}{4}$, add row three to row two, and subtract three times row three from row one. This gives us the pair

$$\begin{bmatrix} 1 & 0 & 0 \\ 0 & 1 & 0 \\ 0 & 0 & 1 \end{bmatrix} = I_3,$$

$$\begin{bmatrix} \frac{3}{4} & -\frac{1}{4} & -\frac{1}{4} \\ -\frac{1}{4} & \frac{3}{4} & -\frac{1}{4} \\ -\frac{1}{4} & -\frac{1}{4} & \frac{3}{4} \end{bmatrix}. \tag{18}$$

We check that this last matrix is, in fact, A^{-1} by computing AA^{-1}:

$$\begin{bmatrix} 2 & 1 & 1 \\ 1 & 2 & 1 \\ 1 & 1 & 2 \end{bmatrix} \begin{bmatrix} \frac{3}{4} & -\frac{1}{4} & -\frac{1}{4} \\ -\frac{1}{4} & \frac{3}{4} & -\frac{1}{4} \\ -\frac{1}{4} & -\frac{1}{4} & \frac{3}{4} \end{bmatrix}$$

$$= \begin{bmatrix} 1 & 0 & 0 \\ 0 & 1 & 0 \\ 0 & 0 & 1 \end{bmatrix}.$$

So far we have confined our attention to the row rank of a matrix. The reason for this was that it was the pertinent concept in analyzing systems of linear equations. We recall that the row rank of an $m \times n$ matrix A is just the dimension in $V_n(R)$ of the subspace spanned by the n-tuples which are the rows of A. It is natural to ask if there is an analogous concept for the columns of A. The columns of A are m-tuples and hence the pertinent question is: what is the dimension of the subspace of $V_m(R)$ spanned by the columns of A? It is a rather unexpected result that the row rank and the column rank of any matrix are the same. This means, for example, that in a 3×100 matrix of row rank 2, there can only be two linearly independent columns in any subset of the 100 columns of A.

To prove that the row rank and the column rank are the same, we must examine what happens to the column rank when an elementary row operation is performed on the matrix. In answer to this problem we have:

Theorem 4.4. *If A is an $m \times n$ matrix, then the column rank of A is unaltered when A is subjected to an elementary row operation.*

Proof. We break the proof into three parts, one for each of the three types of elementary row operations. Suppose first, however, that A has column rank k and that columns $j_1 \cdots j_k$ of A constitute a basis for the space spanned by the columns of A. This means that if $A^{(t)}$ is any column of A, then there exist constants, $c_{t1}, \ldots, c_{tk}$, such that

$$A^{(t)} = c_{t1} A^{(j_1)} + \cdots + c_{tk} A^{(j_k)}$$

$$= c_{t1} \begin{bmatrix} a_{1j_1} \\ a_{2j_1} \\ \vdots \\ a_{mj_1} \end{bmatrix} + \cdots + c_{tk} \begin{bmatrix} a_{1j_k} \\ a_{2j_k} \\ \vdots \\ a_{mj_k} \end{bmatrix}. \tag{19}$$

First suppose that A is subjected to a type I elementary row operation in which rows numbered p and q are interchanged. Then all columns in the new matrix look exactly like the columns in A, except that the entries in positions p and q in each of the new columns are interchanged. It is clear that each of the columns of the new matrix can be written as in (19), since we are just looking at the same series of m equalities (the equality of the components on the two sides of (19) in an altered order).

Suppose next that we perform a type III operation on row p of A by multiplying through by a nonzero constant d. What this does to each of the columns of A is to replace the pth entry by d times the pth entry. It is obvious in looking at (19) again that the series of m equations expressing the equality of the two sides of (19) will be altered only in that both sides of the pth equation will be multiplied by d. Thus a type III elementary row operation leaves the column rank unaltered.

Finally, suppose we add d times row q to row p of A, producing a matrix H. The effect that this has on column $A^{(t)}$ is to replace it by the following column:

$$H^{(t)} = \begin{bmatrix} a_{1t} \\ a_{2t} \\ \vdots \\ a_{p-1,t} \\ a_{pt} + da_{qt} \\ a_{p+1,t} \\ \vdots \\ a_{mt} \end{bmatrix}.$$

The m equations expressing the equality on both sides of (19) are identical for H except that the pth equation is altered. But, since

$$a_{pt} = c_{t1}a_{pj_1} + \cdots + c_{tk}a_{pj_k} \tag{20}$$

and

$$a_{qt} = c_{t1}a_{qj_1} + \cdots + c_{tk}a_{qj_k}, \tag{21}$$

we see that multiplying (21) by d and adding it to (20) results in the statement of equality of the pth components of $H^{(t)}$ and

$$c_{t1}H^{(j_1)} + \cdots + c_{tk}H^{(j_k)}.$$

We illustrate the argument in Theorem 4.4 with an example. Consider the 3×4 matrix

$$A = \begin{bmatrix} 1 & 6 & 3 & 4 \\ 1 & 2 & -1 & 1 \\ -1 & 2 & 5 & 2 \end{bmatrix}.$$

We assert that the first two columns of A form a basis for the column space of A, i.e., the column rank of A is 2 and $A^{(1)}$ and $A^{(2)}$ span the column space of A. First observe that

$$\begin{bmatrix} 3 \\ -1 \\ 5 \end{bmatrix} = -3 \begin{bmatrix} 1 \\ 1 \\ -1 \end{bmatrix} + \begin{bmatrix} 6 \\ 2 \\ 2 \end{bmatrix}, \tag{22}$$

$$\begin{bmatrix} 4 \\ 1 \\ 2 \end{bmatrix} = -\tfrac{1}{2} \begin{bmatrix} 1 \\ 1 \\ -1 \end{bmatrix} + \tfrac{3}{4} \begin{bmatrix} 6 \\ 2 \\ 2 \end{bmatrix}. \tag{23}$$

These correspond to the equations (19), in which j_1 is 1 and j_2 is 2. Suppose we were to perform an elementary row operation of type I, say, interchange rows one and three. This produces the matrix

$$\begin{bmatrix} -1 & 2 & 5 & 2 \\ 1 & 2 & -1 & 1 \\ 1 & 6 & 3 & 4 \end{bmatrix}.$$

It is clear that the equations (22) and (23) change into

$$\begin{bmatrix} 5 \\ -1 \\ 3 \end{bmatrix} = -3 \begin{bmatrix} -1 \\ 1 \\ 1 \end{bmatrix} + \begin{bmatrix} 2 \\ 2 \\ 6 \end{bmatrix}$$

and

$$\begin{bmatrix} 2 \\ 1 \\ 4 \end{bmatrix} = -\tfrac{1}{2} \begin{bmatrix} -1 \\ 1 \\ 1 \end{bmatrix} + \tfrac{3}{4} \begin{bmatrix} 2 \\ 2 \\ 6 \end{bmatrix}.$$

As another example, suppose we perform a type II operation on *A* in which we add -1 times row one to row two. This results in the matrix

$$\begin{bmatrix} 1 & 6 & 3 & 4 \\ 0 & -4 & -4 & -3 \\ -1 & 2 & 5 & 2 \end{bmatrix}.$$

This operation replaces (22) and (23) by the following equations:

$$\begin{bmatrix} 3 \\ -1-3 \\ 5 \end{bmatrix} = -3 \begin{bmatrix} 1 \\ 1-1 \\ -1 \end{bmatrix} + \begin{bmatrix} 6 \\ 2-6 \\ 2 \end{bmatrix},$$

$$\begin{bmatrix} 4 \\ 1-4 \\ 2 \end{bmatrix} = -\tfrac{1}{2} \begin{bmatrix} 1 \\ 1-1 \\ -1 \end{bmatrix} + \tfrac{3}{4} \begin{bmatrix} 6 \\ 2-6 \\ 2 \end{bmatrix},$$

which become, respectively,

$$\begin{bmatrix} 3 \\ -4 \\ 5 \end{bmatrix} = -3 \begin{bmatrix} 1 \\ 0 \\ -1 \end{bmatrix} + \begin{bmatrix} 6 \\ -4 \\ 2 \end{bmatrix},$$

$$\begin{bmatrix} 4 \\ -3 \\ 2 \end{bmatrix} = -\tfrac{1}{2} \begin{bmatrix} 1 \\ 0 \\ -1 \end{bmatrix} + \tfrac{3}{4} \begin{bmatrix} 6 \\ -4 \\ 2 \end{bmatrix}.$$

In other words, the relations which express columns three and four as linear combinations of columns one and two remain the same for the matrix after the type II elementary operations are performed. We omit the entirely similar argument for type III operations.

Theorem 4.4 enables us to prove that the row rank and the column rank are the same.

Theorem 4.5. *If A is an m × n matrix, then the row rank and the column rank of A are equal.*

Proof. The idea of this proof is to perform a sequence of elementary row operations on the matrix A to reduce it to the Hermite normal form, B. We then examine B and determine its column rank. The column rank of B must be the same as the column rank of A, because B was obtained from A by a sequence of elementary row operations each of which (according to Theorem 4.4) leaves the column rank unaltered. Thus our problem is to determine the column rank of the matrix B in Hermite normal form. Suppose, then, that the row rank of A is r. Now, according to Theorem 3.1, the last $m - r$ rows of B must be zero and there exist precisely r columns of B (in the statement of Theorem 3.1 these are called $B^{(n_1)}, \ldots, B^{(n_r)}$) which in succession are the m-tuples

$$e_1 = \begin{bmatrix} 1 \\ \vdots \\ 0 \\ 0 \\ \vdots \\ 0 \end{bmatrix}, \quad e_2 = \begin{bmatrix} 0 \\ 1 \\ \vdots \\ 0 \\ \vdots \\ 0 \end{bmatrix}, \ldots, e_r = \begin{bmatrix} 0 \\ \vdots \\ 0 \\ 1 \\ 0 \\ \vdots \\ 0 \end{bmatrix}. \tag{24}$$

Now, any column of B has nonzero entries only in its first r positions, say,

$$B^{(j)} = \begin{bmatrix} b_{1j} \\ b_{2j} \\ \vdots \\ b_{rj} \\ 0 \\ \vdots \\ 0 \end{bmatrix}.$$

But then we can write

$$B^{(j)} = b_{1j} e_1 + \cdots + b_{rj} e_r;$$

i.e., any column of B can be expressed as a linear combination of the columns (24), and we know, of course, that the columns (24) are linearly independent. Hence the column rank of B is r and the proof is complete.

We illustrate the computation of the column rank of the matrix

$$\begin{bmatrix} 1 & 6 & 3 & 4 \\ 1 & 2 & -1 & 1 \\ -1 & 2 & 1 & 2 \end{bmatrix}$$

by reducing it to Hermite normal form. First add row one to row three and then subtract row one from row two. This results in the matrix

$$\begin{bmatrix} 1 & 6 & 3 & 4 \\ 0 & -4 & -4 & -3 \\ 0 & 8 & 4 & 6 \end{bmatrix}.$$

Now add 2 times row two to row three, then multiply row two by $-\frac{1}{4}$, which results in the matrix

$$\begin{bmatrix} 1 & 6 & 3 & 4 \\ 0 & 1 & 1 & \frac{3}{4} \\ 0 & 0 & -4 & 0 \end{bmatrix}.$$

Add -6 times row two to row one to produce the matrix

$$\begin{bmatrix} 1 & 0 & -3 & -\frac{1}{2} \\ 0 & 1 & 1 & \frac{3}{4} \\ 0 & 0 & -4 & 0 \end{bmatrix}.$$

Now, multiply row three by $-\frac{1}{4}$, subtract row three from row two, and add 3 times row three to row one. This results in the matrix

$$\begin{bmatrix} 1 & 0 & 0 & -\frac{1}{2} \\ 0 & 1 & 0 & \frac{3}{4} \\ 0 & 0 & 1 & 0 \end{bmatrix}, \tag{25}$$

which is in Hermite normal form. The matrix (25) has row rank 3 and hence has column rank 3 as well.

Definition 4.2. (*Rank of a matrix.*) *The common value of the row rank and the column rank of a matrix A is called the **rank** of A. It is denoted by $\rho(A)$.*

At the beginning of this section we saw how elementary row operations could be accomplished by premultiplying a matrix by the corresponding type of elementary matrix (see Definition 4.1). In precisely the same way in which we define the three types of elementary row operations we can define the three types of elementary column operations:

Type I: interchange two columns;

Type II: add to a column a multiple of another column;

Type III: multiply a column by a nonzero number.

By arguments almost identical to those used for elementary row operations, we can see that the three types of elementary column operations can be accomplished by postmultiplication of A by appropriate elementary matrices. For example, suppose A is a 3×4 matrix and we wish to add c times column two to column four. Consider the following elementary matrix:

$$E = \begin{bmatrix} 1 & 0 & 0 & 0 \\ 0 & 1 & 0 & c \\ 0 & 0 & 1 & 0 \\ 0 & 0 & 0 & 1 \end{bmatrix}. \tag{26}$$

The matrix (26) was obtained from the 4×4 identity matrix I_4 by performing the desired column operation on I_4. It is nevertheless an elementary matrix as defined in Definition 4.1, since it could also be obtained from I_4 by adding c times row four to row two. Now, if A is a 3×4 matrix, say, then we compute that

$$AE = \begin{bmatrix} a_{11} & a_{12} & a_{13} & a_{14} \\ a_{21} & a_{22} & a_{23} & a_{24} \\ a_{31} & a_{32} & a_{33} & a_{34} \end{bmatrix} \begin{bmatrix} 1 & 0 & 0 & 0 \\ 0 & 1 & 0 & c \\ 0 & 0 & 1 & 0 \\ 0 & 0 & 0 & 1 \end{bmatrix}$$

$$= \begin{bmatrix} a_{11} & a_{12} & a_{13} & ca_{12} + a_{14} \\ a_{21} & a_{22} & a_{23} & ca_{22} + a_{24} \\ a_{31} & a_{32} & a_{33} & ca_{32} + a_{34} \end{bmatrix}.$$

Similar sorts of computations can be used to verify that elementary column operations on a matrix can be accomplished by postmultiplication of a matrix by an appropriate elementary matrix, i.e., "appropriate" elementary matrix here means a matrix obtained from the identity matrix by performing the required elementary column operation on it.

Theorem 4.6. *Let A be an m × n matrix of rank r. There exist nonsingular m-square and n-square matrices P and Q, respectively, such that*

$$PAQ = \begin{bmatrix} 1 & 0 & \cdots & 0 & 0 \cdots 0 \\ 0 & 1 & & \vdots & \cdot & \cdot \\ 0 & 0 & \cdot & \vdots & \cdot & \cdot \\ \vdots & \vdots & \cdot & 0 & \cdot & \cdot \\ 0 & \cdots & 0 & 1 & 0 \cdots 0 \\ \hline 0 & \cdots & & 0 & 0 \cdots 0 \\ \vdots & & & \vdots & \vdots & \vdots \\ 0 & \cdots & & 0 & 0 \cdots 0 \end{bmatrix}, \tag{27}$$

in which there are r ones appearing in the matrix (27) *in positions* $(1, 1), \ldots,$ (r, r) *and zeros everywhere else.*

Proof. This theorem is very easy to prove, since we can call upon Theorem 4.2 to obtain a nonsingular matrix P such that $PA = B$ is in Hermite normal form. Now, there are r columns in B which are the m-tuples

$$e_1 = \begin{bmatrix} 1 \\ \vdots \\ 0 \\ 0 \\ \cdot \\ \vdots \\ 0 \end{bmatrix}, \quad e_2 = \begin{bmatrix} 0 \\ 1 \\ \vdots \\ 0 \\ \cdot \\ \vdots \\ 0 \end{bmatrix}, \ldots, e_r = \begin{bmatrix} 0 \\ \vdots \\ 0 \\ 1 \\ 0 \\ \vdots \\ 0 \end{bmatrix}. \tag{28}$$

Using elementary type II column operations with e_1, we can annihilate all the entries appearing in the first row of B except the first entry 1 in e_1. Similarly, we can annihilate all the entries in row k of B by elementary type II column operations by using e_k, except for the kth entry 1 in e_k. Since everything below the rth row in B is zero, the result of this succession of type II column operations will produce a matrix whose only nonzero columns are the m-tuples (28). By type I column operations, we can shift these columns (28) into the first r column positions, producing the matrix on the right in (27). Now, each of the indicated elementary column operations may be accomplished by a postmultiplication (i.e., multiplying on the right) by an elementary matrix which we know to be nonsingular.

Definition 4.3. **(Equivalence.)** *Two m × n matrices A and B are said to be* **equivalent** *if there exist two nonsingular matrices P and Q for which* $PAQ = B$. *If A is an m × n matrix of rank r, then the matrix on the right in (27) is called the* **canonical form** *of A under equivalence.*

Theorem 4.7. *Two m × n matrices A and B are equivalent if and only if they have the same rank.*

Proof. Suppose A and B have the same rank r. Then, according to Theorem 4.6, both A and B are equivalent to the same canonical form that appears in (27), i.e., the $m \times n$ matrix with ones in the positions $(1, 1), \ldots, (r, r)$ and zeros elsewhere. Hence there exist nonsingular m-square matrices P and P_1 and nonsingular n-square matrices Q and Q_1 such that

$$PAQ = P_1 B Q_1. \tag{29}$$

Multiply (29) on the left by P_1^{-1} and on the right by Q_1^{-1} to obtain

$$(P_1^{-1}P)A(QQ_1^{-1}) = B. \tag{30}$$

Since $P_1^{-1}P$ and QQ_1^{-1} are nonsingular, it follows that A and B are equivalent. Conversely, suppose that A and B are equivalent, so that $PAQ = B$ for appropriate nonsingular matrices P and Q. Both P and Q are products of elementary matrices [see Theorem 4.3(c)], and hence the rank of A must be the same as the rank of PAQ. (Remember that rank is unaltered by elementary row and column operations.)

For example, the matrices

$$A = \begin{bmatrix} 0 & 1 & 1 \\ 1 & 2 & 1 \\ 1 & 1 & 1 \end{bmatrix}$$

and

$$B = \begin{bmatrix} 1 & 1 & 1 \\ 0 & 1 & 1 \\ 0 & 0 & 1 \end{bmatrix}$$

are equivalent. For, by a sequence of elementary row operations, both A

and B can easily be reduced to the identity matrix I_3. Hence they have the same rank, namely 3, and are thus equivalent.

Quiz
Answer *true* or *false*:

1. Premultiplying a $3 \times m$ matrix A by the elementary matrix

$$E = \begin{bmatrix} 1 & 0 & 1 \\ 0 & 1 & 0 \\ 0 & 0 & 1 \end{bmatrix}$$

has the effect of adding row three of A to row one of A.

2. The 2×3 matrix

$$\begin{bmatrix} 1 & 0 & 0 \\ 0 & 1 & 0 \end{bmatrix}$$

is an elementary matrix.

3. Every elementary matrix is nonsingular.

4. The elementary matrix

$$\begin{bmatrix} 0 & 0 & 1 \\ 0 & 1 & 0 \\ 1 & 0 & 0 \end{bmatrix}$$

is equal to its own inverse.

5. The inverse of the matrix

$$\begin{bmatrix} 1 & 0 & 2 \\ 0 & 1 & 0 \\ 0 & 0 & 1 \end{bmatrix}$$

is

$$\begin{bmatrix} 1 & 0 & -2 \\ 0 & 1 & 0 \\ 0 & 0 & 1 \end{bmatrix}.$$

6. The inverse of the matrix

$$\begin{bmatrix} 4 & 0 & 0 \\ 0 & 1 & 0 \\ 0 & 0 & 1 \end{bmatrix}$$

is

$$\begin{bmatrix} -4 & 0 & 0 \\ 0 & 1 & 0 \\ 0 & 0 & 1 \end{bmatrix}.$$

7. If A is the product of elementary matrices, then A is nonsingular.

8. The matrix

$$\begin{bmatrix} 0 & 1 \\ 1 & 0 \end{bmatrix}$$

is singular.

9. The Hermite normal form of a nonsingular matrix is the identity matrix.

10. The canonical form of the 1×4 matrix

$$[1 \quad 1 \quad 1 \quad 1]$$

is

$$[1 \quad 0 \quad 0 \quad 0].$$

Exercises

1. Express the matrix

$$\begin{bmatrix} 1 & 1 & 1 \\ 0 & 1 & 1 \\ 0 & 0 & 1 \end{bmatrix}$$

as a product of elementary matrices.

2. Find the rank of the matrix

$$\begin{bmatrix} 1 & 0 & -1 & 2 & 5 \\ 0 & 0 & 0 & 1 & 1 \\ 1 & -1 & -1 & 2 & 3 \end{bmatrix}.$$

3. Find the inverse of the matrix

$$\begin{bmatrix} 1 & 0 & 0 & 1 \\ 0 & 1 & 1 & 0 \\ 0 & 1 & -1 & 0 \\ -1 & 0 & 0 & 1 \end{bmatrix}$$

by performing the same sequence of elementary row operations on I_4 that are required to reduce A to its Hermite normal form I_4.

4. Find the canonical form of the matrix

$$\begin{bmatrix} 1 & 1 \\ 1 & 1 \\ 1 & 1 \end{bmatrix}.$$

5. Are the following two matrices equivalent?

$$A = \begin{bmatrix} 1 & 1 & 1 \\ 1 & 1 & 1 \\ 0 & 0 & 0 \end{bmatrix}, \quad B = \begin{bmatrix} 0 & 0 & 0 \\ 0 & 0 & 0 \\ 0 & 0 & 1 \end{bmatrix}.$$

Matrices

6. Let E_{ij} be the $m \times n$ matrix whose only nonzero entry is a 1 appearing in the (i, j) position. Prove that these matrices are all equivalent to one another and determine their common canonical form.

7. Find the canonical form of the matrix

$$\begin{bmatrix} 1 & 1 & 1 & -1 \\ 1 & 1 & 1 & 1 \\ 1 & 1 & 1 & 1 \end{bmatrix}.$$

8. Compute the rank of the matrix

$$\begin{bmatrix} 1 & 1 & 1 & 1 \\ 1 & 2 & 4 & 8 \\ 1 & 3 & 9 & 27 \\ 1 & 4 & 16 & 64 \end{bmatrix}.$$

9. Find the inverse of the matrix

$$\begin{bmatrix} 5 & -1 & -1 & -1 & -1 \\ -1 & 5 & -1 & -1 & -1 \\ -1 & -1 & 5 & -1 & -1 \\ -1 & -1 & -1 & 5 & -1 \\ -1 & -1 & -1 & -1 & 5 \end{bmatrix}.$$

10. Show by example that two 3×4 matrices of the same rank need not have the same Hermite normal form.

11. Prove that if A and B are equivalent matrices, then B and A are equivalent.

12. Prove that A is always equivalent to itself.

13. Prove that if A is equivalent to B and B is equivalent to C, then A is equivalent to C.

14. Prove that if A is a matrix and c is a nonzero number, then A and cA are equivalent.

15. Prove that if A is an n-square matrix, then A and A^T are equivalent. (*Hint: A* and A^T have the same rank in view of Theorem 4.5. Apply Theorem 4.7.)

3
Determinants

3.1. THE DETERMINANT FUNCTION

A matrix may be regarded as a representation of a linear transformation or merely as an array of numbers. In either case it is a fairly complicated entity. We often can describe certain distinguishing characteristics of a matrix, or describe the relation between matrices, by means of certain numbers associated with a matrix. Of course, a rule that associates with every matrix a specific number defines a number-valued function on matrices. One of the most important of these number-valued functions defined on square matrices is the determinant function. This function has been studied extensively for over 200 years. The most astonishing fact in the history of determinants is that the concept of a determinant (i.e., of the value of the determinant function on a matrix) preceded by some 100 years the concept of a matrix. Actually, the two concepts were badly confused until the beginning of this century.

We shall define inductively the determinant function from $M_n(C)$, the set of n-square complex matrices, to the set of complex numbers C (or from $M_n(R)$ to R). The value of the determinant function for an n-square matrix A is called the *determinant* of A and is denoted by $\det(A)$. We shall also require the following notation. If $A = (a_{ij})$ is an n-square matrix, then $A(i|j)$ denotes the $(n-1)$-square matrix obtained from A by deleting the ith row and the jth column of A. Similarly, $A(i_1, \ldots, i_r | j_1, \ldots, j_r)$ is the $(n-r)$-square matrix obtained from A by deleting the rows numbered $i_1, \ldots, i_r$ and the columns numbered $j_1, \ldots, j_r$. The matrix $A(i_1, \ldots, i_r | j_1, \ldots, j_r)$ is called a *submatrix* of A.

Example 1.1.

Let

$$A = \begin{bmatrix} a_{11} & a_{12} & a_{13} & a_{14} \\ a_{21} & a_{22} & a_{23} & a_{24} \\ a_{31} & a_{32} & a_{33} & a_{34} \\ a_{41} & a_{42} & a_{43} & a_{44} \end{bmatrix};$$

then

$$A(2 \mid 1) = \begin{bmatrix} a_{12} & a_{13} & a_{14} \\ a_{32} & a_{33} & a_{34} \\ a_{42} & a_{43} & a_{44} \end{bmatrix}$$

and

$$A(2, 4 \mid 1, 2) = \begin{bmatrix} a_{13} & a_{14} \\ a_{33} & a_{34} \end{bmatrix}.$$

Definition 1.1. (**Determinant.**) *Let* $A = (a_{ij})$ *be an n-square matrix. If* $n = 1$, *we define*

$$\det(A) = a_{11};$$

if $n \geq 2$, *then*

$$\det(A) = \sum_{j=1}^{n} (-1)^{1+j} a_{1j} \det(A(1 \mid j)).$$

In other words, we define the determinant of a 1×1 *matrix to be the entry, then we define the determinant of an* $n \times n$ *matrix,* $n > 1$, *in terms of determinants of* $(n-1) \times (n-1)$ *matrices. The determinant of a submatrix of A is called a* **subdeterminant** *of A. The subdeterminant* $\det(A(i \mid j))$ *is also called the* **minor** *of* a_{ij} *in A.*

Example 1.2.

(a) Let

$$A = \begin{bmatrix} a_{11} & a_{12} \\ a_{21} & a_{22} \end{bmatrix}.$$

Then

$$\det(A) = (-1)^{1+1}a_{11}\det(A(1\,|\,1)) + (-1)^{1+2}a_{12}\det(A(1\,|\,2))$$

$$= a_{11}a_{22} - a_{12}a_{21}.$$

(b) Let

$$A = \begin{bmatrix} a_{11} & a_{12} & a_{13} \\ a_{21} & a_{22} & a_{23} \\ a_{31} & a_{32} & a_{33} \end{bmatrix}.$$

Then

$$\det(A) = (-1)^{1+1}a_{11}\det(A(1\,|\,1)) + (-1)^{1+2}a_{12}\det(A(1\,|\,2))$$
$$+ (-1)^{1+3}a_{13}\det(A(1\,|\,3))$$

$$= a_{11}\det\left(\begin{bmatrix} a_{22} & a_{23} \\ a_{32} & a_{33} \end{bmatrix}\right) - a_{12}\det\left(\begin{bmatrix} a_{21} & a_{23} \\ a_{31} & a_{33} \end{bmatrix}\right)$$

$$+ a_{13}\det\left(\begin{bmatrix} a_{21} & a_{22} \\ a_{31} & a_{32} \end{bmatrix}\right)$$

$$= a_{11}(a_{22}a_{33} - a_{23}a_{32}) - a_{12}(a_{21}a_{33} - a_{23}a_{31})$$
$$+ a_{13}(a_{21}a_{32} - a_{22}a_{31})$$

$$= a_{11}a_{22}a_{33} + a_{12}a_{23}a_{31} + a_{13}a_{21}a_{32} - a_{11}a_{23}a_{32}$$
$$- a_{12}a_{21}a_{33} - a_{13}a_{22}a_{31}.$$

(c) Let

$$B = \begin{bmatrix} 1 & 2 & 3 \\ -2 & 1 & 0 \\ 1 & -1 & 1 \end{bmatrix}.$$

Then

$$\det(B) = 1\det\left(\begin{bmatrix} 1 & 0 \\ -1 & 1 \end{bmatrix}\right) - 2\det\left(\begin{bmatrix} -2 & 0 \\ 1 & 1 \end{bmatrix}\right) + 3\det\left(\begin{bmatrix} -2 & 1 \\ 1 & -1 \end{bmatrix}\right)$$

$$= 1(1 - 0) - 2(-2 - 0) + 3(2 - 1)$$

$$= 8.$$

(d) Show that $\det(I_n) = 1$. We use induction on n. Clearly $\det(I_1) = 1$. We now assume that $\det(I_{n-1}) = 1$ and prove the formula for the $n \times n$ identity matrix. Since every entry in the first row, except the $(1, 1)$ entry, is 0, it follows directly from Definition 1.1 that

$$\det(I_n) = 1 \det(I_n(1 \mid 1))$$
$$= \det(I_{n-1})$$
$$= 1.$$

Some remarkable properties of the determinant function are set out in the following theorem.

Theorem 1.1. *Let* $A = (a_{ij})$ *be an n-square matrix.*
(a) *For any* i, $1 \le i \le n$,

$$\det(A) = \sum_{j=1}^{n} (-1)^{i+j} a_{ij} \det(A(i \mid j)). \tag{1}$$

[Formula (1) is called the *expansion of the determinant of* A *by its ith row*. The number $(-1)^{i+j} \det(A(i \mid j))$ is called the *cofactor* of a_{ij}.]
(b) *If* $B = (b_{ij})$ *is the matrix obtained by interchanging the rth row and the sth row* $(r < s)$ *of* A, *then* $\det(B) = -\det(A)$.
(c) *If two rows of* A *are identical, then* $\det(A) = 0$.
(d) *If* C *is the matrix obtained from* A *by multiplying each entry in the sth row of* A *by a scalar* k, *then* $\det(C) = k \det(A)$.
(e) *For fixed distinct integers* r *and* s, $1 \le r$, $s \le n$ *and a scalar* k, *let* $D = (d_{ij})$ *be defined by*

$$d_{rj} = a_{rj} + k a_{sj}, \qquad j = 1, \ldots, n,$$

and

$$d_{ij} = a_{ij}, \qquad \text{otherwise;}$$

that is, D *is the matrix obtained from* A *by adding* k *times row* s *to row* r. *Then*

$$\det(D) = \det(A).$$

Proof.

(a) We use induction on n. For $n = 2$ it suffices to prove (1) for $i = 2$. Now, the right side of (1) is equal to

$$(-1)^{2+1}a_{21}a_{12} + (-1)^{2+2}a_{22}a_{11} = a_{11}a_{22} - a_{12}a_{21}.$$

But by Example 1.2(a), the latter expression in the elements of A is precisely $\det(A)$. Suppose now that (1) holds for all m-square matrices, $m < n$. Then, by definition,

$$\det(A) = \sum_{j=1}^{n} (-1)^{1+j} a_{1j} \det(A(1 \mid j)).$$

Now for $1 < i \leq n$, by the induction hypothesis,

$$\det(A(1 \mid j)) = \sum_{t=1}^{j-1} (-1)^{(i-1)+t} a_{it} \det(A(1, i \mid t, j))$$

$$+ \sum_{t=j+1}^{n} (-1)^{(i-1)+(t-1)} a_{it} \det(A(1, i \mid j, t)). \quad (2)$$

Therefore,

$$\det(A) = \sum_{j=1}^{n} (-1)^{1+j} a_{1j} \left\{ \sum_{t=1}^{j-1} (-1)^{i+t-1} a_{it} \det(A(1, i \mid t, j)) \right.$$

$$+ \left. \sum_{t=j+1}^{n} (-1)^{i+t} a_{it} \det(A(1, i \mid j, t)) \right\}, \quad (3)$$

and the right side of (3) is just the summation of $n(n - 1)$ terms of the form

$$e_{jt} a_{1j} a_{it} \det(A(1, i \mid t, j)), \qquad j \neq t,$$

where

$$e_{jt} = \begin{cases} (-1)^{i+j+t} & \text{if } t < j, \\ (-1)^{i+j+t+1} & \text{if } t > j. \end{cases}$$

Thus, interchanging the roles of j and t, (3) can be written

$$\det(A) = \sum_{t=1}^{n} (-1)^{i+t} a_{it} \left\{ \sum_{j=1}^{t-1} (-1)^{1+j} a_{1j} \det(A(1, i \mid j, t)) \right.$$

$$+ \left. \sum_{j=t+1}^{n} (-1)^{1+(j-1)} a_{1j} \det(A(1, i \mid t, j)) \right\}. \quad (4)$$

Note that the expression in the braces on the right side of (4) is, by Definition 1.1, equal to $\det(A(i \mid t))$. Hence

$$\det(A) = \sum_{t=1}^{n} (-1)^{i+t} a_{it} \det(A(i \mid t)),$$

which is (1). The reader should satisfy himself that our assertions about the right side of (4) and about (3) are correct—also that the step from (3) to (4) is justified. Indeed, the latter is nothing more than the so-called distributive law.

(b) We first prove the result in case $s = r + 1$, i.e., when the interchanged rows are adjacent. Expand the determinant of B by its rth row:

$$\det(B) = \sum_{j=1}^{n} (-1)^{r+j} b_{rj} \det(B(r \mid j)).$$

Now, $b_{rj} = a_{sj}$, $B(r \mid j) = A(s \mid j)$, and

$$(-1)^{r+j} = (-1)^{s-1+j}$$
$$= -(-1)^{s+j}.$$

Thus

$$\det(B) = -\sum_{j=1}^{n} (-1)^{s+j} a_{sj} \det(A(s \mid j))$$
$$= -\det(A).$$

In the general case, any interchange of rows r and s, written $(r \quad s)$, can be accomplished by a succession of $2(s - r) - 1$ consecutive adjacent interchanges of rows:

$$(r \quad r+1), (r+1 \quad r+2), \ldots, (s-2 \quad s-1), (s-1 \quad s), (s-2 \quad s-1),$$
$$\ldots, (r+1 \quad r+2), (r \quad r+1),$$

in this order. Hence

$$\det(B) = (-1)^{2(s-r)-1} \det(A)$$
$$= -\det(A).$$

(c) Let the rth row and the sth row of A be identical. Let B be the matrix obtained from A by interchanging these two rows. Then, by part **(b)**,

$$\det(B) = -\det(A).$$

But the two rows are identical and therefore $A = B$. It follows that

$$\det(A) = \det(B)$$
$$= -\det(A),$$

and thus $\det(A)$ must be 0.

(d) Expand the determinant of $C = (c_{ij})$ by its sth row

$$\det(C) = \sum_{j=1}^{n} (-1)^{s+j} c_{sj} \det(C(s|j)).$$

But $c_{sj} = k a_{sj}$ and $C(s|j) = A(s|j)$ for $j = 1, \ldots, n$. Therefore,

$$\det(C) = \sum_{j=1}^{n} (-1)^{s+j} k a_{sj} \det(A(s|j))$$
$$= k \det(A).$$

(e) Let $B = (b_{ij})$ be the matrix defined by

$$b_{rj} = a_{sj}, \qquad j = 1, \ldots, n,$$
$$b_{ij} = a_{ij}, \qquad i = 1, \ldots, r-1, r+1, \ldots, n, \quad j = 1, \ldots, n.$$

That is to say, the rth and the sth rows of B are the same as the sth row of A; all other rows of B are equal to the corresponding rows of A. We have, by (c), that $\det(B) = 0$. Now expand the determinant of D by its rth row:

$$\det(D) = \sum_{j=1}^{n} (-1)^{r+j} d_{rj} \det(D(r|j))$$

$$= \sum_{j=1}^{n} (-1)^{r+j} (a_{rj} + k a_{sj}) \det(A(r|j))$$

$$= \sum_{j=1}^{n} (-1)^{r+j} a_{rj} \det(A(r|j)) + k \sum_{j=1}^{n} (-1)^{r+j} a_{sj} \det(A(r|j))$$

$$= \det(A) + k \sum_{j=1}^{n} (-1)^{r+j} b_{rj} \det(B(r|j))$$

$$= \det(A) + k \det(B)$$

$$= \det(A).$$

This concludes the proof of the Theorem 1.1. Note that part **(e)** of the theorem states that the determinant of A is unchanged if we apply to A a type II elementary row operation. This often enables us to simplify the computation of a determinant.

Example 1.3.

(a) Let

$$A = \begin{bmatrix} 1 & -2 & 2 \\ 3 & 1 & 2 \\ -2 & 4 & 1 \end{bmatrix}.$$

Add -3 times the first row to the second row of A and twice the first row to the third row. The determinant of the resulting matrix

$$B = \begin{bmatrix} 1 & -2 & 2 \\ 0 & 7 & -4 \\ 0 & 0 & 5 \end{bmatrix}$$

is equal, by Theorem 1.1(e), to $\det(A)$. But it is clear (expand by the third row) that $\det(B) = 35$.

(b) Suppose that every entry in the rth row of $A = (a_{ij})$ is 0. Then, expanding $\det(A)$ by its rth row, we have

$$\det(A) = \sum_{j=1}^{n} (-1)^{r+j} 0 \det(A(r \,|\, j))$$

$$= 0.$$

Theorem 1.2. *Let $A = (a_{ij})$ be an n-square matrix. Then*

$$\det(A^T) = \det(A).$$

Proof. Use induction on n. The theorem is trivial for $n = 1$. Assume that it holds for all m-square matrices, $m < n$. Since the (i, j) entry of A^T is a_{ji}, we have from (1),

$$\det(A^T) = \sum_{j=1}^{n} (-1)^{i+j} a_{ji} \det(A^T(i \,|\, j)).$$

Observe that $A^T(i|j) = (A(j|i))^T$, and therefore by induction,

$$\det(A^T(i|j)) = \det((A(j|i))^T)$$
$$= \det(A(j|i)),$$

since $A(j|i)$ is $(n-1)$-square. For each $i = 1, \ldots, n$, we have

$$\det(A^T) = \sum_{j=1}^{n} (-1)^{i+j} a_{ji} \det(A^T(i|j)),$$

and summing both sides of this latter equality for $i = 1, \ldots, n$, we obtain

$$\sum_{i=1}^{n} \det(A^T) = \sum_{i=1}^{n} \sum_{j=1}^{n} (-1)^{i+j} a_{ji} \det(A^T(i|j))$$
$$= \sum_{i=1}^{n} \sum_{j=1}^{n} (-1)^{i+j} a_{ji} \det(A(j|i)).$$

If we interchange the order of summation of i and j on the right hand side of the last formula, we have

$$n \det(A^T) = \sum_{j=1}^{n} \sum_{i=1}^{n} (-1)^{j+i} a_{ji} \det(A(j|i)).$$

On the other hand,

$$\sum_{i=1}^{n} (-1)^{j+i} a_{ji} \det(A(j|i))$$

is the expansion of $\det(A)$ by the jth row, and hence

$$\sum_{i=1}^{n} \left(\sum_{j=1}^{n} (-1)^{j+i} a_{ji} \det(A(j|i)) \right) = n \det(A).$$

Thus $n \det(A^T) = n \det(A)$ and therefore $\det(A^T) = \det(A)$.

We saw in Examples 1.2(a) and (b) that if $A = (a_{ij})$ is a 2-square matrix, then

$$\det(A) = a_{11} a_{22} - a_{12} a_{21},$$

and if $A = (a_{ij})$ is a 3-square matrix, then

$$\det(A) = a_{11}a_{22}a_{33} + a_{12}a_{23}a_{31} + a_{13}a_{21}a_{32} - a_{11}a_{23}a_{32}$$
$$- a_{13}a_{22}a_{31} - a_{12}a_{21}a_{33}.$$

Note that in both cases the determinant is a sum of products of entries of A, exactly one entry being taken from each row and from each column of A. Observe also that the product of the n main diagonal elements a_{ii}, $i = 1$, $\dots, n$, occurs with coefficient 1. We now show that this is true in general. Call a product of n entries of an $n \times n$ matrix $A = (a_{ij})$ a *diagonal product* if the product contains exactly one entry from each row and from each column of A. The product $a_{11} \cdots a_{nn}$ is called the *main diagonal product* of A.

Theorem 1.3. *The determinant of a square matrix $A = (a_{ij})$ is a sum of diagonal products of A, each multiplied by ± 1. The main diagonal product occurs with coefficient* 1.

Proof. We use induction on n. We have

$$\det(A) = \sum_{j=1}^{n} (-1)^{1+j} a_{1j} \det(A(1 \mid j)), \tag{5}$$

where $A(1 \mid j)$, $j = 1, \dots, n$, are $(n - 1)$-square matrices, and therefore, by the induction hypothesis, $\det(A(1 \mid j))$ is a sum of diagonal products of $A(1 \mid j)$ each multiplied by ± 1. But diagonal products of $A(1 \mid j)$ are just products of entries of A, exactly one entry being taken from each of rows numbered $2, \dots, n$ and from each of columns numbered $1, \dots, j - 1$, $j + 1, \dots, n$. Thus $a_{1j} \det(A(1 \mid j))$ is the sum of diagonal products, times ± 1, of the matrix A, and the first part of the theorem follows. To find the coefficient of the main diagonal product of A, note that the only terms on the right side of (5), involving a_{11} as a factor, are the terms of $a_{11} \det(A(1 \mid 1))$. It follows that the main diagonal product $a_{11}a_{22} \cdots a_{nn}$ occurs in (5) with the same coefficient as the coefficient of the product $a_{22} \cdots a_{nn}$ in $\det(A(1 \mid 1))$. But the latter is the main diagonal product of the matrix $A(1 \mid 1)$, which, by the induction hypothesis, has coefficient 1.

It is an immediate consequence of Theorem 1.2 that all parts of Theorem 1.1 have analogues in which the roles of rows and columns are interchanged. We state them without proofs.

Theorem 1.4. *Let* $A = (a_{ij})$ *be an n-square matrix.*

(a) *For any* j, $1 \leq j \leq n$,

$$\det(A) = \sum_{i=1}^{n} (-1)^{i+j} a_{ij} \det(A(i \mid j)). \tag{6}$$

(Formula (6) is called the *expansion of the determinant of A by its jth column*.)

(b) *If B is the matrix obtained by interchanging the* rth *column and the* sth *column* $(r < s)$ *of A, then*

$$\det(B) = -\det(A).$$

(c) *If two columns of A are identical, then* $\det(A) = 0$.

(d) *If C is the matrix obtained from A by multiplying each entry in the* sth *column of A by a scalar k, then*

$$\det(C) = k \det(A).$$

(e) *For fixed distinct integers r and s,* $1 \leq r$, $s \leq n$ *and a scalar k, let* $D = (d_{ij})$ *be defined by*

$$d_{ir} = a_{ir} + ka_{is}, \qquad i = 1, \ldots, n,$$

and

$$d_{ij} = a_{ij}, \qquad otherwise.$$

Then $\det(D) = \det(A)$.

Quiz

Answer *true* or *false*:

(Unless otherwise stated, all matrices are n-square.)

1. For any A and B, $\det(A + B) = \det(A) + \det(B)$.
2. For any scalar k and any matrix A, $\det(kA) = k \det(A)$.
3. If A is an n-square matrix, then $\det(-A) = (-1)^n \det(A)$.
4. Let $D = (d_{ij})$ be a diagonal n-square matrix (i.e., $d_{ij} = 0$ whenever $i \neq j$). Then $\det(D) = \prod_{i=1}^{n} d_{ii}$.
5. Let

$$G = \begin{bmatrix} 0 & 0 & 1 \\ 0 & 1 & 0 \\ 1 & 0 & 0 \end{bmatrix}.$$

Then $\det(G) = 1$.

6. Let $T = (t_{ij})$ be an upper triangular n-square matrix (i.e., $t_{ij} = 0$ whenever $i > j$). Then $\det(T) = \prod_{i=1}^{n} t_{ii}$.

7. Let

$$A = \begin{bmatrix} \cos\theta & \sin\theta \\ \sin\theta & -\cos\theta \end{bmatrix}.$$

Then $\det(A) = -1$.

8. If $A = (a_{ij})$ is an 8-square matrix, $a_{18} = a_{81} = 1$, $a_{1j} = a_{i1} = 0$, $i, j = 1, \ldots, 7$, then $\det(A) = \det(A(1, 8 \mid 1, 8))$.

9. If $A = (a_{ij})$ is the matrix in Question 7, then the cofactor of a_{12} in A is $\sin\theta$.

10. If no entry of a square matrix P is equal to 0, then $\det(P) \neq 0$.

Exercises

1. Let

$$A = \begin{bmatrix} 3 & 1 & 0 \\ -1 & 2 & 1 \\ 1 & 1 & 1 \end{bmatrix} \quad \text{and} \quad B = \begin{bmatrix} 1 & 1 & -1 \\ 1 & 1 & 2 \\ 3 & 2 & 1 \end{bmatrix}.$$

Compute AB, BA, $\det(A)$, $\det(B)$, $\det(AB)$, and $\det(BA)$. Verify that $\det(A)\det(B) = \det(AB) = \det(BA)$.

2. Find a value for x such that

$$\det\left(\begin{bmatrix} x & 0 & 2 \\ 1 & x & 0 \\ 1 & -2 & x \end{bmatrix}\right) = 0.$$

3. Let $A = (a_{ij})$, $B = (b_{ij})$, and $C = (c_{ij})$ be n-square matrices satisfying

$$\begin{aligned} a_{1j} &= b_{1j} + c_{1j}, & j &= 1, \ldots, n, \\ a_{ij} &= b_{ij} = c_{ij}, & i &= 2, \ldots, n, \quad j = 1, \ldots, n. \end{aligned}$$

Show that $\det(A) = \det(B) + \det(C)$.

4. Let

$$A = (a_{ij}) = \begin{bmatrix} 1 & 1 & \cdots & 1 \\ r_1 & r_2 & & r_n \\ r_1^2 & r_2^2 & & r_n^2 \\ \vdots & \vdots & & \vdots \\ r_1^{n-1} & r_2^{n-1} & \cdots & r_n^{n-1} \end{bmatrix};$$

i.e., $a_{ij} = r_j^{i-1}$ (A is called the *Vandermonde*, or *alternant*, matrix). Prove the formula

$$\det(A) = \prod_{1 \leq i < j \leq n} (r_j - r_i)$$

for the special cases $n = 2$ and $n = 3$.

5. Let $S = (s_{ij})$ be a *skew-symmetric* n-square real matrix; i.e., let $s_{ij} = -s_{ji}$, $i, j = 1, \ldots, n$. Show that if n is odd, then $\det(S) = 0$. [*Hint*: $S^T = -S$ and $\det(S) = \det(S^T)$.]

3.2. PROPERTIES OF DETERMINANTS

The determinant function is related in a remarkable way to the concept of nonsingularity and, more generally, to the rank of a matrix. In this section we shall also obtain a formula for the inverse of a matrix in terms of its determinant and the cofactors of its entries. We also prove an alternative definition of the rank of a matrix. In fact, this definition historically preceded the more modern definition given in Chapter 2.

Definition 2.1. (*Adjugate.*) *Let* $A = (a_{ij})$ *be an n-square matrix and let* $B = (b_{ij})$ *be the n-square matrix defined by*

$$b_{ij} = (-1)^{i+j} \det(A(j \mid i)), \qquad i, j = 1, \ldots, n.$$

In other words, the (i, j) *entry of B is the cofactor of* a_{ji} *in A. The matrix B is called the* **adjugate** *of A and is denoted by* adj A.

Example 2.1. Find the adjugate of

$$A = \begin{bmatrix} 1 & 3 & 2 \\ -1 & -1 & -1 \\ 2 & 3 & -2 \end{bmatrix}.$$

We compute the cofactors of a_{ij}, $i, j = 1, 2, 3$:

The cofactor of a_{11} is $(-1)^{1+1} \det\left(\begin{bmatrix} -1 & -1 \\ 3 & -2 \end{bmatrix}\right) = 5$;

a_{12}: $(-1)^{1+2} \det\left(\begin{bmatrix} -1 & -1 \\ 2 & -2 \end{bmatrix}\right) = -4$;

a_{13}: $(-1)^{1+3} \det\left(\begin{bmatrix} -1 & -1 \\ 2 & 3 \end{bmatrix}\right) = -1$;

a_{21}: $(-1)^{2+1} \det\left(\begin{bmatrix} 3 & 2 \\ 3 & -2 \end{bmatrix}\right) = 12$;

a_{22}: $(-1)^{2+2} \det\left(\begin{bmatrix} 1 & 2 \\ 2 & -2 \end{bmatrix}\right) = -6$;

a_{23}: $(-1)^{2+3} \det\left(\begin{bmatrix} 1 & 3 \\ 2 & 3 \end{bmatrix}\right) = 3$;

a_{31}: $(-1)^{3+1} \det\left(\begin{bmatrix} 2 & 2 \\ -1 & -1 \end{bmatrix}\right) = -1$;

a_{32}: $(-1)^{3+2} \det\left(\begin{bmatrix} 1 & 2 \\ -1 & -1 \end{bmatrix}\right) = -1$;

a_{33}: $(-1)^{3+3} \det\left(\begin{bmatrix} 1 & 3 \\ -1 & -1 \end{bmatrix}\right) = 2$.

Therefore,

$$\text{adj } A = \begin{bmatrix} 5 & 12 & -1 \\ -4 & -6 & -1 \\ -1 & 3 & 2 \end{bmatrix}.$$

The entries in adj A are cofactors of the entries in A. We may expect, therefore, that if we multiply A by adj A, then in some entries of the product, the entries of A may multiply their own cofactor and perhaps produce the determinant of A. Let us try an experiment. We compute

$$A \text{ adj } A = \begin{bmatrix} 1 & 3 & 2 \\ -1 & -1 & -1 \\ 2 & 3 & -2 \end{bmatrix} \begin{bmatrix} 5 & 12 & -1 \\ -4 & -6 & -1 \\ -1 & 3 & 2 \end{bmatrix}$$

$$= \begin{bmatrix} -9 & 0 & 0 \\ 0 & -9 & 0 \\ 0 & 0 & -9 \end{bmatrix}$$

$$= -9I_3.$$

We can also evaluate the determinant of A directly and find that $\det(A) = -9$. Is this striking result generally true or is it due to some peculiar property of the matrix A? We answer this question in Theorem 2.1.

Theorem 2.1. *If A is an n-square matrix, then*

$$A \text{ adj } A = (\text{adj } A)A$$

$$= \det(A)I_n. \tag{1}$$

Proof. Let adj $A = B = (b_{ij})$ and let $AB = C = (c_{ij})$. We compute, for $i = 1, \ldots, n$,

$$c_{ii} = \sum_{t=1}^{n} a_{it}b_{ti}$$

$$= \sum_{t=1}^{n} a_{it}(-1)^{i+t} \det(A(i \mid t))$$

$$= \det(A);$$

for $i \neq j$,

$$c_{ij} = \sum_{t=1}^{n} a_{it} b_{tj}$$

$$= \sum_{t=1}^{n} (-1)^{j+t} a_{it} \det(A(j \mid t)). \qquad (2)$$

Now let $D = (d_{ij})$ be the matrix whose jth row is the same as the ith row of A and all the other entries of D are equal to corresponding entries in A, i.e.,

$$d_{jt} = a_{it}, \qquad t = 1, \ldots, n,$$

$$d_{st} = a_{st}, \qquad s \neq j, t = 1, \ldots, n.$$

Then D has two identical rows, namely, its jth and ith rows, and therefore, by Theorem 1.1(c), $\det(D) = 0$. Also,

$$\det(A(j \mid t)) = \det(D(j \mid t)), \qquad t = 1, \ldots, n.$$

Therefore equation (2) gives

$$c_{ij} = \sum_{t=1}^{n} (-1)^{j+t} d_{jt} \det(D(j \mid t))$$

$$= \det(D)$$

$$= 0,$$

i.e.,

$$C = A(\operatorname{adj} A)$$

$$= \det(A) I_n.$$

Applying this identity to A^T we also obtain

$$A^T(\operatorname{adj} A^T) = \det(A^T) I_n.$$

But $\operatorname{adj} A^T = (\operatorname{adj} A)^T$ [see Exercise 10] and $\det(A^T) = \det(A)$, and therefore

$$A^T(\operatorname{adj} A)^T = \det(A) I_n. \qquad (3)$$

Taking the transpose of both sides of (3), we have

$$(\text{adj } A)A = \det(A)I_n.$$

Equations (1) provide a formula for the inverse of A when $\det(A) \neq 0$. What happens when $\det(A) = 0$? Before we consider this question let us list the following equivalent statements that we have already established:

(a) A has an inverse;
(b) A is nonsingular;
(c) the rank of A is n;
(d) the row rank of A is n;
(e) the rows of A are linearly independent;
(f) the column rank of A is n;
(g) the columns of A are linearly independent;
(h) the Hermite normal form of A is I_n;
(i) A is a product of elementary matrices;
(j) the only solution of the system of equations $Ax = 0$ is $x = 0$.

To this list we now add another equivalent statement.

Theorem 2.2. *An n-square matrix A is nonsingular if and only if* $\det(A) \neq 0$. *If* $\det(A) \neq 0$, *then*

$$A^{-1} = \frac{1}{\det(A)} \text{ adj } A. \tag{4}$$

Proof. The second part of the theorem follows immediately from (1). Now let $\det(A) = 0$. We prove by induction that A is singular. If $n = 1$, then $\det(A) = 0$ implies that $A = 0$. Suppose that the theorem holds for all $(n - 1)$-square matrices, i.e., that for an $(n - 1)$-square matrix a zero determinant implies singularity, and suppose that it fails for A, namely, that A is nonsingular in spite of our hypothesis that $\det(A) = 0$. We shall obtain a contradiction. If $\det(A) = 0$, then (1) gives

$$A(\text{adj } A) = 0,$$

and therefore (assuming that A is nonsingular)

$$A^{-1}A \text{ adj } A = 0$$

or

$$\text{adj } A = 0.$$

In other words, all the minors of A are zero. Now let B be the $(n-1) \times n$ matrix consisting of the first $n-1$ rows of A. Since any $(n-1)$-square matrix consisting of $n-1$ columns of B has a zero determinant (it is a minor of A), we can conclude, using the induction hypothesis, that each of these $(n-1)$-square matrices is singular, i.e., of rank less than $n-1$. Therefore B can have at most $n-2$ linearly independent columns and, by Theorem 4.5, Chapter 2, at most $n-2$ linearly independent rows. Thus the rows of B and therefore those of A are linearly dependent, which contradicts our assumption that A is nonsingular.

Example 2.2. Find the inverse of the matrix

$$A = \begin{bmatrix} 1 & 3 & 2 \\ -1 & -1 & -1 \\ 2 & 3 & -2 \end{bmatrix}.$$

In Example 2.1 we found that

$$\operatorname{adj} A = \begin{bmatrix} 5 & 12 & -1 \\ -4 & -6 & -1 \\ -1 & 3 & 2 \end{bmatrix},$$

and that $\det(A) = -9$. Therefore, by (4),

$$A^{-1} = -\tfrac{1}{9} \begin{bmatrix} 5 & 12 & -1 \\ -4 & -6 & -1 \\ -1 & 3 & 2 \end{bmatrix}.$$

(Compare with Exercise 7, Section 2.3.)

Theorem 2.2 states that the rank of an n-square matrix is n if and only if its determinant is nonzero. This is actually a special case of a more general theorem relating rank to determinants. If X is a k-square submatrix of Y, the determinant of X is called a *subdeterminant* of Y of order k.

Theorem 2.3. *Let A be an $m \times n$ matrix and let k be a positive integer. Then $\rho(A) \geq k$ if and only if A contains a nonzero subdeterminant of order k.*

Proof. Suppose that $\rho(A) \geq k$. Then the row rank of A is at least k and A contains k linearly independent rows. Let these rows be numbered

$t_1, \ldots, t_k$ and let B be the $k \times n$ matrix whose ith row is row t_i of A. Then the row rank of B is k and therefore $\rho(B) = k$. It follows that the column rank of B is k and therefore that B contains k linearly independent columns. Let C be the k-square matrix consisting of these columns. Now the columns of C are linearly independent and therefore $\rho(C) = k$. It follows, by Theorem 2.2, that $\det(C) \neq 0$. Since C is a submatrix of A, we have proved that A must contain a nonzero subdeterminant of order k. Conversely, if A contains a nonzero subdeterminant of order k, then, by Theorem 2.2, A has a k-square nonsingular submatrix D. Let D lie in rows $s_1, \ldots, s_k$ of A. Since D is nonsingular, its rows are linearly independent. But then rows $s_1, \ldots, s_k$ of A are linearly independent. Hence the row rank of A, and thus $\rho(A)$, must be at least equal to k.

An immediate consequence of Theorem 2.3 is the following well-known result.

Theorem 2.4. *The rank of an $m \times n$ matrix A is equal to r ($r > 0$) if and only if at least one subdeterminant of A of order r is nonzero and all subdeterminants of A of order $r + 1$ are zero.*

Proof. If $\rho(A) = r$, then, by Theorem 2.3, the matrix A contains a nonzero subdeterminant of order r. Moreover, A cannot contain a nonzero subdeterminant of order $r + 1$, for then, by the same theorem, its rank could not be less than $r + 1$. The converse is equally obvious.

Example 2.2. Let $v_1 = (1, 2, 0, -1)$, $v_2 = (2, -2, 1, 1)$, and $v_3 = (1, 8, -1, -4)$. Find the dimension of $\langle v_1, v_2, v_3 \rangle$. Let

$$A = \begin{bmatrix} 1 & 2 & 0 & -1 \\ 2 & -2 & 1 & 1 \\ 1 & 8 & -1 & -4 \end{bmatrix}.$$

Then $\dim\langle v_1, v_2, v_3 \rangle$ is the row rank of A. The problem is to evaluate $\rho(A)$. We use Theorem 2.4. Virtually all the subdeterminants of A of order 2 are nonzero. For example,

$$\det\left(\begin{vmatrix} 1 & 2 \\ 2 & -2 \end{vmatrix} \right) = -6 \neq 0.$$

Thus, by Theorem 2.3, $\rho(A) \geq 2$. Now the 3-square submatrices of A are

$$\begin{bmatrix} 1 & 2 & 0 \\ 2 & -2 & 1 \\ 1 & 8 & -1 \end{bmatrix}, \quad \begin{bmatrix} 1 & 2 & -1 \\ 2 & -2 & 1 \\ 1 & 8 & -4 \end{bmatrix}, \quad \begin{bmatrix} 1 & 0 & -1 \\ 2 & 1 & 1 \\ 1 & -1 & -4 \end{bmatrix}, \quad \begin{bmatrix} 2 & 0 & -1 \\ -2 & 1 & 1 \\ 8 & -1 & -4 \end{bmatrix}.$$

It is easy to check that each of these matrices has a zero determinant. Hence by Theorem 2.4, $\rho(A) = 2 = \dim\langle v_1, v_2, v_3 \rangle$.

The most striking and characteristic property of determinants is embodied in the next theorem.

Theorem 2.5. *If A and B are n-square matrices, then*

$$\det(AB) = \det(A)\det(B). \tag{5}$$

Proof. First suppose that A is singular. Then AB must be singular. For, since A is singular, $\rho(A) < n$, and hence the Hermite normal form of A has a zero nth row. It follows that AB is equivalent to a matrix with a zero nth row and therefore $\rho(AB) < n$. Thus if A is singular then, by Theorem 2.2, both sides of (5) are equal to 0. If A is nonsingular, then it is a product of elementary matrices (see Theorem 4.3; Chapter 2). Let $A = E_1 \cdots E_k$, where $E_1, \ldots, E_k$ are elementary matrices. We use induction on k. If E_1 is a type I elementary matrix (see Definition 4.1; Chapter 2), then $\det(E_1 B) = -\det(B)$, by Theorem 1.1(b). If E_1 is of type II, then $\det(E_1 B) = \det(B)$, by Theorem 1.1(e). If E_1 is of type III (multiply a row by $c \neq 0$), then $\det(E_1 B) = c \det(B)$, by Theorem 1.1(d). In particular, for types I, II and III, respectively, we have

$$\det(E_1) = \det(E_1 I_n) = -\det(I_n) = -1,$$
$$\det(E_1) = \det(I_n) = 1,$$
$$\det(E_1) = c \det(I_n) = c.$$

Thus in each case

$$\det(E_1 B) = \det(E_1)\det(B).$$

This proves the theorem when $k = 1$. Assume now that $k > 1$ and that the theorem holds if the first of the two matrices is a product of $k - 1$

elementary matrices. Then, using this induction hypothesis and the special case established above, we obtain

$$\begin{aligned}
\det(AB) &= \det(E_1 E_2 \cdots E_k B) \\
&= \det(E_1(E_2 \cdots E_k B)) \\
&= \det(E_1)\det(E_2 \cdots E_k B) \\
&= \det(E_1)\det(E_2 \cdots E_k)\det(B) \\
&= \det(E_1 E_2 \cdots E_k)\det(B) \\
&= \det(A)\det(B).
\end{aligned}$$

We continue with one of the most famous results in mathematics: the so-called *Cramer's rule*. For two centuries this result dominated the theory of equations and the teaching of algebra in general. In spite of the fact that the result itself must be considered nowadays of no theoretical significance and of no practical value, it is of considerable historical interest. It was announced by Cramer in his famous treatise of 1750, and it is one of the very first results involving determinants.

Theorem 2.6. *Let* $x = (x_1, \ldots, x_n)$, $b = (b_1, \ldots, b_n)$, *and let*

$$Ax = b \tag{6}$$

be a system of n linear equations in n unknowns $x_1, \ldots, x_n$. *For* $j = 1, \ldots, n$, *let* A_j *denote the n-square matrix whose jth column is the n-tuple b and whose remaining columns are the corresponding columns of A. Suppose that* $\det(A) \neq 0$. *Then*

$$x_j = \frac{\det(A_j)}{\det(A)}, \quad j = 1, \ldots, n. \tag{7}$$

Proof. Multiply both sides of (6) by adj A:

$$(\text{adj } A)Ax = (\text{adj } A)b$$

or, by Theorem 2.1,

$$\det(A)x = (\text{adj } A)b. \tag{8}$$

Equating the jth coordinates on both sides of (8) we get

$$x_j \det(A) = \sum_{t=1}^{n} (-1)^{t+j} \det(A(t\,|\,j))b_t, \tag{9}$$

since the (j, t) entry in adj A is $(-1)^{t+j}\det(A(t|j))$. Now expand the determinant of A_j by its jth column

$$\det(A_j) = \sum_{t=1}^{n} (-1)^{t+j} b_t \det(A_j(t|j))$$

$$= \sum_{t=1}^{n} (-1)^{t+j} b_t \det(A(t|j)),$$

and thus (9) becomes

$$x_j \det(A) = \det(A_j),$$

which is formula (7).

Example 2.3. Use Cramer's rule to solve the system

$$\begin{array}{rcl}
3x_1 - 2x_2 + x_3 - x_4 & = & -4 \\
x_1 + 3x_2 - x_3 + 2x_4 & = & 3 \\
2x_1 + x_2 \qquad + x_4 & = & 1 \\
x_2 + x_3 + x_4 & = & 6.
\end{array} \qquad (10)$$

We can write the system in the matrix form

$$Ax = b, \qquad (11)$$

where

$$A = \begin{bmatrix} 3 & -2 & 1 & -1 \\ 1 & 3 & -1 & 2 \\ 2 & 1 & 0 & 1 \\ 0 & 1 & 1 & 1 \end{bmatrix},$$

$x = (x_1, x_2, x_3, x_4)$ and $b = (-4, 3, 1, 6)$. Then, using the notation of Theorem 2.6,

$$A_1 = \begin{bmatrix} -4 & -2 & 1 & -1 \\ 3 & 3 & -1 & 2 \\ 1 & 1 & 0 & 1 \\ 6 & 1 & 1 & 1 \end{bmatrix}, \qquad A_2 = \begin{bmatrix} 3 & -4 & 1 & -1 \\ 1 & 3 & -1 & 2 \\ 2 & 1 & 0 & 1 \\ 0 & 6 & 1 & 1 \end{bmatrix},$$

$$A_3 = \begin{bmatrix} 3 & -2 & -4 & -1 \\ 1 & 3 & 3 & 2 \\ 2 & 1 & 1 & 1 \\ 0 & 1 & 6 & 1 \end{bmatrix}, \qquad A_4 = \begin{bmatrix} 3 & -2 & 1 & -4 \\ 1 & 3 & -1 & 3 \\ 2 & 1 & 0 & 1 \\ 0 & 1 & 1 & 6 \end{bmatrix}.$$

We compute:

$$\det(A) = -2, \qquad \det(A_1) = 2, \qquad \det(A_2) = -2,$$
$$\det(A_3) = -6, \qquad \det(A_4) = -4.$$

Therefore the solution of (10) is

$$x_1 = \frac{2}{-2} = -1, \qquad x_2 = \frac{-2}{-2} = 1, \qquad x_3 = \frac{-6}{-2} = 3, \qquad x_4 = \frac{-4}{-2} = 2.$$

In view of Theorem 2.6, it is natural to ask about the system of equations (6) in which $b = 0$. Clearly $x = 0$ is then a solution for any A. We have the following theorem.

Theorem 2.7. *Let A be an $n \times n$ matrix. The homogeneous system of equations*

$$Ax = 0 \qquad\qquad (12)$$

has a nonzero solution if and only if $\det(A) = 0$.

Proof. If $\det(A)$ is not zero, we know from Theorem 2.2 that A is nonsingular. Then multiply both sides of (12) by A^{-1} to obtain

$$A^{-1}Ax = 0$$

or

$$x = 0.$$

Thus, if $\det(A) \neq 0$, then $x = 0$ is the only solution of (12). Suppose now that the system (12) is satisfied by a nonzero vector v. According to Theorem 3.2(a), Chapter 2, if r is the rank of A, then $n - r$ must be at least 1. In other words, the row rank of A is strictly less than n. But then Theorem 4.3(b), Chapter 2, tells us that A cannot be nonsingular, i.e., A is singular and therefore, by Theorem 2.2, $\det(A) = 0$.

As a final application of Theorem 2.5 we can very easily prove the following result.

Theorem 2.8. *Let A be an $n \times n$ matrix. If, for some $n \times n$ matrix B, $AB = I_n$ or $BA = I_n$, then A is nonsingular and $B = A^{-1}$.*

Proof. From

$$AB = I_n \tag{13}$$

we compute, using Theorem 2.5, that

$$1 = \det(I_n)$$
$$= \det(AB)$$
$$= \det(A)\det(B)$$

and hence $\det(A) \neq 0$. Hence, by Theorem 2.2, A is nonsingular, i.e., A^{-1} exists. Thus from (13) we have

$$A^{-1}(AB) = A^{-1}I_n,$$
$$(A^{-1}A)B = A^{-1},$$
$$B = A^{-1}.$$

For the case $BA = I_n$ the argument is similar.

Quiz

Answer *true* or *false*:

1. The adjugate of $\begin{bmatrix} a & b \\ c & d \end{bmatrix}$ is $\begin{bmatrix} d & -c \\ -b & a \end{bmatrix}$.

2. If A is a singular square matrix, then adj $A = 0$.

3. If A is a singular square matrix, then $A(\text{adj } A) = 0$.

4. The rank of

$$\begin{bmatrix} 1 & 2 & 1 \\ 2 & 1 & -1 \\ 1 & 5 & 4 \end{bmatrix}$$

is 2.

5. If A is a *nilpotent* square matrix (i.e., $A^k = 0$ for some positive integer k), then $\det(A) = 0$.

6. If A is an *idempotent* matrix (i.e., $A^2 = A$), then $\det(A) = 1$.

7. If A and B are n-square matrices, then $\det(AB) = \det(BA)$.

8. If A is a nonsingular matrix, then $\det(A^{-1}) = (\det(A))^{-1}$.

9. If A and B are n-square matrices, $\det(B) \neq 0$, then $\det(BAB^{-1}) = \det(A)$.

10. If A is a singular matrix, then $\det(\text{adj } A) = 0$.

Exercises

1. Use formula (4) to find the inverse of

$$\begin{bmatrix} 2 & 1 & 3 \\ 1 & 1 & 2 \\ 1 & -1 & 1 \end{bmatrix}.$$

2. Let $v_1 = (1, 3, 2)$, $v_2 = (5, 3, 1)$, $v_3 = (1, -1, -1)$, and $v_4 = (1, 7, 5)$. Find the dimension of $\langle v_1, v_2, v_3, v_4 \rangle$.

3. If every subdeterminant of A of order k is zero, show that every subdeterminant of A of order greater than k is zero.

4. Find numbers x and y such that the vectors $(x, 1, 3, 2)$, $(1, -1, 1, 1)$, and $(1, 2, 2, y)$ are linearly dependent.

5. Show that $\text{adj}(kA) = k^{n-1}\text{adj } A$ for any scalar k and any n-square matrix A.

6. Let A be an n-square matrix. Prove that

$$\det(\text{adj } A) = (\det(A))^{n-1}.$$

7. Show that if A and B are nonsingular, then

$$\text{adj}(AB) = \text{adj } B \text{ adj } A.$$

8. Show that if A is a nonsingular n-square matrix ($n \geq 2$), then

$$\text{adj}(\text{adj } A) = A(\det(A))^{n-2}.$$

9. Use Cramer's rule to solve the system

$$\begin{aligned} x_1 + 2x_2 - 3x_3 - x_4 &= -1 \\ 2x_1 + x_2 + x_3 + x_4 &= 1 \\ x_1 - x_2 + x_3 &= -2 \\ 3x_1 + x_2 + x_4 &= 0. \end{aligned}$$

10. Show that $\text{adj } A^T = (\text{adj } A)^T$ without using Theorem 2.1.

4

Characteristic Roots

4.1. VECTOR SPACES

Mathematicians study the properties of well-known mathematical objects (such as integers, real numbers, or sets of numbers) as well as the properties of abstract systems. By an abstract system we mean any unspecified structure that satisfies a prescribed set of criteria, called *postulates*. For example, any nonempty set of objects G for which a binary operation (denoted by $+$ and called "addition") is defined is said to form an *abelian group* if the following postulates hold:

(i) for any x and y in G, $x + y$ is a well-defined element in G;

(ii) for any x, y, and z in G,

$$(x + y) + z = x + (y + z);$$

(iii) there exists an element in G, called *zero* and denoted by 0, such that

$$x + 0 = x$$

for all x in G;

(iv) for each x in G, there exists an element in G, denoted by $-x$, such that

$$x + (-x) = 0;$$

(v) for any x and y in G,

$$x + y = y + x.$$

147

For example, the integers form an abelian group under ordinary addition. Also, complex n-tuples form an abelian group under addition as defined in Definition 6.1, Chapter 1.

Example 1.1. Let G be an abelian group. Suppose that

$$a + b = a \tag{1}$$

for some a and b in G. Then $b = 0$. For, we have from (1),

$$-a + (a + b) = -a + a,$$
$$(-a + a) + b = 0,$$
$$0 + b = 0,$$
$$b = 0.$$

Also, we can show that

$$a + c = 0 \tag{2}$$

implies $c = -a$. For, from (2),

$$-a + (a + c) = -a + 0,$$
$$(-a + a) + c = -a,$$
$$0 + c = -a,$$
$$c = -a.$$

Abelian groups and other important abstract systems have been studied extensively in mathematics. In this section we give the definition of an abstract complex (real) vector space.

Definition 1.1. (*Vector space*). *A complex (real)* **vector space** *V is a nonempty set of elements, called* **vectors**, *together with two operations, called* **vector addition** *and* **scalar multiplication**, *which satisfy the following postulates:*

    (1) *the vectors of V form an abelian group under vector addition;*
    (2) *the scalar product of a complex (real) number c and a vector v, denoted by cv, is a vector in V;*

(3) *if c, c_1, and c_2 are complex (real) numbers and v, v_1, and v_2 are vectors in V, then*

$$(c_1 + c_2)v = c_1 v + c_2 v,$$

$$c(v_1 + v_2) = cv_1 + cv_2,$$

$$c_1(c_2 v) = (c_1 c_2)v,$$

$$1v = v.$$

In the context of complex (real) vector spaces, complex (real) numbers are called **scalars**. *The identity element in the additive group of vectors is called the* **zero vector** *and is denoted by $\underline{0}$ or simply by 0 if no confusion with the number zero is likely. Also, if v_1 and v_2 are vectors, then for simplicity we write $v_1 - v_2$ instead of $v_1 + (-v_2)$.*

The following are examples of complex or real vector spaces:

(a) $V_n(C)$ as defined in Chapter 1 is a complex vector space;

(b) the set of $m \times n$ matrices, under matrix addition and scalar multiplication, forms a vector space;

(c) complex numbers form a real vector space under ordinary addition and multiplication; they also form a complex vector space;

(d) the set of all symmetric n-square matrices [a square matrix $A = (a_{ij})$ is symmetric if $a_{ij} = a_{ji}$ for all i, j] forms a real vector space under matrix addition and scalar multiplication;

(e) the set of all polynomials with real coefficients forms a real vector space;

(f) the set of all real solutions of

$$2\frac{d^2 y}{dx^2} + 3\frac{dy}{dx} + y = 0$$

forms a real vector space.

Example 1.2. Let $\underline{0}$ be the zero vector in a vector space V. Prove that, for any v in V,

$$0v = \underline{0}$$

and

$$-1v = -v.$$

We have

$$1v = (1 + 0)v$$
$$= 1v + 0v,$$

and thus, by Example 1.1, $0v$ is the zero vector $\underline{0}$. Also,

$$\underline{0} = 0v$$
$$= (1 + (-1))v$$
$$= 1v + (-1)v$$
$$= v + (-1)v,$$

which proves that $(-1)v$ is $-v$.

Virtually all the definitions in Section 1.6 apply *mutatis mutandis* to abstract vector spaces. In particular, the following definitions are exact restatements of the corresponding definitions for $V_n(C)$: *subspace* of an abstract vector space V, *linear combination*, *subspace spanned* by a set of vectors, and *linear dependence* and *independence* of vectors in V. If V contains a finite set of vectors that span V, then V is said to be *finite-dimensional*. All the examples of vector spaces immediately preceding Example 1.2 except (e) are finite dimensional. Henceforth we shall restrict ourselves to finite-dimensional vector spaces. We refer the student to Chapter 1, Section 1.6, in particular Theorem 6.2 and Definitions 6.4 and 6.5. Precisely as in Theorem 6.2, Section 1.6, we denote the subspace spanned by the set of vectors $X = \{v_1, \ldots, v_k\}$ by $\langle v_1, \ldots, v_k \rangle$, or simply by $\langle X \rangle$.

Definition 1.2. (Basis). *If* $W = \langle v_1, \ldots, v_k \rangle$ *and the vectors* $v_1, \ldots, v_k$ *are linearly independent, then they are said to form a* **basis** *of the (finite-dimensional) space* W.

Theorem 1.1. *Let* V *be a finite-dimensional nonzero (i.e.,* $V \neq \{0\}$*) vector space. Then*
  (a) *the space* V *has a basis;*
  (b) *if* $v_1, , \ldots, v_k$ *is a basis of* V *and* $u_1, \ldots, u_r$ *are linearly independent vectors in* V, *then* $r \leq k$ *and for some set of* $k - r$ *of the basis vectors, say* $v_{r+1}, \ldots, v_k$, *the set* $u_1, \ldots, u_r, v_{r+1}, \ldots, v_k$ *is a basis of* V;

(c) *any two bases of V contain the same number of elements.*

Proof.

(a) Since V is a finite-dimensional space, there exists a finite set X in V such that $\langle X \rangle = V$. Consider all the subsets of X. Some of these must be linearly independent, as V is nonzero and thus not all vectors in X can be zero. There is a finite number of such linearly independent subsets. We can therefore find a linearly independent subset $\{v_1, \ldots, v_k\}$ of X with the property that no linearly independent subset of X contains more than k vectors. We assert that $V = \langle v_1, \ldots, v_k \rangle$ and that $v_1, \ldots, v_k$ therefore form a basis of V. For, let u be any vector in X. It suffices to show that $u \in \langle v_1, \ldots, v_k \rangle$. Now, by the maximality of $v_1, \ldots, v_k$, the vectors $u, v_1, \ldots, v_k$ must be linearly dependent. Otherwise the $k + 1$ vectors $u, v_1, \ldots, v_k$ would be linearly independent, and this would contradict the fact that no linearly independent subset of X consists of more than k vectors. In other words, there exist scalars $c_0, c_1, \ldots, c_k$, not all 0, such that

$$c_0 u + c_1 v_1 + \cdots + c_k v_k = 0. \tag{3}$$

Clearly c_0 cannot be 0, otherwise (3) would imply that $v_1, \ldots, v_k$ are linearly dependent. But then

$$u = (-c_0^{-1} c_1) v_1 - \cdots - (c_0^{-1} c_k) v_k \in \langle v_1, \ldots, v_k \rangle.$$

At this point we have proved that every vector in the set X is a linear combination of $v_1, \ldots, v_k$. Let v be any vector in V. Then, since $V = \langle X \rangle$, we know that v is a linear combination of an appropriate set of vectors $x_1, \ldots, x_m$ in X, i.e.,

$$v = \sum_{j=1}^{m} d_j x_j.$$

Now each x_j is in X and therefore, as we have just seen, is a linear combination of $v_1, \ldots, v_k$. If we replace each x_j in the preceding sum by its expression in terms of $v_1, \ldots, v_k$, then v will be expressed as a linear combination of $v_1, \ldots, v_k$, i.e., $v \in \langle v_1, \ldots, v_k \rangle$. Hence $V = \langle v_1, \ldots, v_k \rangle$.

Parts **(b)** and **(c)** of the theorem are proved exactly as in Chapter 1, Theorem 6.4**(b)** and **(c)**.

Definition 1.3. (**Dimension**). *Let* V *be a finite-dimensional vector space. The* **dimension** *of* V, *denoted by* $\dim V$, *is the number of vectors in a basis of* V. *If* V *consists of the single vector* $\underline{0}$, *we set* $\dim V = 0$. *If* $\dim V = n$, *i.e., a basis of* V *consists of* n *vectors, we sometimes say that* V *is* **n-dimensional.**

The proof of the following theorem is identical to the proof of Theorem 6.5 in Chapter 1.

Theorem 1.2. *Let* V *be a finite-dimensional vector space.*
   (a) *If* U *is a proper subspace of* V, *then* $\dim U < \dim V$.
   (b) *If* U *and* W *are subspaces of* V *and* $\dim U + \dim W > n$, *then* $\dim(U \cap W) > 0$.

For example, let U be the subspace of $V_3(R)$ consisting of all vectors (x_1, x_2, x_3) whose coordinates satisfy $x_1 + x_2 + x_3 = 0$ and let W be the subspace of vectors (x_1, x_2, x_3) whose coordinates satisfy $x_1 - x_2 - x_3 = 0$. Then $\dim U = \dim W = 2$ and $\dim U + \dim W > \dim V_3(R)$. Clearly $U \cap W$ consists of all vectors (x_1, x_2, x_3) whose coordinates satisfy the system of equations

$$x_1 + x_2 + x_3 = 0,$$
$$x_1 - x_2 - x_3 = 0;$$

i.e., $U \cap W = \langle (0, 1, -1) \rangle$.

We now define linear transformations on abstract vector spaces and discuss the relations between linear transformations and matrices. The development is very similar to the one in Chapter 2, where we were interested specifically in linear transformations on spaces of n-tuples.

Definition 1.4. (**Linear transformation**). *Let* U *and* V *be complex vector spaces* (*or both real vector spaces*), *not necessarily distinct. The function* $T: U \to V$ *is called a* **linear transformation** *if*

$$T(c_1 u_1 + c_2 u_2) = c_1 T(u_1) + c_2 T(u_2)$$

for any vectors u_1 *and* u_2 *in* U *and any scalars* c_1 *and* c_2.

Now, let $G = \{g_1, \ldots, g_n\}$ be a basis of U and let $H = \{h_1, \ldots, h_m\}$ be a basis of V. Then the vectors $T(g_j)$, $j = 1, \ldots, n$, are in V, and therefore there exist scalars a_{ij}, $i = 1, \ldots, m$, $j = 1, \ldots, n$, such that

$$T(g_1) = a_{11} h_1 + a_{21} h_2 + \cdots + a_{m1} h_m,$$
$$T(g_2) = a_{12} h_1 + a_{22} h_2 + \cdots + a_{m2} h_m,$$
$$\vdots \qquad\qquad\qquad\qquad \vdots \qquad\qquad (4)$$
$$T(g_n) = a_{1n} h_1 + a_{2n} h_2 + \cdots + a_{mn} h_m.$$

It is clear that once the bases G and H are given, the linear transformation T is completely determined by the scalars a_{ij}, $i = 1, \ldots, m$, $j = 1, \ldots, n$. For, if $u = \sum_{j=1}^{n} c_j g_j$ is any vector in U, then

$$
\begin{aligned}
T(u) &= T\left(\sum_{j=1}^{n} c_j g_j\right) \\
&= \sum_{j=1}^{n} c_j T(g_j) \\
&= \sum_{j=1}^{n} c_j \sum_{i=1}^{m} a_{ij} h_i \\
&= \sum_{i=1}^{m} \left(\sum_{j=1}^{n} a_{ij} c_j\right) h_i, \qquad (5)
\end{aligned}
$$

and therefore the value of T at u is completely determined by the a_{ij}.

Definition 1.5. **(Matrix representation).** *The $m \times n$ matrix*

$$
A = \begin{bmatrix}
a_{11} & a_{12} & \cdots & a_{1n} \\
a_{21} & a_{22} & \cdots & a_{2n} \\
\vdots & & & \vdots \\
a_{m1} & a_{m2} & \cdots & a_{mn}
\end{bmatrix},
$$

*whose entries are the coefficients a_{ij} appearing in (4), is called the **matrix representation** of T with respect to the bases G and H. We write*

$$A = [T]_G^H.$$

Examples 1.3.

   (a) Suppose $T: V_2(R) \to V_2(R)$ is the rotation of the plane through an angle θ. Let $T((x_1, x_2)) = (y_1, y_2)$. Then [see formulas (7) in Section 1.3]

$$y_1 = x_1 \cos \theta - x_2 \sin \theta, \tag{6}$$
$$y_2 = x_1 \sin \theta + x_2 \cos \theta.$$

In particular, for the basis vectors $g_1 = (1, 0)$ and $g_2 = (0, 1)$, formulas (6) give

$$T(g_1) = g_1 \cos \theta + g_2 \sin \theta,$$
$$T(g_2) = -g_1 \sin \theta + g_2 \cos \theta.$$

Thus

$$[T]_G^G = \begin{bmatrix} \cos \theta & -\sin \theta \\ \sin \theta & \cos \theta \end{bmatrix}.$$

(b) Let S be the linear transformation that sends each point P in the plane into its mirror image across the horizontal axis (see Quiz Question 4, Section 1.3). If $g_1 = (1, 0)$ and $g_2 = (0, 1)$ as before, then clearly

$$S(g_1) = g_1,$$
$$S(g_2) = -g_2,$$

and therefore

$$[S]_G^G = \begin{bmatrix} 1 & 0 \\ 0 & -1 \end{bmatrix}.$$

The basic results in Chapter 2 on the matrix representation of a product and a sum of linear transformations are generalized without difficulty.

Theorem 1.3. *Let* $T: U \to V$, $S: V \to W$, *and* $R: U \to V$. *Let* $G = \{g_1, \ldots, g_n\}$, $H = \{h_1, \ldots, h_m\}$, *and* $K = \{k_1, \ldots, k_r\}$ *be bases of U, V, and W, respectively. Then*

$$[S]_H^K[T]_G^H = [ST]_G^K \tag{7}$$

and

$$[R]_G^H + [T]_G^H = [R + T]_G^H. \tag{8}$$

Proof. Let $[S]_H^K = (a_{ij})$, $[T]_G^H = (b_{ij})$, and $[ST]_G^K = (c_{ij})$. Then c_{ij} is the coefficient of k_i in the expression for $(ST)(g_j)$ as a linear combination of $k_1, \ldots, k_r$. Now

$$(ST)(g_j) = S(Tg_j)$$

$$= S\left(\sum_{t=1}^{m} b_{tj} h_t\right)$$

$$= \sum_{t=1}^{m} b_{tj} S(h_t)$$

$$= \sum_{t=1}^{m} b_{tj} \sum_{i=1}^{r} a_{it} k_i$$

$$= \sum_{i=1}^{r} \left(\sum_{t=1}^{m} a_{it} b_{tj}\right) k_i.$$

Thus

$$c_{ij} = \sum_{t=1}^{m} a_{it} b_{tj},$$

which is the (i, j) entry of the matrix $[S]_H^K[T]_G^H$. Formula (8) is proved quite easily, and we leave the proof to the reader.

It should be noted that the matrix $[T]_G^H$ depends not only on T, but also on the two bases G and H. For example, if I_U is the identity transformation on a vector space U, then $[I_U]_G^G$ is the identity matrix I_n, but if H is any other basis of U, then $[I_U]_G^H \neq I_n$. However, matrices $[T]_G^G$ and $[T]_H^H$, representing the same linear transformation with respect to different bases, are related in an important way.

Theorem 1.4. Let G and H be two bases of U and let $T : U \rightarrow U$ be a linear transformation. If $A = [T]_G^G$ and $B = [T]_H^H$, then there exists a nonsingular matrix C such that

$$A = CBC^{-1}. \tag{9}$$

Proof. We use formula (7) and compute

$$A = [T]_G^G$$

$$= [I_U T I_U]_G^G$$

$$= [I_U]_H^G[T]_H^H[I_U]_G^H. \tag{10}$$

Now we set $C = [I_U]_H^G$ and show that $[I_U]_G^H = C^{-1}$. In fact,

$$[I_U]_H^G[I_U]_G^H = [I_U]_G^G$$

$$= I_n,$$

and therefore the matrix $[I_U]_G^H$ is the inverse of the matrix $[I_U]_H^G$. Thus, by (10),

$$A = CBC^{-1}.$$

The converse of Theorem 1.4 is also true. That is to say, if A and B are matrices for which (9) holds and $A = [T]_G^G$, then there exists a basis H of U such that $B = [T]_H^H$. We shall not prove the converse here.

Example 1.4. Let $G = \{g_1, g_2\}$ and $H = \{h_1, h_2\}$, where $g_1 = (1, 1)$, $g_2 = (1, -1)$, $h_1 = (2, 1)$, and $h_2 = (-1, 3)$. Then G and H are two bases of $V_2(R)$. Let $T: V_2(R) \to V_2(R)$ be defined by

$$T((x_1, x_2)) = (x_1 + 2x_2, 2x_1 - x_2). \tag{11}$$

We compute $A = [T]_G^G$ and $B = [T]_H^H$. From (11) we have

$$T(g_1) = (3, 1),$$
$$T(g_2) = (-1, 3),$$

and we easily compute

$$T(g_1) = 2g_1 + g_2,$$
$$T(g_2) = g_1 - 2g_2.$$

Similarly, we compute

$$T(h_1) = (4, 3),$$
$$T(h_2) = (5, -5),$$

and

$$T(h_1) = \tfrac{15}{7}h_1 + \tfrac{2}{7}h_2,$$
$$T(h_2) = \tfrac{10}{7}h_1 - \tfrac{15}{7}h_2.$$

We have therefore,

$$A = [T]_G^G = \begin{bmatrix} 2 & 1 \\ 1 & -2 \end{bmatrix},$$

$$B = [T]_H^H = \begin{bmatrix} \frac{15}{7} & \frac{10}{7} \\ \frac{2}{7} & -\frac{15}{7} \end{bmatrix}.$$

We next compute $C = [I_U]_H^G$, where $U = V_2(R)$:

$$I_U(h_1) = \tfrac{3}{2}g_1 + \tfrac{1}{2}g_2,$$

$$I_U(h_2) = g_1 - 2g_2,$$

and these equations yield

$$C = \begin{bmatrix} \frac{3}{2} & 1 \\ \frac{1}{2} & -2 \end{bmatrix}.$$

Finally, we verify Theorem 1.4 for the linear transformation T and bases G and H. We compute

$$C^{-1} = \begin{bmatrix} \frac{4}{7} & \frac{2}{7} \\ \frac{1}{7} & -\frac{3}{7} \end{bmatrix},$$

and then

$$CBC^{-1} = \begin{bmatrix} 2 & 1 \\ 1 & -2 \end{bmatrix}$$

$$= A.$$

Theorem 1.4 suggests that any two matrices A and B related by an equation such as (9) have many intrinsic properties in common. This is indeed the case. In Section 4.2 we shall consider the following problem: given a linear transformation $T: V \rightarrow V$, find a basis G of V so hat the matrix representation $[T]_G^G$ has some simple form.

Definition 1.6.   (Similarity). *A matrix A is said to be **similar** to a matrix B if there exists a nonsingular matrix C such that $A = CBC^{-1}$.*

Theorem 1.4 states, therefore, that matrices that are representations of the same linear transformation are similar.

Quiz

Answer *true* or *false*:

1. Let U be an n-dimensional vector space and let $T: U \to U$ be defined by $T(u) = 0$ for every u in U. Then T is a linear transformation.

2. If T is as defined in Question 1 and if G and H are bases of U, then $\lfloor T \rfloor_G^H = 0_n$.

3. If I_U is the identity transformation on U and G and H are bases of U, then $[I_U]_G^H = I_n$.

4. If $S: U \to U$ is a linear transformation, G and H are bases of U and if $[S]_G^H = I_n$, then $S = I_U$.

5. The set M_n of n-square matrices with matrix addition and scalar multiplication forms a vector space of dimension n^2.

6. The matrices

$$\begin{bmatrix} 1 & 0 \\ 1 & 1 \end{bmatrix} \quad \text{and} \quad \begin{bmatrix} 1 & 0 \\ 0 & 1 \end{bmatrix}$$

   are similar.

7. Similar matrices have the same rank. (See Theorem 4.6, Chapter 2.)

8. If A and B are similar, then $\det(A) = \det(B)$. (See Theorem 2.5, Chapter 3.)

9. If A, B, and C are square matrices and $AC = CB$, then A and B are similar. (*Hint:* Try $C = 0$.)

10. If A is similar to B, then A^2 is similar to B^2. (*Hint:* If $A = SBS^{-1}$, then compute A^2.)

Exercises

1. Let $T: V_2(R) \to V_3(R)$ be the linear transformation defined by

$$T((x_1, x_2)) = (x_1 + x_2, x_1 - x_2, x_1).$$

   If $G = \{(1, -1), (1, 1)\}$ and $H = \{(1, 0, 1), (-1, 0, 1), (1, 1, 1)\}$ are the bases of $V_2(R)$ and $V_3(R)$, respectively, then find the matrix representation

$$[T]_G^H.$$

2. Let $V = V_2(R)$ and choose bases $G = \{(1, 1), (0, 1)\}$, $H = \{(-1, 0), (2, 3)\}$. Find $[I_V]_G^H$, $[I_V]_H^G$, and show that $[I_V]_G^H [I_V]_H^G = I_2$ by direct computation.

3. Show that the following pairs of matrices are similar:

$$\begin{bmatrix} 1 & 0 \\ 0 & 2 \end{bmatrix}, \quad \begin{bmatrix} 2 & 0 \\ 0 & 1 \end{bmatrix};$$

$$\begin{bmatrix} 0 & 1 \\ 0 & 0 \end{bmatrix}, \quad \begin{bmatrix} 0 & 0 \\ 1 & 0 \end{bmatrix};$$

$$\begin{bmatrix} 1 & 0 \\ 0 & 2 \end{bmatrix}, \quad \begin{bmatrix} 1 & 2 \\ 0 & 2 \end{bmatrix}.$$

4. Let E_{ij} denote the n-square matrix with 1 in its (i, j) position and 0 elsewhere. Show that the n^2 matrices E_{ij}, $i, j = 1, \ldots, n$, form a basis for the space of n-square matrices.

5. Let T_n denote the space of all upper triangular n-square matrices. Find the dimension of T_n.

6. Let T be a linear tranformation on $M_2(R)$, the space of 2-square real matrices, defined by

$$T\left(\begin{bmatrix} a_{11} & a_{12} \\ a_{21} & a_{22} \end{bmatrix}\right) = \begin{bmatrix} 2a_{11} & a_{12} + a_{21} \\ a_{12} - a_{21} & 3a_{22} \end{bmatrix}.$$

If $G = \{E_{11}, E_{12}, E_{21}, E_{22}\}$, where E_{ij}, $i, j = 1, 2$, are the matrices defined in Exercise 4, find $[T]_G^G$.

7. Let $H = \{F_1, F_2, F_3, F_4\}$ be a basis for $M_2(R)$, where $F_1 = I_2$,

$$F_2 = \begin{bmatrix} 1 & 0 \\ 0 & -1 \end{bmatrix}, \qquad F_3 = \begin{bmatrix} 0 & 1 \\ 1 & 0 \end{bmatrix}, \qquad \text{and} \qquad F_4 = \begin{bmatrix} 0 & 1 \\ -1 & 0 \end{bmatrix}.$$

Let T be the linear transformation defined in Exercise 6. Find the matrix $B = [T]_H^H$ and a matrix C such that

$$CBC^{-1} = [T]_G^G,$$

where G is the basis defined in Exercise 6.

8. Show that:
   (a) every square matrix is similar to itself;
   (b) if A is similar to B, then B is similar to A;
   (c) if A is similar to B and B is similar to C, then A is similar to C.

9. Show that for any nonzero numbers x and y, the matrices

$$\begin{bmatrix} 1 & x \\ 0 & 1 \end{bmatrix} \qquad \text{and} \qquad \begin{bmatrix} 1 & y \\ 0 & 1 \end{bmatrix}$$

are similar. What is the necessary condition that

$$\begin{bmatrix} 1 & x \\ 0 & 1 \end{bmatrix}$$

be similar to

$$\begin{bmatrix} 1 & 0 \\ 0 & 1 \end{bmatrix}?$$

10. Let V be a finite-dimensional vector space. Let $L(V, V)$ be the set of all linear transformations $T: V \to V$. Define addition and scalar multiplication on $L(V, V)$ as follows: if T_1 and T_2 are in $L(V, V)$, then

$$(T_1 + T_2)v = T_1 v + T_2 v$$

for all $v \in V$; if T is in $L(V, V)$, then

$$(cT)v = c(Tv)$$

for all $v \in V$ and all scalars c.

Show that:
  (a) $T_1 + T_2$ and cT are linear transformations.
  (b) $L(V, V)$, with addition and scalar multiplication defined as above, forms a vector space.
11. Prove formula (8).

4.2. CHARACTERISTIC ROOTS AND CHARACTERISTIC VECTORS

In Section 4.1 we suggested that given a linear transformation $T: V \to V$, it may be possible to find a basis G of V such that the matrix $[T]_G^G$ has some special, simple form. For example, it may be possible to choose G so that $[T]_G^G$ is upper triangular, or perhaps symmetric, or even diagonal. Diagonal matrices have an exceptionally simple and "transparent" structure: the rank of $D = \mathrm{diag}(d_1, \ldots, d_n)$ is clearly equal to the number of nonzero entries; the determinant of D is just the product $d_1 \cdots d_n$; the product of D and $F = \mathrm{diag}(f_1, \ldots, f_n)$ is $DF = FD = \mathrm{diag}(d_1 f_1, \ldots, d_n f_n)$, while $D + F = \mathrm{diag}(d_1 + f_1, \ldots, d_n + f_n)$. We shall try to find conditions for a given linear transformation to have a diagonal matrix representation or, equivalently, for a given matrix to be similar to a diagonal matrix.

Suppose that A is similar to $D = \mathrm{diag}(d_1, \ldots, d_n)$, i.e., that $A = SDS^{-1}$ for some nonsingular matrix S. Then

$$AS = SD, \tag{1}$$

or, equating the columns on both sides of (1),

$$(AS)^{(j)} = (SD)^{(j)}, \qquad j = 1, \ldots, n.$$

Recall that $(XY)^{(j)} = XY^{(j)}$ for any matrices X and Y for which the product XY is defined (see Exercise 9, Section 2.1). We have, therefore,

$$AS^{(j)} = SD^{(j)}.$$

But if D is a diagonal matrix, then $D^{(j)} = d_j e_j$, where e_j is the n-tuple with 1 as its jth coordinate and 0's elsewhere. It is also obvious that $Xe_j = X^{(j)}$ for any $n \times n$ matrix X. Thus

$$AS^{(j)} = SD^{(j)}$$
$$= d_j S e_j$$
$$= d_j S^{(j)}, \qquad j = 1, \ldots, n. \tag{2}$$

We also note that $S^{(j)} \neq 0$, since the matrix S is nonsingular. Before we enshrine the preceding remarks in a theorem, we define two important concepts.

Definition 2.1. **(Characteristic roots and characteristic vectors).** *Let A be an n × n matrix with complex (real) entries. If v_t is a nonzero complex (real) n-tuple satisfying*

$$Av_t = \lambda_t v_t, \tag{3}$$

where λ_t is a scalar, then v_t is called a **characteristic vector** *of A corresponding to the* **characteristic root** *λ_t of A. Characteristic vectors and characteristic roots are also called* **eigenvectors** *and* **eigenvalues**, *or* **latent vectors** *and* **latent roots**.

Example 2.1. Find, by direct computation, the characteristic roots and corresponding characteristic vectors of the matrix

$$A = \begin{bmatrix} 2 & 2 \\ 3 & 1 \end{bmatrix}.$$

We want to solve the system

$$\begin{bmatrix} 2 & 2 \\ 3 & 1 \end{bmatrix} \begin{bmatrix} x_1 \\ x_2 \end{bmatrix} = \lambda \begin{bmatrix} x_1 \\ x_2 \end{bmatrix} \tag{4}$$

for x_1, x_2, and λ. The statement (4) is equivalent to

$$2x_1 + 2x_2 = \lambda x_1,$$
$$3x_1 + x_2 = \lambda x_2,$$

i.e.,

$$(\lambda - 2)x_1 - 2x_2 = 0,$$
$$-3x_1 + (\lambda - 1)x_2 = 0. \tag{5}$$

Now, a necessary and sufficient condition for the system (5) to have a non-zero solution (x_1, x_2) is that

$$\det\left(\begin{bmatrix} \lambda - 2 & -2 \\ -3 & \lambda - 1 \end{bmatrix}\right) = 0$$

(see Theorem 2.7, Chapter 3); i.e.,

$$\lambda^2 - 3\lambda - 4 = 0$$

or

$$(\lambda - 4)(\lambda + 1) = 0.$$

Thus (5) has nonzero solution (x_1, x_2) if and only if $\lambda = 4$ or $\lambda = -1$. If $\lambda = 4$, then (5) is equivalent to the system

$$x_1 - x_2 = 0,$$

and, for example, $(1, 1)$ is a characteristic vector corresponding to the characteristic root 4. If $\lambda = -1$, then (5) becomes

$$3x_1 + 2x_2 = 0,$$

and $(2, -3)$ is a characteristic vector corresponding to the characteristic root -1.

We are now ready to state our first result. Call a square matrix *diagonalizable* (*triangularizable*) if it is similar to a diagonal (triangular) matrix.

Theorem 2.1. *An n-square matrix A is diagonalizable if and only if A has n linearly independent characteristic vectors.*

Proof. We have already established [see (2)] that if $A = SDS^{-1}$, where $D = \text{diag}(\lambda_1, \ldots, \lambda_n)$, then

$$AS^{(j)} = \lambda_j S^{(j)}, \qquad j = 1, \ldots, n.$$

Thus the columns of S are characteristic vectors of A. But S is nonsingular and, therefore, its columns are linearly independent. Hence A has n linearly independent characteristic vectors. To prove the converse, assume that A has n linearly independent characteristic vectors $v_1, \ldots, v_n$, i.e., that

$$Av_j = \lambda_j v_j, \qquad j = 1, \ldots, n,$$

where $v_j \neq 0$. Let S be the $n \times n$ matrix whose jth column is equal to

$v_j, j = 1, \ldots, n$. Thus

$$AS^{(j)} = \lambda_j S^{(j)}$$
$$= \lambda_j S e_j$$
$$= SD^{(j)}, \qquad j = 1, \ldots, n,$$

where $D = \text{diag}(\lambda_1, \ldots, \lambda_n)$. But $AS^{(j)} = (AS)^{(j)}$ and $SD^{(j)} = (SD)^{(j)}$.

Thus

$$(AS)^{(j)} = (SD)^{(j)}, \qquad j = 1, \ldots, n,$$

i.e.,

$$AS = SD. \tag{6}$$

Now the columns of S are linearly independent and thus the rank of S is n. Therefore, by Theorem 4.3(b), Chapter 2, S is nonsingular. Hence we can pre-multiply both sides of (6) by S^{-1} and obtain

$$S^{-1}AS = D.$$

We have proved that if A has n linearly independent characteristic vectors $v_1, \ldots, v_n$, then A is similar to $\text{diag}(\lambda_1, \ldots, \lambda_n)$, where λ_j is the characteristic root corresponding to $v_j, j = 1, \ldots, n$.

Example 2.2. Diagonalize the matrix

$$A = \begin{bmatrix} 2 & 2 \\ 3 & 1 \end{bmatrix}.$$

We found in Example 2.1 that the characteristic roots of A are 4 and -1, with corresponding characteristic vectors $(1, 1)$ and $(2, -3)$. Let

$$S = \begin{bmatrix} 1 & 2 \\ 1 & -3 \end{bmatrix}.$$

We compute

$$S^{-1} = -\frac{1}{5} \begin{bmatrix} -3 & -2 \\ -1 & 1 \end{bmatrix},$$

and

$$S^{-1}AS = \begin{bmatrix} 4 & 0 \\ 0 & -1 \end{bmatrix}.$$

We return now to the problem of finding characteristic roots and characteristic vectors of a given n-square matrix A, i.e., the problem of solving

$$Av = \lambda v \tag{7}$$

for the vector v, $v \neq 0$, and the scalar λ. The right side of (7) is equal to $\lambda I_n v$ and the system (7) is equivalent to

$$(\lambda I_n - A)v = 0. \tag{8}$$

Nonzero solutions for v are precisely nonzero vectors in the null space of $\lambda I_n - A$. By Theorem 2.7, Chapter 3, the null space of $\lambda I_n - A$ contains nonzero vectors if and only if

$$\det(\lambda I_n - A) = 0. \tag{9}$$

Definition 2.2. **(Characteristic equation).** *Let $A = (a_{ij})$ be an $n \times n$ real or complex matrix. The matrix*

$$\lambda I_n - A = \begin{bmatrix} \lambda - a_{11} & -a_{12} & \cdots & -a_{1n} \\ -a_{21} & \lambda - a_{22} & & -a_{2n} \\ \vdots & \vdots & \ddots & \vdots \\ -a_{n1} & -a_{n2} & \cdots & \lambda - a_{nn} \end{bmatrix}$$

*is called the **characteristic matrix** of A. The determinant of the characteristic matrix of A, $\det(\lambda I_n - A)$, is called the **characteristic polynomial** (or the **characteristic function**) of A. Equation (9) is called the **characteristic equation** of A.*

The roots of the characteristic equation of A are, of course, the characteristic roots of A. For, we saw that λ can be a characteristic root [see (8)] if and only if $\lambda I_n - A$ is singular, i.e., $\det(\lambda I_n - A) = 0$. We assert that the degree of the characteristic polynomial of an n-square matrix is n. For by Theorem 1.3, Chapter 3, one of the terms in $\det(\lambda I_n - A)$ is $\prod_{i=1}^{n} (\lambda - a_{ii})$, and all other terms involve products with fewer than n factors of the form $\lambda - a_{ii}$. Thus λ^n appears in the characteristic polynomial precisely once, and every other term in the characteristic polynomial must have degree less than n. Now, it is proved in more advanced books that every complex polynomial of degree n has exactly n roots (not necessarily distinct). Thus every $n \times n$ complex matrix has exactly n characteristic roots. Clearly the characteristic polynomial of a matrix with real entries has real coefficients but not necessarily real roots.

Characteristic vectors corresponding to a characteristic root λ_t of a matrix A are nonzero vectors in the null space of the matrix $\lambda_t I_n - A$. It follows that any nonzero linear combination of characteristic vectors corresponding to λ_t is a characteristic vector corresponding to λ_t [see Theorem 3.2(a), Chapter 2]. In particular, this is true of a nonzero scalar multiple of such a characteristic vector.

Example 2.3.

(a) Find the characteristic roots and corresponding characteristic vectors of

$$A = \begin{bmatrix} 2 & -3 & 3 \\ 4 & -5 & 3 \\ 4 & -4 & 2 \end{bmatrix}.$$

The characteristic matrix of A is

$$\lambda I_3 - A = \begin{bmatrix} \lambda - 2 & 3 & -3 \\ -4 & \lambda + 5 & -3 \\ -4 & 4 & \lambda - 2 \end{bmatrix}.$$

We compute the characteristic polynomial of A:

$$\det(\lambda I_3 - A) = \lambda^3 + \lambda^2 - 4\lambda - 4. \tag{10}$$

Recall the well-known theorem in algebra stating that the rational roots of a polynomial $\lambda^n + a_{n-1}\lambda^{n-1} + \cdots + a_1\lambda + a_0$ with integer coefficients $a_0, \ldots, a_{n-1}$ are, in fact, integers which divide a_0. Thus the only possible rational roots of $\lambda^3 + \lambda^2 - 4\lambda - 4$ are divisors of -4. We try in turn $1, -1, 2, -2, 4,$ and -4 and find that $-1, 2,$ and -2 are the roots of the characteristic equation, i.e., the characteristic roots of A. Substitute $\lambda = -1$

in the characteristic matrix of A and solve the system

$$\begin{bmatrix} -3 & 3 & -3 \\ -4 & 4 & -3 \\ -4 & 4 & -3 \end{bmatrix} \begin{bmatrix} x_1 \\ x_2 \\ x_3 \end{bmatrix} = 0. \tag{11}$$

The system (11) is equivalent to

$$-3x_1 + 3x_2 - 3x_3 = 0,$$
$$-4x_1 + 4x_2 - 3x_3 = 0,$$

i.e.,

$$x_1 = x_2,$$
$$x_3 = 0.$$

Thus $(1, 1, 0)$ is a characteristic vector corresponding to -1. Next, substitute $\lambda = 2$ in the characteristic matrix and solve the system

$$\begin{bmatrix} 0 & 3 & -3 \\ -4 & 7 & -3 \\ -4 & 4 & 0 \end{bmatrix} \begin{bmatrix} x_1 \\ x_2 \\ x_3 \end{bmatrix} = 0$$

to obtain a characteristic vector $(1, 1, 1)$ corresponding to 2. Finally, solve the system

$$(-2I_3 - A)v = 0,$$

i.e.,

$$\begin{bmatrix} -4 & 3 & -3 \\ -4 & 3 & -3 \\ -4 & 4 & -4 \end{bmatrix} \begin{bmatrix} x_1 \\ x_2 \\ x_3 \end{bmatrix} = 0,$$

to obtain $(0, 1, 1)$ as a characteristic vector corresponding to the characteristic root -2. Since the three characteristic vectors which we found are obviously linearly independent, we can set

$$S = \begin{bmatrix} 1 & 1 & 0 \\ 1 & 1 & 1 \\ 0 & 1 & 1 \end{bmatrix}$$

and verify that

$$S^{-1}AS = \text{diag}(-1, 2, -2).$$

(b) Show that the matrix

$$B = \begin{bmatrix} 1 & 2 & 1 \\ 1 & -1 & 1 \\ 2 & 0 & 1 \end{bmatrix}$$

is not similar to a diagonal matrix. We compute the characteristic polynomial of B:

$$\det(\lambda I_3 - B) = \lambda^3 - \lambda^2 - 5\lambda - 3.$$

Substitute 1, -1, 3, and -3, in turn, for λ and find that -1 and 3 are roots. We can divide $\lambda^3 - \lambda^2 - 5\lambda - 3$ by $(\lambda + 1)(\lambda - 3)$ and thus obtain the factorization

$$\lambda^3 - \lambda^2 - 5\lambda - 3 = (\lambda + 1)^2(\lambda - 3).$$

Hence the characteristic roots of B are -1, -1, and 3. Now,

$$(-1)I_3 - B = \begin{bmatrix} -2 & -2 & -1 \\ -1 & 0 & -1 \\ -2 & 0 & -2 \end{bmatrix}$$

is of rank 2, and therefore its null space is of dimension $3 - 2 = 1$ [see Theorem 3.2(a), Chapter 2]. Solving the system

$$((-1)I_3 - B)v = 0,$$

we find that $v_0 = (2, -1, -2)$ is a characteristic vector corresponding to -1; any other characteristic vector corresponding to -1 is a nonzero multiple of v_0. Similarly,

$$3I_3 - B = \begin{bmatrix} 2 & -2 & -1 \\ -1 & 4 & -1 \\ -2 & 0 & 2 \end{bmatrix}$$

is of rank 2, and therefore every characteristic vector corresponding to 3 is a nonzero multiple of any nonzero solution vector of

$$(3I_3 - B)v = 0;$$

we find that $(2, 1, 2)$ is a characteristic vector corresponding to 3. We have now run out of characteristic roots of B and have no more than two linearly independent characteristic vectors. It follows from Theorem 2.1 that B cannot be similar to a diagonal matrix.

At the beginning of this section we enumerated several important, special properties of diagonal matrices. To this list we must add the following: the characteristic roots of $D = \text{diag}(d_1, \ldots, d_n)$ are the numbers $d_1, \ldots, d_n$. For, the characteristic matrix of D, $\lambda I_n - D$, is itself diagonal, and therefore the characteristic polynomial $\det(\lambda I_n - D)$ is just the product $\prod_{i=1}^{n} (\lambda - d_i)$. Unfortunately, as we have discovered in Example 2.3(b), not every square matrix can be diagonalized. However, we shall show that every matrix is similar to an upper triangular matrix. Now, we saw [Quiz Question 6, Section 3.1] that if $T = (t_{ij})$ is an n-square upper triangular matrix, then the determinant of T is just the product $\prod_{i=1}^{n} t_{ii}$, and since the characteristic matrix $\lambda I_n - T$ is also upper triangular, the characteristic polynomial of T is $\prod_{i=1}^{n} (\lambda - t_{ii})$. It follows that the characteristic roots of T are just the main diagonal entries $t_{11}, \ldots, t_{nn}$.

The mere fact that a matrix is in some way related to another matrix of a simpler structure is not, by itself, of great importance. After all, any non-singular matrix is equivalent to the identity matrix. In fact, the only significant property common to equivalent matrices is their rank. We know that if two matrices are similar, then they are equivalent (see Definition 4.3, Chapter 2). The converse, of course, is not true; e.g., the identity matrix obviously is not similar to any other matrix, since $SI_n S^{-1} = I_n$ for any nonsingular matrix S. This means that similar matrices not only have the same rank but share some other properties as well. The following theorem underlines the importance of similarity to a diagonal, or even a triangular, matrix.

Theorem 2.2. *Similar matrices have the same characteristic polynomial.*

Proof. Let A and B be $n \times n$ matrices and suppose that $A = SBS^{-1}$.

Then

$$\begin{aligned}
\det(\lambda I_n - A) &= \det(\lambda I_n - SBS^{-1}) \\
&= \det(S(\lambda I_n - B)S^{-1}) \\
&= \det(S)\det(\lambda I_n - B)\det(S^{-1}) \\
&= \det(S)\det(S^{-1})\det(\lambda I_n - B) \\
&= \det(SS^{-1})\det(\lambda I_n - B) \\
&= \det(\lambda I_n - B).
\end{aligned}$$

It follows from Theorem 2.2 that similar matrices have the same characteristic roots (including multiplicities). The converse is not true. For example, the matrix B in Example 2.3(b) has the same characteristic roots as the matrix $\mathrm{diag}(-1, -1, 3)$, yet B is not diagonalizable; therefore, it cannot be similar to $\mathrm{diag}(-1, -1, 3)$.

Let A be an n-square matrix and let

$$\det(\lambda I_n - A) = \lambda^n + c_{n-1}\lambda^{n-1} + \cdots + c_1\lambda + c_0. \tag{12}$$

If $\lambda_1, \ldots, \lambda_n$ are the characteristic roots of A, then it is a well-known result in the elementary theory of equations that

$$-c_{n-1} = \lambda_1 + \lambda_2 + \cdots + \lambda_n,$$

and

$$(-1)^n c_0 = \lambda_1\lambda_2 \cdots \lambda_n.$$

On the other hand, we can substitute 0 for λ in (12) and obtain [see Theorem 1.1(d) and Quiz Question 3, Section 3.1]

$$\begin{aligned}
c_0 &= \det(-A) \\
&= (-1)^n \det(A).
\end{aligned}$$

It is also easy to see that

$$c_{n-1} = -(a_{11} + a_{22} + \cdots + a_{nn}).$$

Thus we have proved

Theorem 2.3. *If* $A = (a_{ij})$ *is an* $n \times n$ *matrix with characteristic roots* $\lambda_1, \ldots, \lambda_n$, *then*

$$\det(A) = \prod_{i=1}^{n} \lambda_i \qquad (13)$$

and

$$\sum_{i=1}^{n} a_{ii} = \sum_{i=1}^{n} \lambda_i. \qquad (14)$$

The sum $\sum_{i=1}^{n} a_{ii}$ is of importance in the theory of matrices and is given a special name.

Definition 2.3. **(Trace).** *If* $A = (a_{ij})$ *is an* $n \times n$ *matrix, then the **trace** of* A, *denoted by* tr A, *is defined by*

$$\text{tr } A = \sum_{i=1}^{n} a_{ii}.$$

Thus, by (14), if $\lambda_1, \ldots, \lambda_n$ are characteristic roots of A, then

$$\text{tr } A = \sum_{i=1}^{n} \lambda_i.$$

Theorems 2.2 and 2.3 imply, therefore, that similar matrices have the same traces and determinants.

Example 2.4. Let $A = SBS^{-1}$, where

$$B = \begin{bmatrix} 1 & 1 & 0 \\ 1 & 2 & 1 \\ 0 & 1 & 3 \end{bmatrix}, \qquad S = \begin{bmatrix} 1 & 1 & 0 \\ 1 & 1 & 1 \\ 1 & 0 & 1 \end{bmatrix}.$$

Compute A and verify that $\det(A) = \det(B)$ and tr $A = $ tr B. We have

$$A = SBS^{-1}$$

$$= \begin{bmatrix} 1 & 1 & 0 \\ 1 & 1 & 1 \\ 1 & 0 & 1 \end{bmatrix} \begin{bmatrix} 1 & 1 & 0 \\ 1 & 2 & 1 \\ 0 & 1 & 3 \end{bmatrix} \begin{bmatrix} 1 & -1 & 1 \\ 0 & 1 & -1 \\ -1 & 1 & 0 \end{bmatrix}$$

$$= \begin{bmatrix} 1 & 2 & -1 \\ -2 & 6 & -2 \\ -2 & 4 & -1 \end{bmatrix},$$

and, therefore,

$$\det(A) = 1(-6+8) - 2(2-4) - 1(-8+12)$$
$$= 2,$$
$$\operatorname{tr} A = 1 + 6 - 1$$
$$= 6.$$

We also compute

$$\det(B) = 1(6-1) - 1(3-0) + 0$$
$$= 2,$$
$$\operatorname{tr} B = 1 + 2 + 3$$
$$= 6.$$

We now return to triangularization of matrices.

Theorem 2.4. *Every square matrix is similar to an upper triangular matrix.*

Proof. Let $A = (a_{ij})$ be an n-square matrix. We use induction on n. The theorem holds trivially for $n = 1$. Assume that every $(n-1)$-square matrix is similar to an upper triangular matrix. Let λ_1 be a characteristic root of A and let v_1 be a corresponding characteristic vector. Let P be any nonsingular matrix whose first column $P^{(1)}$ is v_1. Such a P can always be constructed, for, v_1 may be completed to a basis of $V_n(R)$ with $v_2, \ldots, v_n$ [see Theorem 6.4(b), Chapter 1], and using these n-tuples as columns, we conclude from the linear independence of the v_i, $i = 1, \ldots, n$, that P is nonsingular [see Theorems 4.3(b) and 4.5, Chapter 2]. Then we compute that

$$\begin{aligned} (P^{-1}AP)^{(1)} = P^{-1}AP^{(1)} \quad &= P^{-1}Av_1 \\ = P^{-1}(\lambda_1 v_1) \quad &= \lambda_1 P^{-1}P^{(1)} \\ = \lambda_1(P^{-1}P)^{(1)} \quad &= \lambda_1(I_n)^{(1)} \\ = \lambda_1 e_1, \end{aligned}$$

where e_1 is the n-tuple with 1 as its first coordinate and 0 as its other coordinates. Thus $P^{-1}AP$ is of the form

$$
\begin{bmatrix}
\lambda_1 & \times \cdots \times \\
\hline
0 & \\
\vdots & A_1 \\
0 &
\end{bmatrix},
$$

where $\times$ represents unspecified entries while A_1 is an $(n-1)$-square submatrix of $P^{-1}AP$. By the induction hypothesis, there exists a nonsingular $(n-1)$-square matrix Q_1 such that $Q_1^{-1}A_1Q_1$ is upper triangular. Let $Q = (q_{ij})$ be the $n \times n$ matrix

$$
\begin{bmatrix}
1 & 0 \cdots 0 \\
\hline
0 & \\
\vdots & Q_1 \\
0 &
\end{bmatrix};
$$

i.e., $q_{11} = 1$, $q_{1j} = q_{i1} = 0$ for $i, j = 2, \ldots, n$, and $Q(1\,|\,1) = Q_1$. Then it is easy to see that

$$
Q^{-1} =
\begin{bmatrix}
1 & 0 \cdots 0 \\
\hline
0 & \\
\vdots & Q_1^{-1} \\
0 &
\end{bmatrix}
$$

and that

$$
Q^{-1}(P^{-1}AP)Q =
\begin{bmatrix}
\lambda_1 & \times \cdots \times \\
\hline
0 & \\
\vdots & Q_1^{-1}A_1Q_1 \\
0 &
\end{bmatrix},
\tag{15}
$$

where the $\times$ again represent unspecified entries. Now, $Q_1^{-1}A_1Q_1$ is an upper triangular $(n-1)$-square matrix, and therefore the matrix (15) is upper triangular. Denote it by T and set $PQ = S$. Then

$$Q^{-1}(P^{-1}AP)Q = T,$$

and therefore

$$A = PQTQ^{-1}P^{-1}$$
$$= STS^{-1}.$$

Example 2.5. Triangularize the matrix

$$B = \begin{bmatrix} 1 & 2 & 1 \\ 1 & -1 & 1 \\ 2 & 0 & 1 \end{bmatrix}.$$

We saw in Example 2.3(b) that -1 is a characteristic root of B and $(2, -1, -2)$ is a characteristic vector of B corresponding to -1. Let

$$P = \begin{bmatrix} 2 & 0 & 0 \\ -1 & 1 & 0 \\ -2 & 0 & 1 \end{bmatrix},$$

which clearly is nonsingular. In fact,

$$P^{-1} = \frac{1}{2} \begin{bmatrix} 1 & 0 & 0 \\ 1 & 2 & 0 \\ 2 & 0 & 2 \end{bmatrix}.$$

[Obviously, it would be advantageous to choose for P a matrix whose second column is $(2, 1, 2)$, the other characteristic vector which we found in Example 2.3(b). However, the purpose of the present example is to illustrate the constructive method of the proof of Theorem 2.4, and P was selected with this purpose in mind.] We compute

$$P^{-1}BP = \begin{bmatrix} -1 & 1 & \frac{1}{2} \\ \hline 0 & 0 & \frac{3}{2} \\ 0 & 2 & 2 \end{bmatrix}.$$

Let

$$B_1 = \begin{bmatrix} 0 & \frac{3}{2} \\ 2 & 2 \end{bmatrix}.$$

Then

$$\det(\lambda I_2 - B_1) = \lambda^2 - 2\lambda - 3$$
$$= (\lambda + 1)(\lambda - 3),$$

and we compute the characteristic vector u of B_1 corresponding to -1:

$$\begin{bmatrix} -1 & -\frac{3}{2} \\ -2 & -3 \end{bmatrix} u = 0;$$

therefore $u = (3, -2)$. Set

$$Q_1 = \begin{bmatrix} 3 & -1 \\ -2 & 1 \end{bmatrix}$$

and

$$Q = \begin{bmatrix} 1 & 0 & 0 \\ 0 & 3 & -1 \\ 0 & -2 & 1 \end{bmatrix}.$$

Let $PQ = S$. Then

$$S^{-1}BS = Q^{-1}(P^{-1}BP)Q$$
$$= \begin{bmatrix} -1 & 2 & -\frac{1}{2} \\ 0 & -1 & \frac{3}{2} \\ 0 & 0 & 3 \end{bmatrix},$$

which is upper triangular.

We shall demonstrate an important application of Theorem 2.4. First, however, we prove a preliminary result on upper triangular matrices.

Theorem 2.5. *If* $A = (a_{ij})$ *and* $B = (b_{ij})$ *are n-square upper triangular matrices, then:*

(a) *the matrix* $S = (s_{ij}) = A + B$ *is upper triangular, and* $s_{ii} = a_{ii} + b_{ii}$, $i = 1, \ldots, n$;

(b) *the matrix* $Q = (q_{ij}) = kA$ *is upper triangular for any scalar* k, *and* $q_{ii} = ka_{ii}$, $i = 1, \ldots, n$;

(c) *the matrix* $P = (p_{ij}) = AB$ *is upper triangular, and* $p_{ii} = a_{ii}b_{ii}$, $i = 1, \ldots, n$.

Proof. Parts (a) and (b) follow directly from the definitions. We prove (c). Recall that, since A and B are upper triangular, $a_{ij} = b_{ij} = 0$ whenever $i > j$. Suppose that $i > j$. We compute

$$p_{ij} = \sum_{t=1}^{n} a_{it} b_{tj}$$

$$= \sum_{t=1}^{i-1} a_{it} b_{tj} + \sum_{t=i}^{n} a_{it} b_{tj}. \tag{16}$$

Now, $a_{it} = 0$, $t = 1, \ldots, i - 1$, and $b_{tj} = 0$, $t = i, \ldots, n$, since $i > j$. Hence both sums in (16) are 0, and $p_{ij} = 0$ whenever $i > j$. It follows that P is upper triangular. Moreover,

$$p_{ii} = \sum_{t=1}^{n} a_{it} b_{ti}$$

$$= \sum_{t=1}^{i-1} a_{it} b_{ti} + a_{ii} b_{ii} + \sum_{t=i+1}^{n} a_{it} b_{ti}$$

$$= \sum_{t=1}^{i-1} 0 b_{ti} + a_{ii} b_{ii} + \sum_{t=i+1}^{n} a_{it} 0$$

$$= a_{ii} b_{ii}$$

for $i = 1, \ldots, n$. This completes the proof.

Now, let $f(\lambda) = \sum_{t=0}^{m} c_t \lambda^t$ be a polynomial with complex (or real) coefficients and let A be an n-square matrix. Let $f(A)$ denote the n-square matrix $c_m A^m + c_{m-1} A^{m-1} + \cdots + c_1 A + c_0 I_n$.

Theorem 2.6. *If* $f(\lambda)$ *is a polynomial and* A *an* n-*square matrix with characteristic roots* $\lambda_1, \ldots, \lambda_n$, *then the characteristic roots of the matrix* $f(A)$ *are* $f(\lambda_1), \ldots, f(\lambda_n)$.

Proof. By Theorem 2.4, there exists a matrix S such that $B = S^{-1}AS$ is upper triangular. Let $f(\lambda) = \sum_{t=0}^{m} c_t \lambda^t$. Then

$$f(A) = \sum_{t=0}^{m} c_t A^t$$

$$= \sum_{t=0}^{m} c_t (SBS^{-1})^t. \tag{17}$$

Now, for $t \geq 1$,

$$(SBS^{-1})^t = (SBS^{-1})(SBS^{-1})(SBS^{-1}) \cdots (SBS^{-1})$$

$$= SB(S^{-1}S)B(S^{-1}S)B \cdots (S^{-1}S)BS^{-1}$$

$$= SB^t S^{-1},$$

and, for $t = 0$,

$$(SBS^{-1})^0 = I_n$$

$$= SI_n S^{-1}$$

$$= SA^0 S^{-1}.$$

Therefore, from (17),

$$f(A) = \sum_{t=0}^{m} c_t SB^t S^{-1}$$

$$= S\left(\sum_{t=0}^{m} c_t B^t \right) S^{-1}$$

$$= Sf(B)S^{-1}.$$

Since $B = (b_{ij})$ is upper triangular, it follows from Theorem 2.5(c) that the matrices B^t are upper triangular, and also that the main diagonal entries of B^t are $b_{11}^t, b_{22}^t, \ldots, b_{nn}^t$. Further, by Theorem 2.5(b), the matrices $c_t B^t$ are upper triangular, and the main diagonal entries of $c_t B^t$ are $c_t b_{11}^t, c_t b_{22}^t, \ldots, c_t b_{nn}^t$. Finally, by Theorem 2.5(a), the matrix $\sum_{t=0}^{m} c_t B^t = f(B)$ is upper triangular, and its main diagonal entries are $\sum_{t=0}^{m} c_t b_{11}^t$,

$\sum_{t=0}^{m} c_t b_{22}^t, \ldots, \sum_{t=0}^{m} c_t b_{nn}^t$, i.e., $f(b_{11}), f(b_{22}), \ldots, f(b_{nn})$. But the characteristic roots of an upper triangular matrix are its main diagonal entries, and B and $f(B)$ are both upper triangular. Also, A and B are similar and thus have the same characteristic roots. It follows that

$$b_{ii} = \lambda_i, \qquad i = 1, \ldots, n,$$

$$f(b_{ii}) = f(\lambda_i), \qquad i = 1, \ldots, n.$$

Now, we proved that $f(\lambda_1), \ldots, f(\lambda_n)$ are the characteristic roots of $f(B)$ and that $f(B)$ and $f(A)$ are similar. Therefore $f(\lambda_1), \ldots, f(\lambda_n)$ are the characteristic roots of $f(A)$.

Example 2.6. Let $f(\lambda) = \lambda^2 - 2\lambda + 4$ and let

$$A = \begin{bmatrix} 0 & -1 & -1 \\ 1 & 2 & 1 \\ 1 & 1 & 2 \end{bmatrix}.$$

Compute the characteristic roots λ_1, λ_2, and λ_3 of A and verify Theorem 2.6. We have

$$\det(\lambda I_3 - A) = \det\left(\begin{bmatrix} \lambda & 1 & 1 \\ -1 & \lambda - 2 & -1 \\ -1 & -1 & \lambda - 2 \end{bmatrix}\right)$$

$$= \lambda^3 - 4\lambda^2 + 5\lambda - 2$$

$$= (\lambda - 1)^2(\lambda - 2),$$

and therefore $\lambda_1 = \lambda_2 = 1$ and $\lambda_3 = 2$. Now,

$$f(A) = A^2 - 2A + 4I_3$$

$$= \begin{bmatrix} -2 & -3 & -3 \\ 3 & 4 & 3 \\ 3 & 3 & 4 \end{bmatrix} - \begin{bmatrix} 0 & -2 & -2 \\ 2 & 4 & 2 \\ 2 & 2 & 4 \end{bmatrix} + \begin{bmatrix} 4 & 0 & 0 \\ 0 & 4 & 0 \\ 0 & 0 & 4 \end{bmatrix}$$

$$= \begin{bmatrix} 2 & -1 & -1 \\ 1 & 4 & 1 \\ 1 & 1 & 4 \end{bmatrix}.$$

Therefore the characteristic polynomial of $f(A)$ is

$$\det(\lambda I_3 - f(A)) = \det\left(\begin{bmatrix} \lambda - 2 & 1 & 1 \\ -1 & \lambda - 4 & -1 \\ -1 & -1 & \lambda - 4 \end{bmatrix}\right)$$

$$= \lambda^3 - 10\lambda^2 + 33\lambda - 36$$

$$= (\lambda - 3)^2(\lambda - 4).$$

Hence the characteristic roots of $f(A)$ are 3, 3, and 4. On the other hand, we can compute directly that $f(\lambda_1) = f(\lambda_2) = 1^2 - 2 \cdot 1 + 4 = 3$, while $f(\lambda_3) = 2^2 - 2 \cdot 2 + 4 = 4$, and thus the conclusions of Theorem 2.6 are verified in this case.

Suppose that A is an n-square matrix with characteristic roots $\lambda_1, \ldots, \lambda_n$ and characteristic polynomial $p(\lambda)$. Then, by Theorem 2.6, the characteristic roots of $p(A)$ are $p(\lambda_1), \ldots, p(\lambda_n)$. But the λ_i are the roots of the characteristic equation of A, and therefore $p(\lambda_1) = \cdots = p(\lambda_n) = 0$. That is, all the characteristic roots of $p(A)$ are 0. This fact by itself does not, of course, imply that $p(A) = 0$, for there exist nonzero matrices all of whose characteristic roots are 0, e.g.,

$$\begin{bmatrix} 1 & -1 \\ 1 & -1 \end{bmatrix}.$$

However, every square matrix does satisfy its characteristic equation, as we shall show in the next celebrated theorem.

Theorem 2.7.   (Cayley-Hamilton Theorem). *If A is a square matrix and $p(\lambda)$ its characteristic polynomial, then $p(A) = 0$.*

Proof. Recall that if X is any $n \times n$ matrix, then

$$X \operatorname{adj}(X) = I_n \det(X) \tag{18}$$

[see Theorem 2.1, Chapter 3]. We apply the identity (18) to the characteristic matrix of A:

$$(\lambda I_n - A) \operatorname{adj}(\lambda I_n - A) = I_n \det(\lambda I_n - A). \tag{19}$$

Let

$$p(\lambda) = \det(\lambda I_n - A)$$

$$= \sum_{t=0}^{n} c_t \lambda^t,$$

and let $\mathrm{adj}(\lambda I_n - A) = B(\lambda) = (b_{ij}(\lambda))$. The entries of $B(\lambda)$ are polynomials in λ. Suppose that no $b_{ij}(\lambda)$ is of degree greater than m. Let

$$b_{ij}(\lambda) = q_m^{(i,j)}\lambda^m + \cdots + q_1^{(i,j)}\lambda + q_0^{(i,j)},$$

where some of the coefficients may be 0, and let Q_s be the $n \times n$ matrix whose (i,j) entry is $q_s^{(i,j)}$, i.e., the coefficient of λ^s in the (i,j) entry of $B(\lambda)$. Then

$$B(\lambda) = \sum_{s=0}^{m} \lambda^s Q_s.$$

The identity (19) becomes

$$(\lambda I_n - A) \sum_{s=0}^{m} \lambda^s Q_s = \sum_{t=0}^{n} \lambda^t c_t I_n. \tag{20}$$

For $m > n$, we equate the coefficients (that is, matrices) of λ^j, $j = m+1$, $m, \ldots, n+1$, on both sides of (20):

$$Q_m \qquad\qquad\quad = 0$$

$$Q_{m-1} - AQ_m \quad = 0,$$

$$Q_{m-2} - AQ_{m-1} = 0, \tag{21}$$

$$\vdots \qquad\qquad \vdots$$

$$Q_n - AQ_{n+1} \quad\; = 0.$$

Equations (21) imply that $Q_s = 0$, $s = n, \ldots, m$. Now equate the coefficients of $\lambda^j, j = n, \ldots, 1, 0$, on both sides of (20):

$$Q_{n-1} \qquad\qquad = c_n I_n,$$
$$Q_{n-2} - AQ_{n-1} = c_{n-1} I_n,$$
$$Q_{n-3} - AQ_{n-2} = c_{n-2} I_n, \qquad\qquad (22)$$
$$\vdots \qquad\qquad \vdots$$
$$Q_1 - AQ_2 \qquad = c_2 I_n,$$
$$Q_0 - AQ_1 \qquad = c_1 I_n,$$
$$-AQ_0 \qquad = c_0 I_n.$$

Premultiply the first equation in (22) by A^n, the second by $A^{n-1}, \ldots$, the $(n-1)$st by A^2, and the nth by A:

$$A^n Q_{n-1} \qquad\qquad = c_n A^n,$$
$$A^{n-1} Q_{n-2} - A^n Q_{n-1} \qquad = c_{n-1} A^{n-1},$$
$$A^{n-2} Q_{n-3} - A^{n-1} Q_{n-2} = c_{n-2} A^{n-2} \qquad (23)$$
$$\vdots \qquad\qquad \vdots$$
$$A^2 Q_1 - A^3 Q_2 \qquad = c_2 A^2,$$
$$A Q_0 - A^2 Q_1 \qquad = c_1 A,$$
$$-AQ_0 \qquad = c_0 I_n,$$

and add the resulting equations (23). The left side collapses to 0 while the right side yields

$$c_n A^n + c_{n-1} A^{n-1} + \cdots + c_1 A + c_0 I_n = p(A).$$

Thus we have

$$p(A) = 0.$$

Example 2.7. Let

$$A = \begin{bmatrix} 1 & 3 & 2 \\ -1 & -1 & -1 \\ 2 & 3 & -2 \end{bmatrix}.$$

Find a polynomial $f(\lambda)$ such that $A^{-1} = f(A)$. We compute directly the characteristic polynomial of A:

$$\det(\lambda I_3 - A) = \lambda^3 + 2\lambda^2 + \lambda + 9.$$

Now, by the Cayley-Hamilton theorem,

$$A^3 + 2A^2 + A + 9I_3 = 0.$$

Therefore,

$$A(A^2 + 2A + I_3) = -9I_3,$$

i.e.,

$$A(-\tfrac{1}{9}A^2 - \tfrac{2}{9}A - \tfrac{1}{9}I_3) = I_3.$$

Thus

$$A^{-1} = -\tfrac{1}{9}A^2 - \tfrac{2}{9}A - \tfrac{1}{9}I_3 \qquad (24)$$

and

$$f(\lambda) = -\tfrac{1}{9}\lambda^2 - \tfrac{2}{9}\lambda - \tfrac{1}{9}.$$

We verify the formula (24):

$$A^{-1} = -\tfrac{1}{9}\begin{bmatrix} 2 & 6 & -5 \\ -2 & -5 & 1 \\ -5 & -3 & 5 \end{bmatrix} - \tfrac{2}{9}\begin{bmatrix} 1 & 3 & 2 \\ -1 & -1 & -1 \\ 2 & 3 & -2 \end{bmatrix} - \tfrac{1}{9}\begin{bmatrix} 1 & 0 & 0 \\ 0 & 1 & 0 \\ 0 & 0 & 1 \end{bmatrix}$$

$$= -\tfrac{1}{9}\begin{bmatrix} 5 & 12 & -1 \\ -4 & -6 & -1 \\ -1 & 3 & 2 \end{bmatrix},$$

which agrees with the result obtained in Example 2.2, Chapter 3.

We conclude this section with a useful sufficient condition for a matrix to be diagonalizable.

Theorem 2.8. *An n-square matrix with n distinct characteristic roots is diagonalizable.*

Proof. Let A be a matrix with distinct characteristic roots $\lambda_1, \ldots, \lambda_n$. In view of Theorem 2.1, it suffices to prove that A has n linearly independent characteristic vectors. Suppose that $v_1, \ldots, v_n$ are characteristic vectors corresponding to $\lambda_1, \ldots, \lambda_n$, respectively. Suppose that $v_1, \ldots, v_n$ are linearly dependent. We show that this assumption leads to a contradiction. Since v_1 is a characteristic vector, it is different from 0. Therefore there exists an integer k, $1 \leq k < n$, such that $v_1, \ldots, v_k$ are linearly independent, while $v_1, \ldots, v_k, v_{k+1}$ are linearly dependent, i.e.,

$$c_1 v_1 + \cdots + c_k v_k + c_{k+1} v_{k+1} = 0 \tag{25}$$

for some scalars $c_1, \ldots, c_{k+1}$, not all 0. Then

$$c_1 A v_1 + \cdots + c_k A v_k + c_{k+1} A v_{k+1} = 0,$$

and, since $v_1, \ldots, v_{k+1}$ are characteristic vectors of A,

$$c_1 \lambda_1 v_1 + \cdots + c_k \lambda_k v_k + c_{k+1} \lambda_{k+1} v_{k+1} = 0. \tag{26}$$

Now, multiply both sides of (25) by λ_{k+1} and subtract from (26):

$$c_1 (\lambda_1 - \lambda_{k+1}) v_1 + \cdots + c_k (\lambda_k - \lambda_{k+1}) v_k = 0.$$

Since $v_1, \ldots, v_k$ are linearly independent, we must have

$$c_t (\lambda_t - \lambda_{k+1}) = 0, \qquad t = 1, \ldots, k.$$

But $\lambda_1, \ldots, \lambda_{k+1}$ are distinct and therefore $\lambda_t - \lambda_{k+1} \neq 0$, $t = 1, \ldots, k$. It follows that $c_1 = \cdots = c_k = 0$. Also, by (25), $c_{k+1} = 0$. This contradicts our assumption that $c_1, \ldots, c_{k+1}$ are not all equal to 0, i.e., that $v_1, \ldots, v_{k+1}$ are linearly dependent.

Quiz
Answer *true* or *false*:

1. If two matrices have the same characteristic roots (including multiplicities), then they are similar. (*Hint:* Consider

$$\begin{bmatrix} 1 & 0 \\ 0 & 1 \end{bmatrix} \quad \text{and} \quad \begin{bmatrix} 1 & 1 \\ 0 & 1 \end{bmatrix}.)$$

2. If two matrices are similar, then they have the same characteristic roots (including multiplicities).

3. The matrices

$$\begin{bmatrix} 1 & 4 & 1 \\ 0 & 2 & 5 \\ 0 & 0 & 3 \end{bmatrix} \quad \text{and} \quad \begin{bmatrix} 2 & -1 & 2 \\ 0 & 1 & 7 \\ 0 & 0 & 3 \end{bmatrix}$$

are similar. (*Hint:* What are the characteristic roots of each matrix? Apply Theorem 2.8.)

4. The matrices

$$\begin{bmatrix} 1 & 1 & 1 \\ 0 & 1 & 1 \\ 0 & 0 & 1 \end{bmatrix} \quad \text{and} \quad \begin{bmatrix} 1 & 1 & 1 \\ 1 & 1 & 0 \\ 1 & 0 & 0 \end{bmatrix}$$

are similar. (*Hint:* Compute the trace of each matrix.)

5. The matrix

$$\begin{bmatrix} 1 & 1 \\ 0 & 1 \end{bmatrix}$$

is similar to a diagonal matrix.

6. If v is a characteristic vector of A, and B is similar to A, then v is a characteristic vector of B.

7. If all characteristic roots of A are 0, then $A = 0$. (*Hint:* Consider triangular matrices.)

8. If A is a square matrix, then A and A^T have the same characteristic polynomial.

9. If A is similar to a diagonal matrix, then the characteristic roots of A are distinct.

10. If k characteristic roots of A are 0, then the rank of A is $n - k$.

Exercises

1. Let

$$A = \begin{bmatrix} -4 & 5 & 1 \\ -3 & 4 & 1 \\ -3 & 3 & 2 \end{bmatrix}.$$

Find a matrix S such that $S^{-1}AS$ is diagonal.

2. Let

$$B = \begin{bmatrix} 1 & -1 & 2 & 0 \\ 1 & -1 & 0 & 2 \\ 2 & 0 & 1 & -1 \\ 0 & 2 & 1 & -1 \end{bmatrix}.$$

Find an upper triangular matrix similar to B.

3. Let A be an n-square matrix with characteristic roots $\lambda_1, \ldots, \lambda_n$ and let α be a scalar. Show that:
   (a) the characteristic roots of αA are $\alpha\lambda_1, \ldots, \alpha\lambda_n$;
   (b) the characteristic roots of $A + \alpha I_n$ are $\lambda_1 + \alpha, \ldots, \lambda_n + \alpha$.

4. Show that if the rank of a square matrix A is r, then the number of nonzero characteristic roots cannot exceed r.

5. Let J be the $n \times n$ matrix all of whose entries are 1. Use the result in Exercise 4 to find all the characteristic roots of J.

6. Use the results in Exercises 3(b) and 5 to find the characteristic roots of the matrix

$$\begin{bmatrix} 1 & -2 & -2 & -2 \\ -2 & 1 & -2 & -2 \\ -2 & -2 & 1 & -2 \\ -2 & -2 & -2 & 1 \end{bmatrix}.$$

7. Let A and B be n-square matrices and let α and β be scalars. Show that

$$\text{tr}(\alpha A + \beta B) = \alpha\,\text{tr}(A) + \beta\,\text{tr}(B).$$

8. Show that if A and B are $n \times n$ matrices and at least one of A and B is non-singular, then AB and BA have the same characteristic roots. (*Hint:* Show that AB and BA are similar.)

9. Show that a square matrix is singular if and only if it has a zero characteristic root.

10. Prove that if A is nilpotent (i.e., $A^k = 0$ for some positive integer k), then all the characteristic roots of A are 0.

11. Prove that if A is idempotent (i.e., $A^2 = A$), then every characteristic root of A is either 0 or 1. (*Hint:* Let S be a matrix such that $S^{-1}AS$ is triangular. Then $(S^{-1}AS)^2 = S^{-1}A^2S = S^{-1}AS$ and each main diagonal entry of $S^{-1}AS$ is equal to its square.)

12. Let A be a matrix with characteristic roots $\lambda_1, \ldots, \lambda_n$. Show that if $\lambda_1, \ldots, \lambda_k$ $(1 < k \leq n)$ are distinct, then corresponding characteristic vectors must be linearly independent. (*Hint:* Use the method of the proof of Theorem 2.8.)

4.3.   SOME SPECIAL TYPES OF MATRICES

Many of the real matrices that occur in linear algebra [see, e.g., Chapter 5], geometry, physics, and other sciences are symmetric matrices. In this section we shall study some properties of symmetric matrices and their complex counterparts. We shall also consider some other special types of matrices. Henceforth in this section R will denote the set of real numbers and C will denote the set of complex numbers.

Recall that if A is a matrix, then A^* denotes the conjugate transpose of A, that is, the matrix whose (i, j) entry is the complex conjugate of the (j, i) entry of A. [See Section 2.2, Chapter 2.]

Definition 3.1. (*Hermitian and skew-hermitian matrices*). *A square complex matrix H is called **hermitian** if $H^* = H$. A square matrix S is said to* be **skew-hermitian** if $S^* = -S$. A real hermitian matrix is called (*real*) **symmetric** and a real skew-hermitian matrix is called (*real*) **skew-symmetric**.

For example, the matrices

$$\begin{bmatrix} 3 - i2 \\ -1 + i3 \\ - i4 \end{bmatrix},$$

ic, respec-

ly as a sum

calculation

and therefore S is skew-hermitian. To prove the uniqueness, suppose that

$$A = K + T, \tag{1}$$

where K is hermitian and T is skew-hermitian. Then

$$A^* = K^* + T^*$$
$$= K - T. \tag{2}$$

Add equation (1) to equation (2) and multiply by $\frac{1}{2}$. We obtain

$$\tfrac{1}{2}(A + A^*) = K,$$

i.e.,

$$H = K.$$

Similarly, if we subtract (2) from (1) and multiply by $\frac{1}{2}$ we get

$$\tfrac{1}{2}(A - A^*) = T,$$

i.e.,

$$S = T.$$

Surprisingly enough, Theorem 3.1, for all its elegance, does not seem to have many important applications. The most striking properties of hermitian and skew-hermitian matrices are those relating to their characteristic roots and characteristic vectors.

Let λ and μ be characteristic roots of a hermitian $n \times n$ matrix H, and let u and v be corresponding characteristic vectors. Suppose that $\lambda \neq \bar{\mu}$. (*N.B.:* We shall show later that all characteristic roots of a hermitian matrix are real, but this fact is irrelevant here.) It is convenient in the present discussion to regard the n-tuples u and v as $n \times 1$ matrices. Thus

$$Hu = \lambda u, \tag{3}$$

$$Hv = \mu v. \tag{4}$$

Premultiply both sides of equation (3) by v^* and both sides of equation (4) by u^*:

$$v^*Hu = \lambda v^*u, \tag{5}$$

$$u^*Hv = \mu u^*v. \tag{6}$$

Now take the conjugate transpose of both sides of (6) to obtain

$$v^*H^*u = \bar{\mu}v^*u,$$

and, since H is hermitian, we conclude that

$$v^*Hu = \bar{\mu}v^*u. \tag{7}$$

Comparing (5) and (7) we obtain

$$\lambda v^*u = \bar{\mu}v^*u,$$

and, since $\lambda \neq \bar{\mu}$,

$$v^*u = 0. \tag{8}$$

Let u be the n-tuple $(x_1, \ldots, x_n)$ and v the n-tuple $(y_1, \ldots, y_n)$. Then (8) reads

$$\sum_{j=1}^{n} x_j \bar{y}_j = 0. \tag{9}$$

Note that for real vectors u and v and $n = 2$, the left side of (9) is just the standard inner product of the vectors u and v (Definition 5.1, Chapter 1). Moreover, for real vectors and $n = 2$, formula (9) tells us that the two vectors are orthogonal. We shall extend our definition of the standard inner product to complex n-tuples and study some of the consequences before we return to hermitian matrices.

Definition 3.2. (**Standard inner product**). *The standard inner product of two complex n-tuples,* $u = (x_1, \ldots, x_n)$ *and* $v = (y_1, \ldots, y_n)$, *denoted by* *(u, v), is the complex number*

$$\sum_{j=1}^{n} x_j \bar{y}_j.$$

*If $(u, v) = 0$, the vectors u and v are said to be **orthogonal** (or **perpendicular**). The nonnegative real number $(u, u)^{1/2}$ is called the **length** of u and is denoted by $\|u\|$. If $\|u\| = 1$, then u is said to be a **unit vector**. A set of vectors in $V_n(C)$ is called **orthogonal** if every pair of vectors in the set is orthogonal. If every vector of an orthogonal set is a unit vector, the set is said to be **orthonormal**.*

Thus we saw in (9) that the characteristic vectors u and v corresponding to characteristic roots λ and μ, $\lambda \neq \bar{\mu}$, must be orthogonal.

The following properties of the inner product follow directly from the definition:

(i) $(u, v) = \overline{(v, u)}$;

(ii) $(u, u) > 0$, unless $u = 0$;

(iii) $(c_1 u_1 + c_2 u_2, v) = c_1(u_1, v) + c_2(u_2, v)$, and thus $(v, c_1 u_1 + c_2 u_2)$ $= \bar{c}_1(v, u_1) + \bar{c}_2(v, u_2)$, for any vectors u_1, u_2, and v and any scalars c_1 and c_2.

Theorem 3.2. *An orthogonal set containing no zero vector is linearly independent. In particular, an orthonormal set is linearly independent.*

Proof. Let $v_1, \ldots, v_m$ be an orthogonal set of nonzero vectors, i.e.,

$$(v_i, v_j) = 0 \tag{10}$$

whenever $i \neq j$. Suppose that

$$\sum_{j=1}^{m} c_j v_j = 0 \tag{11}$$

for some scalars $c_1, \ldots, c_m$. Then for any i, $\quad 1 \leq i \leq m$,

$$\left(\sum_{j=1}^{m} c_j v_j, v_i \right) = 0,$$

and, by property (iii),

$$\sum_{j=1}^{m} c_j (v_j, v_i) = 0.$$

Thus, by (10),

$$c_i(v_i, v_i) = 0,$$

and since $v_i \neq 0$ and therefore, by property (ii), $(v_i, v_i) \neq 0$, we must have $c_i = 0$. Moreover, this is true for all i, $1 \leq i \leq m$, and thus $v_1, \ldots, v_m$ are linearly independent.

It follows immediately from Theorem 3.2 that any orthogonal set of n nonzero vectors in $V_n(C)$ (or in $V_n(R)$) forms a basis. In particular, an orthonormal set of n vectors in $V_n(C)$ forms a basis of $V_n(C)$; it is naturally called an *orthonormal* basis of $V_n(C)$.

For example, the set of vectors $v_1 = (1 + i, -1 - i, 0)$, $v_2 = (1 + i, 1 + i, 1)$, and $v_3 = (1 + i, 1 + i, -4)$ is orthogonal. For,

$$\begin{aligned}
(v_1, v_2) &= (1 + i)\overline{(1 + i)} + (-1 - i)\overline{(1 + i)} + 0 \cdot 1 \\
&= (1 + i)(1 - i) + (-1 - i)(1 - i) \\
&= 2 - 2 \\
&= 0,
\end{aligned}$$

$$\begin{aligned}
(v_2, v_3) &= (1 + i)\overline{(1 + i)} + (1 + i)\overline{(1 + i)} + 1(-4) \\
&= 2 + 2 - 4 \\
&= 0,
\end{aligned}$$

$$\begin{aligned}
(v_3, v_1) &= (1 + i)\overline{(1 + i)} + (1 + i)\overline{(-1 - i)} + (-4)0 \\
&= (1 + i)(1 - i) + (1 + i)(-1 + i) \\
&= 2 - 2 \\
&= 0.
\end{aligned}$$

Thus v_1, v_2, and v_3 form a basis of $V_3(C)$. Note that if v is any nonzero n-tuple and $u = v/\|v\|$, then

$$\begin{aligned}
(u, u) &= \left(\frac{v}{\|v\|}, \frac{v}{\|v\|}\right) \\
&= \frac{(v, v)}{\|v\|^2} \\
&= \frac{\|v\|^2}{\|v\|^2} \\
&= 1,
\end{aligned}$$

and u is a unit vector. In the preceding example,

$$\|v_1\| = (2 + 2 + 0)^{1/2}$$

$$= 2,$$

$$\|v_2\| = (2 + 2 + 1)^{1/2}$$

$$= \sqrt{5},$$

$$\|v_3\| = (2 + 2 + 16)^{1/2}$$

$$= 2\sqrt{5}.$$

Hence the vectors $\frac{1}{2}v_1$, $(1/\sqrt{5})v_2$, and $(1/2\sqrt{5})v_3$ form an orthonormal basis of $V_3(C)$.

Theorem 3.3. (*Gram-Schmidt orthonormalization process*). *Let* $v_1, \ldots, v_m$ *be a linearly independent set of vectors in* $V_n(C)$. *Then there exists an orthonormal set of vectors* $u_1, \ldots, u_m$ *such that*

$$\langle u_1, \ldots, u_p \rangle = \langle v_1, \ldots, v_p \rangle, \qquad p = 1, \ldots, m. \tag{12}$$

Proof. Since $v_1, \ldots, v_m$ are linearly independent, none of them is 0. Thus we can set

$$u_1 = \frac{1}{\|v_1\|} v_1.$$

We can continue in the following manner: set

$$u_2 = \frac{1}{\|w_2\|} w_2,$$

where

$$w_2 = v_2 - (v_2, u_1)u_1$$

is nonzero since v_2 and v_1 (and therefore v_2 and u_1) are linearly independent. Also,

$$(u_2, u_1) = \frac{1}{\|w_2\|} (v_2 - (v_2, u_1)u_1, u_1)$$

$$= \frac{1}{\|w_2\|} ((v_2, u_1) - (v_2, u_1)(u_1, u_1))$$

$$= 0,$$

since $(u_1, u_1) = 1$. We therefore have two orthogonal unit vectors such that $\langle u_1, u_2 \rangle = \langle v_1, v_2 \rangle$. We can construct u_3 in a similar manner. However, we shall continue the process by induction. Suppose that we have already constructed an orthonormal set of vectors $u_1, \ldots, u_{k-1}$ satisfying the equalities (12) for $m = k - 1$. Set

$$w_k = v_k - \sum_{t=1}^{k-1} (v_k, u_t)u_t. \tag{13}$$

Then $w_k \neq 0$; otherwise (13) would imply that

$$v_k = \sum_{t=1}^{k-1} (v_k, u_t)u_t \in \langle u_1, \ldots, u_{k-1} \rangle$$

$$= \langle v_1, \ldots, v_{k-1} \rangle,$$

which is impossible, since $v_1, \ldots, v_k$ are linearly independent. Now define

$$u_k = \frac{1}{\|w_k\|} w_k.$$

We prove that $u_1, \ldots, u_k$ are orthonormal. By the induction hypothesis $u_1, \ldots, u_{k-1}$ are orthonormal. It remains to prove that $(u_k, u_j) = 0$ for $j = 1, \ldots, k - 1$. We have

$$(u_k, u_j) = \frac{1}{\|w_k\|} (w_k, u_j)$$

$$= \frac{1}{\|w_k\|} \left(v_k - \sum_{t=1}^{k-1} (v_k, u_t)u_t, \ u_j \right)$$

$$= \frac{1}{\|w_k\|} \left[(v_k, u_j) - \sum_{t=1}^{k-1} (v_k, u_t)(u_t, u_j) \right],$$

and, since $(u_t, u_j) = 0$ for $t \neq j$ and $(u_j, u_j) = 1$, we obtain

$$(u_k, u_j) = \frac{1}{\|w_k\|} [(v_k, u_j) - (v_k, u_j)]$$

$$= 0.$$

Lastly, formula (13) and the fact that $\langle u_1, \ldots, u_{k-1} \rangle = \langle v_1, \ldots, v_{k-1} \rangle$ imply that

$$\langle u_1, \ldots, u_k \rangle \subset \langle u_1, \ldots, u_{k-1}, v_k \rangle$$

$$\subset \langle v_1, \ldots, v_{k-1}, v_k \rangle.$$

Now, $u_1, \ldots, u_k$ form an orthonormal set and thus are linearly independent. Hence

$$\dim \langle u_1, \ldots, u_k \rangle = k$$

$$= \dim \langle v_1, \ldots, v_k \rangle,$$

and we must therefore have [see Theorem 6.5(b), Chapter 1]

$$\langle u_1, \ldots, u_k \rangle = \langle v_1, \ldots, v_k \rangle.$$

Example 3.1. Let $v_1 = (1, 1, 1, 1)$, $v_2 = (1, 0, 0, 0)$, $v_3 = (0, 0, 1, 1)$, and $v_4 = (0, 1, 1, 0)$. Find an orthonormal basis u_1, u_2, u_3, and u_4 of $V_4(R)$ such that $u_1 = v_1/\|v_1\|$. We apply the Gram-Schmidt process (using the notation of Theorem 3.3):

$$u_1 = (\tfrac{1}{2}, \tfrac{1}{2}, \tfrac{1}{2}, \tfrac{1}{2});$$

$$w_2 = v_2 - (v_2, u_1)u_1$$

$$= (1, 0, 0, 0) - \tfrac{1}{2}(\tfrac{1}{2}, \tfrac{1}{2}, \tfrac{1}{2}, \tfrac{1}{2})$$

$$= (\tfrac{3}{4}, -\tfrac{1}{4}, -\tfrac{1}{4}, -\tfrac{1}{4});$$

therefore

$$\|w_2\| = \frac{\sqrt{3}}{2}$$

and

$$u_2 = \left(\frac{3}{2\sqrt{3}}, -\frac{1}{2\sqrt{3}}, -\frac{1}{2\sqrt{3}}, -\frac{1}{2\sqrt{3}}\right);$$

$$w_3 = v_3 - (v_3, u_1)u_1 - (v_3, u_2)u_2$$

$$= (0, 0, 1, 1) - 1\left(\frac{1}{2}, \frac{1}{2}, \frac{1}{2}, \frac{1}{2}\right)$$

$$+ \frac{1}{\sqrt{3}}\left(\frac{3}{2\sqrt{3}}, -\frac{1}{2\sqrt{3}}, -\frac{1}{2\sqrt{3}}, -\frac{1}{2\sqrt{3}}\right)$$

$$= \left(0, -\frac{2}{3}, \frac{1}{3}, \frac{1}{3}\right),$$

and therefore

$$u_3 = \left(0, -\frac{2}{\sqrt{6}}, \frac{1}{\sqrt{6}}, \frac{1}{\sqrt{6}}\right);$$

finally,

$$w_4 = v_4 - (v_4, u_1)u_1 - (v_4, u_2)u_2 - (v_4, u_3)u_3$$

$$= (0, 1, 1, 0) - 1\left(\frac{1}{2}, \frac{1}{2}, \frac{1}{2}, \frac{1}{2}\right)$$

$$+ \frac{1}{\sqrt{3}}\left(\frac{3}{2\sqrt{3}}, -\frac{1}{2\sqrt{3}}, -\frac{1}{2\sqrt{3}}, -\frac{1}{2\sqrt{3}}\right)$$

$$+ \frac{1}{\sqrt{6}}\left(0, -\frac{2}{\sqrt{6}}, \frac{1}{\sqrt{6}}, \frac{1}{\sqrt{6}}\right)$$

$$= \left(0, 0, \frac{1}{2}, -\frac{1}{2}\right),$$

and thus

$$u_4 = \left(0, 0, \frac{1}{\sqrt{2}}, -\frac{1}{\sqrt{2}}\right).$$

In formula (9) we showed that if a hermitian matrix has two distinct real roots [see Theorem 3.7(a) below], then the corresponding characteristic vectors are orthogonal. We shall show that, in fact, an $n \times n$ hermitian matrix H has n orthonormal characteristic vectors and therefore that $U^{-1}HU$ is diagonal [see Theorems 2.1 and 3.2] for some matrix U whose column vectors are orthonormal. We shall first define some important types of matrices.

Definition 3.3. (Unitary and orthogonal matrices). *An n-square complex matrix U is called* **unitary** *if*

$$U^{-1} = U^*,$$

i.e., if

$$UU^* = U^*U = I_n.$$

A unitary matrix with real number entries is called **orthogonal**. *That is, an $n \times n$ real matrix P is orthogonal if*

$$PP^T = P^TP = I_n.$$

For example, the matrix

$$P = \begin{bmatrix} \dfrac{1}{2} & \dfrac{3}{2\sqrt{3}} & 0 & 0 \\[2ex] \dfrac{1}{2} & -\dfrac{1}{2\sqrt{3}} & -\dfrac{2}{\sqrt{6}} & 0 \\[2ex] \dfrac{1}{2} & -\dfrac{1}{2\sqrt{3}} & \dfrac{1}{\sqrt{6}} & \dfrac{1}{\sqrt{2}} \\[2ex] \dfrac{1}{2} & -\dfrac{1}{2\sqrt{3}} & \dfrac{1}{\sqrt{6}} & -\dfrac{1}{\sqrt{2}} \end{bmatrix}$$

is orthogonal, since it is easy to verify that $P^TP = I_n$.

Theorem 3.4.

    (a) *A square matrix is unitary if and only if its rows form an orthonormal set.*

(b) *A square matrix is unitary if and only if its columns form an ortho-normal set.*

(c) *The product of unitary matrices is a unitary matrix.*

(d) *The inverse of a unitary matrix is unitary.*

Proof.

(a) Let $U = (u_{ij})$ be an $n \times n$ matrix. Then the (i, j) entry of UU^* is

$$(UU^*)_{ij} = \sum_{t=1}^{n} U_{it}(U^*)_{tj}$$

$$= \sum_{t=1}^{n} u_{it}\bar{u}_{jt},$$

or, since $U_{(i)} = (u_{i1}, \ldots, u_{in})$ and $U_{(j)} = (u_{j1}, \ldots, u_{jn})$,

$$(UU^*)_{ij} = (U_{(i)}, U_{(j)}). \tag{14}$$

Now, if U is unitary, then $UU^* = I_n$ and $(UU^*)_{ij}$ is 1 or 0, according as $i = j$ or $i \neq j$. Thus, by (14),

$$(U_{(i)}, U_{(i)}) = 1, \tag{15}$$

$$(U_{(i)}, U_{(j)}) = 0 \tag{16}$$

if $i \neq j$. In other words, $U_{(1)}, \ldots, U_{(n)}$ form an orthonormal set. Conversely, if $U_{(1)}, \ldots, U_{(n)}$ form an orthonormal set, then (15), (16), and (14) imply that $UU^* = I_n$ and that U is unitary.

(b) The proof of this part is similar to the proof of (a). We have

$$(U^*U)_{ij} = \sum_{t=1}^{n} (U^*)_{it} U_{tj}$$

$$= \sum_{t=1}^{n} \bar{u}_{ti} u_{tj}.$$

Now, $U^{(i)} = (u_{1i}, \ldots, u_{ni})$ and $U^{(j)} = (u_{1j}, \ldots, u_{nj})$ and therefore

$$(U^{(i)}, U^{(j)}) = \sum_{t=1}^{n} u_{ti}\bar{u}_{tj}$$

$$= \overline{(U^*U)_{ij}}.$$

If U is unitary we have

$$U^*U = I_n,$$

and therefore

$$(U^{(i)}, U^{(j)}) = \delta_{ij},$$

where δ_{ij} is 0 or 1 according as $i \neq j$ or $i = j$. It follows that the columns of U are orthonormal. To prove the converse, simply reverse the steps in the preceding argument.

(c) A square matrix X is unitary if and only if $XX^* = I_n$. Suppose then that U and V are unitary $n \times n$ matrices, i.e.,

$$UU^* = VV^*$$

$$= I_n.$$

We have [see formula (44), Section 2.2, Chapter 2]

$$(UV)(UV)^* = (UV)(V^*U^*)$$

$$= U(VV^*)U^*$$

$$= UI_nU^*$$

$$= UU^*$$

$$= I_n.$$

Therefore the product UV is unitary.

(d) Similarly, if U is unitary, then [see formula (45), Section 2.2, Chapter 2]

$$(U^{-1})(U^{-1})^* = U^{-1}(U^*)^{-1}$$

$$= (U^*U)^{-1}$$

$$= I_n^{-1}$$

$$= I_n,$$

and therefore U^{-1} is unitary.

We are now ready to prove some striking properties of hermitian, skew-hermitian, and unitary matrices.

Definition 3.4. (Unitarily diagonalizable matrix). *An n-square matrix X is called **unitarily diagonalizable** or **normal** if there exists a unitary matrix U such that U^*XU is a diagonal matrix.*

Theorem 3.5. *Hermitian (skew-hermitian, unitary) matrices are unitarily diagonalizable.*

Proof. Let H be an $n \times n$ hermitian matrix. Let λ_1 be a characteristic root of H and v_1 a corresponding characteristic vector. We shall use induction on n and a method similar to that used to prove Theorem 2.4. The theorem holds trivially for $n = 1$. Assume that it holds for all $(n - 1)$-square hermitian matrices. Let $v_2, \ldots, v_n$ be any $n - 1$ n-tuples for which $v_1, v_2, \ldots, v_n$ are linearly independent. Use the Gram-Schmidt process to obtain an orthonormal set of vectors $u_1, \ldots, u_n$ from the basis $v_1, \ldots, v_n$ such that

$$u_1 = \frac{1}{\|v_1\|} v_1.$$

We have

$$Hu_1 = \frac{1}{\|v_1\|} Hv_1$$

$$= \frac{1}{\|v_1\|} \lambda_1 v_1$$

$$= \lambda_1 u_1,$$

and we conclude that u_1 is also a characteristic vector corresponding to λ_1. Let V be the unitary matrix whose columns are $u_1, \ldots, u_n$. Then

$$(V^*HV)^{(1)} = V^*HV^{(1)}$$

$$= V^*Hu_1$$

$$= V^*\lambda_1 u_1$$

$$= \lambda_1 V^* V^{(1)}$$

$$= \lambda_1 (V^* V)^{(1)}$$

$$= \lambda_1 I_n^{(1)}$$

$$= \lambda_1 e_1,$$

where $e_1 = (1, 0, \ldots, 0)$. Thus the first column of V^*HV is the n-tuple $(\lambda_1, 0, \ldots, 0)$. But

$$(V^*HV)^* = V^*H^*V^{**}$$
$$= V^*HV,$$

and therefore V^*HV is hermitian. (Note that this is true for any matrix of the form V^*HV, where V is unitary and H is hermitian.) It follows that the first row of V^*HV is $(\lambda_1, 0, \ldots, 0)$ as well and that

$$V^*HV = \begin{bmatrix} \lambda_1 & 0 \cdots 0 \\ \hline 0 & \\ \vdots & H_1 \\ 0 & \end{bmatrix}$$

where H_1 is an $(n-1)$-square hermitian matrix (H_1 is hermitian because V^*HV is hermitian). By the induction hypothesis there exists a unitary $(n-1)$-square matrix W_1 such that $W_1^*H_1W_1$ is a diagonal matrix. Let

$$W = \begin{bmatrix} 1 & 0 \cdots 0 \\ \hline 0 & \\ \vdots & W_1 \\ 0 & \end{bmatrix}.$$

Then

$$WW^* = \begin{bmatrix} 1 & 0 \cdots 0 \\ \hline 0 & \\ \vdots & W_1 \\ 0 & \end{bmatrix} \begin{bmatrix} 1 & 0 \cdots 0 \\ \hline 0 & \\ \vdots & W_1^* \\ 0 & \end{bmatrix}$$

$$= \begin{bmatrix} 1 & 0 \cdots 0 \\ \hline 0 & \\ \vdots & W_1W_1^* \\ 0 & \end{bmatrix}$$

$$= \begin{bmatrix} 1 & 0 & \cdots & 0 \\ \hline 0 & & & \\ \vdots & & I_{n-1} & \\ 0 & & & \end{bmatrix}$$

$$= I_n,$$

and therefore W is unitary. If we now set $U = VW$, then, by Theorem 3.4(c), U is unitary and

$$U^*HU = W^*(V^*HV)W$$

$$= \begin{bmatrix} \lambda_1 & 0 & \cdots & 0 \\ \hline 0 & & & \\ \vdots & & W_1^*H_1W_1 & \\ 0 & & & \end{bmatrix},$$

which is diagonal.

The proof for skew-hermitian and unitary matrices is almost identical. For, if S is skew-hermitian and V is unitary, then

$$(V^*SV)^* = V^*S^*V^{**}$$

$$= -V^*SV,$$

and V^*SV is skew-hermitian. Similarly, if U is unitary and V is unitary, then U^*VU is unitary, by Theorem 3.4(c) and (d). We can prove then that skew-hermitian and unitary matrices are unitarily diagonalizable by following the method of the proof for hermitian matrices (see Exercise 9).

An important immediate consequence of Theorems 3.5 and 2.1 is the following result.

Theorem 3.6. *An $n \times n$ hermitian (skew-hermitian, unitary) matrix has n orthonormal characteristic vectors.*

Proof. Let H be an n-square hermitian matrix. By Theorem 3.5 there exists a unitary matrix U such that U^*HU is diagonal. But as we saw in the proof of Theorem 2.1, the columns of U are the characteristic vectors of H. Theorem 3.4(b) tells us that the columns of U form an orthonormal set and the proof is complete.

Suppose that $U^*HU = \text{diag}(\lambda_1, \ldots, \lambda_n)$, where U is unitary and H is hermitian. Then $\lambda_1, \ldots, \lambda_n$ are, by Theorem 2.1, the characteristic roots of H corresponding to the characteristic vectors $U^{(1)}, \ldots, U^{(n)}$. In the proof of Theorem 3.5 we saw that U^*HU is hermitian. But the main diagonal entries of any hermitian matrix are real (see Exercise 5). Thus $\lambda_1, \ldots, \lambda_n$ are real. Similarly, if $U^*SU = \text{diag}(\mu_1, \ldots, \mu_n)$ is skew-hermitian, then $\mu_1, \ldots, \mu_n$ must be pure imaginary (see Exercise 5). Finally, if W is a unitary matrix and $U^*WU = \text{diag}(v_1, \ldots, v_n)$ for some unitary U, then the product U^*WU is unitary and hence the length of each of its row vectors must be 1, by Theorem 3.4(a). Since the ith row of $\text{diag}(v_1, \ldots, v_n)$ is $(0, \ldots, 0, v_i, 0, \ldots, 0)$, its length is the absolute value (modulus) of the characteristic root v_i of U^*WU and therefore of W. Thus every characteristic root v_i of W must be of absolute value 1. We therefore have the following important theorem.

Theorem 3.7.
   (a) *The characteristic roots of a hermitian matrix are real.*
   (b) *The characteristic roots of a skew-hermitian matrix are pure imaginary.*
   (c) *The characteristic roots of a unitary matrix are of absolute value* 1.

Quiz
Answer *true* or *false*:

1. The matrix

$$A = \frac{1}{\sqrt{2}} \begin{bmatrix} 0 & -1+i \\ 1+i & 0 \end{bmatrix}$$

   is hermitian.

2. The matrix A in Question 1 is skew-hermitian.

3. The matrix A in Question 1 is unitary.

4. A hermitian matrix is 0 if and only if all its characteristic roots are zero.

5. A matrix S is skew-hermitian if and only if iS is hermitian ($i^2 = -1$).

6. Every characteristic root of a (real) orthogonal matrix is 1 or -1.

7. The determinant of a (real) orthogonal matrix is 1 or -1.

8. The product of two hermitian matrices is hermitian.

9. The inverse of a nonsingular hermitian matrix is hermitian.

10. A unitary matrix cannot be singular.

Exercises

1. Let

$$A = \frac{1}{\sqrt{2}}\begin{bmatrix} 1 & -i \\ i & -1 \end{bmatrix}.$$

(a) Is the matrix A hermitian? (b) skew-hermitian? (c) unitary?

2. Express the matrix

$$\begin{bmatrix} 2+i & 1-i & 3 \\ i & 2 & 1+i \\ 1+2i & 2-i & 2+2i \end{bmatrix}$$

as a sum of a hermitian matrix and a skew-hermitian matrix.

3. Verify that the matrices

$$U = \begin{bmatrix} \frac{2}{3} & \frac{2}{3} & \frac{1}{3} \\ \frac{1}{3} & -\frac{2}{3} & \frac{2}{3} \\ -\frac{2}{3} & \frac{1}{3} & \frac{2}{3} \end{bmatrix}, \quad V = \begin{bmatrix} \frac{3}{5} & 0 & \frac{4}{5} \\ 0 & 1 & 0 \\ \frac{4}{5} & 0 & -\frac{3}{5} \end{bmatrix}$$

are both unitary. Compute U^2, UV, and VU and verify that they are unitary.

4. Show that an orthogonal 2×2 matrix has either of the forms

$$\begin{bmatrix} \cos\theta & -\sin\theta \\ \sin\theta & \cos\theta \end{bmatrix} \quad \text{or} \quad \begin{bmatrix} \cos\theta & \sin\theta \\ \sin\theta & -\cos\theta \end{bmatrix}$$

for some θ.

5. Show that the main diagonal entries of a hermitian matrix are real and that the main diagonal entries of a skew-hermitian matrix are pure imaginary. What are the main diagonal entries of a (real) skew-symmetric matrix?

6. Let D, F, and G be diagonal $n \times n$ matrices whose main diagonal entries are real, pure imaginary, and complex numbers of modulus 1, respectively. If U is a unitary $n \times n$ matrix, show that the matrices U^*DU, U^*FU, and U^*GU are hermitian, skew-hermitian, and unitary, respectively.

7. Let

$$A = \begin{bmatrix} 2 & 0 & 1 \\ 0 & 2 & -1 \\ 1 & -1 & 1 \end{bmatrix}.$$

Find a unitary matrix U such that U^*AU is diagonal.

8. Let $v_1 = (1, 1, 1)$, $v_2 = (2, 1, 0)$, and $v_3 = (0, 1, 1)$. Find an orthogonal set of vectors u_1, u_2, and u_3 such that $\langle u_1 \rangle = \langle v_1 \rangle$ and $\langle u_1, u_2 \rangle = \langle v_1, v_2 \rangle$.

9. Prove in detail that if U is an n-square unitary matrix, then U is unitarily diagonalizable.

5

Quadratic Functions

5.1. CONGRUENCE

A typical question that one encounters in elementary analytic geometry is the following. In the (x_1, x_2) plane find the graph of the set of points satisfying

$$2x_1^2 + 5x_1x_2 + 3x_2^2 = 0. \tag{1}$$

There are a number of ways in which we may go about solving this problem. We could assign values to x_2, solve the resulting quadratic equation (1) for x_1, and plot the points (x_1, x_2) thereby obtained. Of course, since we can only plot a finite number of points, all this does is give us an idea of the shape of the curve and hence is not an altogether successful approach. On the other hand, if we stare at (1) for a time, we see that the left side can be factored into

$$(x_1 + x_2)(2x_1 + 3x_2) = 0. \tag{2}$$

Now the problem of describing the set of points satisfying (1) (or equivalently (2)) is very simple; for, a point $x = (x_1, x_2)$ can satisfy (2) if and only if at least one of the factors $(x_1 + x_2)$, $(2x_1 + 3x_2)$ is equal to zero. In other words, the set of points x in $V_2(R)$ satisfying (1) consists of the points lying on either one of the lines:

$$x_1 + x_2 = 0,$$

$$2x_1 + 3x_2 = 0.$$

202

We see that although originally (1) looked like a quadratic in x_1 and x_2, it is, in fact, the product of two linear expressions in x_1 and x_2. In this chapter we shall develop the necessary tools to decide about general questions like this.

Another typical example is the following. Suppose we consider the quadratic function in x_1 and x_2 given by

$$q(x) = q((x_1, x_2))$$
$$= 2x_1^2 + 2x_2^2 + x_1 x_2. \qquad (3)$$

We can think of q as a function which associates with each point (x_1, x_2) in $V_2(R)$ a number which is determined by the right side of (3). The problem is: describe the set of points $x = (x_1, x_2)$ in $V_2(R)$ for which $q(x) = 1$. We could start out with the usual peasant approach of plotting points as we did with (1), but this is tedious and uninformative. Once again we need an idea. We shall try to "reduce" $q(x)$ to a simpler quadratic function that we already know about. In order to do this, we first consider the following elementary problem, which should be familiar to the reader from what we did in Section 1.3, Chapter 1. Suppose we are given a point $x = (x_1, x_2)$, and we consider the linear transformation T which rotates every point in the plane counterclockwise around the origin through an angle θ. If we look back at formula (7) in Section 1.3, Chapter 1, we see that if $y = T(x)$, then $y = (y_1, y_2)$ is given by

$$y_1 = (\cos \theta)x_1 - (\sin \theta)x_2,$$
$$y_2 = (\sin \theta)x_1 + (\cos \theta)x_2. \qquad (4)$$

If we set

$$P = \begin{bmatrix} \cos \theta & -\sin \theta \\ \sin \theta & \cos \theta \end{bmatrix}, \qquad (5)$$

we can rewrite (4) in the notation

$$y = Px. \qquad (6)$$

We check easily that P is a nonsingular matrix and, in fact,

$$P^{-1} = \begin{bmatrix} \cos \theta & \sin \theta \\ -\sin \theta & \cos \theta \end{bmatrix}. \qquad (7)$$

Once again, in somewhat different language, we are trying to describe the set of points

$$C = \{x = (x_1, x_2) \mid q(x) = 1\}. \tag{8}$$

Let $P(C)$ denote the set of points $y = Px$ as x ranges over C. We know that $P(C)$ is obtained from C by counterclockwise rotation around the origin through an angle θ, so that if we can find what $P(C)$ is, we can discover C by just rotating back through an angle θ. In other words, we shall try to choose the angle θ so that $P(C)$ is a recognizable curve. Now observe that $y \in P(C)$ if and only if $P^{-1}y \in C$. That is to say, $y \in P(C)$ if and only if $q(P^{-1}y) = 1$. Now, from (7),

$$P^{-1}y = \begin{bmatrix} \cos\theta & \sin\theta \\ -\sin\theta & \cos\theta \end{bmatrix}\begin{bmatrix} y_1 \\ y_2 \end{bmatrix}$$
$$= \begin{bmatrix} (\cos\theta)y_1 + (\sin\theta)y_2 \\ (-\sin\theta)y_1 + (\cos\theta)y_2 \end{bmatrix}. \tag{9}$$

Hence, from (3),

$$q(P^{-1}y) = q((y_1\cos\theta + y_2\sin\theta, \, -y_1\sin\theta + y_2\cos\theta))$$
$$= 2(y_1\cos\theta + y_2\sin\theta)^2 + 2(-y_1\sin\theta + y_2\cos\theta)^2$$
$$+ (y_1\cos\theta + y_2\sin\theta)(-y_1\sin\theta + y_2\cos\theta). \tag{10}$$

We shall try to choose θ so that (10) involves only y_1^2 and y_2^2 and no cross terms $y_1 y_2$. Collecting the coefficients of the terms in y_1 and y_2 we have

$$q(P^{-1}y) = (2\cos^2\theta + 2\sin^2\theta - \cos\theta\sin\theta)y_1^2$$
$$+ (2\sin^2\theta + 2\cos^2\theta + \sin\theta\cos\theta)y_2^2$$
$$+ (4\cos\theta\sin\theta - 4\cos\theta\sin\theta + \cos^2\theta - \sin^2\theta)y_1 y_2. \tag{11}$$

Thus, from (11), the coefficient of $y_1 y_2$ in $q(P^{-1}y)$ is $\cos^2\theta - \sin^2\theta$, and if we set $\theta = 45°$ (i.e., $\pi/4$ radians) and use the fact that $\cos(\pi/4) = \sin(\pi/4) = 1/\sqrt{2}$, it follows from (11) that

$$q(P^{-1}y) = \tfrac{3}{2}y_1^2 + \tfrac{5}{2}y_2^2. \tag{12}$$

Now, we know from elementary analytic geometry that the set of points for which

$$q(P^{-1}y) = \tfrac{3}{2}y_1^2 + \tfrac{5}{2}y_2^2$$
$$= 1$$

is an ellipse with center at the origin (Fig. 1).

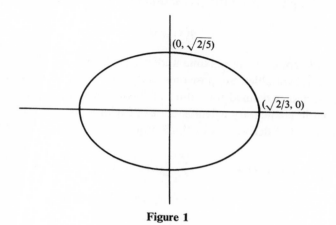

Figure 1

The ellipse in Fig. 1 is a picture of $P(C)$. As we remarked before, C is obtained by a clockwise rotation through 45° of the ellipse in Fig. 1, so the curve C looks as shown in Fig. 2.

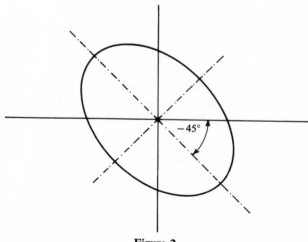

Figure 2

In the preceding example, we were interested in the shape of a curve consisting of all points x such that $q(x) = 1$, where q was the quadratic (3).

As our next example we consider a problem in which it is required to determine if a given quadratic $q(x)$ satisfies the inequality

$$q(x) \geq 0. \tag{13}$$

This example comes from maxima and minima problems involving functions of several variables. Suppose then that $f(u) = f((u_1, \ldots, u_n))$ is a function of n variables defined for values of u lying in some region in $V_n(R)$. It is proved in elementary calculus books (Taylor's theorem) that if f has continuous partial derivatives of third order and if $x = (x_1, \ldots, x_n)$, then

$$f(u + x) = f(u) + \sum_{j=1}^{n} f_j(u)x_j + \tfrac{1}{2} \sum_{i,j=1}^{n} f_{ij}(u)x_i x_j$$

$$+ \text{ terms of degree 3 or more in } x. \tag{14}$$

The numbers $f_j(u)$ and $f_{ij}(u)$ are the first- and second-order partials of f evaluated at u. It is also proved that if u is a stationary point for f, then $f_j(u) = 0$ for $j = 1, \ldots, n$. If we let $a_{ij} = f_{ij}(u)$, $i = 1, \ldots, n, j = 1, \ldots, n$, and define q by

$$q(x) = \sum_{i,j=1}^{n} a_{ij} x_i x_j,$$

then (14) tells us that a stationary point u will be a minimum only if

$$q(x) \geq 0$$

for all x. Thus the problem of finding the maxima and minima of a function f of several variables is really a problem in deciding about the sign of the quadratic function q. It is also proved in calculus texts that the partials f_{ij} satisfy

$$f_{ij}(u) = f_{ji}(u), \qquad i, j = 1, \ldots, n,$$

so that the n-square matrix

$$A = (a_{ij})$$

satisfies

$$A^T = A.$$

In other words, the matrix A is symmetric.

We shall next use the notation for the standard inner product in $V_n(R)$ and show how it can be used to simplify writing the quadratic function q. Recall the Definition 3.2, Chapter 4: let R be the set of real numbers, and for each pair of vectors $x = (x_1, \ldots, x_n)$ and $y = (y_1, \ldots, y_n)$ in $V_n(R)$, let (x, y) denote the number given by

$$(x, y) = \sum_{i=1}^{n} x_i y_i. \tag{15}$$

The number (x, y) is the standard inner product of x and y. We defined the length of the vector x to be

$$\|x\| = (x, x)^{1/2}$$
$$= \left(\sum_{i=1}^{n} x_i^2 \right)^{1/2}.$$

Recall that a vector is a unit vector if its length is 1, i.e., $\|x\| = 1$, and two vectors x and y are said to be orthogonal or perpendicular if their inner product is zero, i.e., $(x, y) = 0$.

In considering maxima-minima problems for functions of several variables, we were led to the question of determining the sign of a quadratic function of the form

$$q(x) = \sum_{i,j=1}^{n} a_{ij} x_i x_j, \tag{16}$$

in which $A = (a_{ij})$ is a symmetric matrix, i.e., $a_{ij} = a_{ji}$, $i, j = 1, \ldots, n$. Thinking of x as a column n-tuple (as we did when we were studying linear equations), we write

$$y = Ax, \tag{17}$$

so that

$$y_i = \sum_{j=1}^{n} a_{ij} x_j. \tag{18}$$

Thus, in terms of the standard inner product, we can use (17) and (18) to write (16) in the following way:

$$q(x) = \sum_{i,j=1}^{n} a_{ij} x_j x_i$$

$$= \sum_{i=1}^{n} x_i \left(\sum_{j=1}^{n} a_{ij} x_j \right)$$

$$= \sum_{i=1}^{n} x_i y_i$$

$$= (x, y)$$

$$= (x, Ax). \tag{19}$$

The form (19) will be particularly useful to us. One should observe in (19) that the multiplicity of indices has disappeared from view. Our next result will provide us with a simple computational device which will prove to be very fruitful in analyzing $q(x) = (x, Ax)$.

Theorem 1.1. *Let P be any n × n matrix. Then for all x and y in $V_n(R)$,*

$$(Px, y) = (x, P^T y). \tag{20}$$

Proof. Let $P = (p_{ij})$. Then the *i*th component of $z = Px$ is

$$z_i = \sum_{j=1}^{n} p_{ij} x_j.$$

The left side of (20) is, of course, (z, y), and

$$(z, y) = \sum_{i=1}^{n} z_i y_i$$

$$= \sum_{i=1}^{n} \sum_{j=1}^{n} p_{ij} x_j y_i$$

$$= \sum_{i,j=1}^{n} p_{ij} y_i x_j.$$

On the other hand, since the (i, j) entry of P^T is p_{ji}, we see that the *i*th component of $w = P^T y$ is given by

$$w_i = \sum_{j=1}^{n} p_{ji} y_j.$$

Hence the right side of (20) is

$$(x, P^T y) = (x, w)$$

$$= \sum_{i=1}^{n} x_i w_i$$

$$= \sum_{i=1}^{n} x_i \sum_{j=1}^{n} p_{ji} y_j$$

$$= \sum_{i,j=1}^{n} p_{ji} y_j x_i . \tag{21}$$

Now, the indices i and j appearing in (21) are dummies after all, so we can replace j by i and i by j to obtain

$$\sum_{i,j=1}^{n} p_{ji} y_j x_i = \sum_{i,j=1}^{n} p_{ij} y_i x_j . \tag{22}$$

But the right side of (22) is exactly what we obtained for the value $(Px, y) = (z, y)$. In other words,

$$(Px, y) = (x, P^T y).$$

We intend to use this last result in the following way. If P is a nonsingular $n \times n$ matrix, we know that as x ranges over $V_n(R)$, so does Px. Thus [see (19)]

$$q(x) = (x, Ax)$$

is greater than or equal to zero for all x if and only if

$$q(Px) \geq 0$$

for all x, since Px ranges over $V_n(R)$ as x does. But according to Theorem 1.1,

$$q(Px) = (Px, APx)$$
$$= (x, P^T APx).$$

In other words, in studying the quadratic function

$$q(x) = (x, Ax),$$

we can replace A by the matrix $P^T A P$, where P is any nonsingular matrix. It will be ideal for us if we can select the matrix P so that $P^T A P$ is a diagonal matrix. We know, however, from Theorem 3.5, Chapter 4, that there exists an orthogonal matrix P, i.e., one for which $P^T P = I_n$, such that

$$
P^T A P = \begin{bmatrix} \lambda_1 & & & \\ & \lambda_2 & & \mathbf{0} \\ & & \ddots & \\ \mathbf{0} & & & \ddots \\ & & & & \lambda_n \end{bmatrix},
\tag{23}
$$

in which $\lambda_1, \ldots, \lambda_n$ are the characteristic roots of the symmetric matrix A. Using this choice of P, we compute from (23) that

$$
(x, P^T A P x) = (x, D x),
\tag{24}
$$

in which D is the diagonal matrix on the right in (23). But

$$
D x = (\lambda_1 x_1, \lambda_2 x_2, \ldots, \lambda_n x_n),
$$

and hence from (24) we have

$$
q(P x) = \sum_{i=1}^{n} \lambda_i x_i^2.
\tag{25}
$$

We have done all the work necessary to state and prove the following theorem.

Theorem 1.2. *Let A be an n-square symmetric matrix. The quadratic function*

$$
q(x) = \sum_{i,j=1}^{n} a_{ij} x_i x_j
$$

$$
= (x, A x)
$$

is positive (negative) for all nonzero vectors x if and only if every characteristic root of A is positive (negative).

Proof. As in (25), choose an orthogonal matrix P so that

$$
q(P x) = \sum_{i=1}^{n} \lambda_i x_i^2,
\tag{26}
$$

where $\lambda_1, \ldots, \lambda_n$ are the characteristic roots of A. Clearly if $\lambda_i > 0$, $i = 1, \ldots, n$, then the right side of (26) is positive for any nonzero vector x.

Conversely, if the right side of (26) is positive for any nonzero x, choose

$$x = (0, \ldots, 0, 1, 0, \ldots, 0),$$

where the 1 occurs in the ith position. For this x, the right side of (26) has the value λ_i, and hence λ_i is positive. But as we saw before, $q(x)$ is positive for all nonzero x if and only if $q(Px)$ is positive for all nonzero x. Precisely the same argument works when the word "positive" is replaced by the word "negative."

Consider the following example. Show that for all real numbers x_1, x_2, and x_3, not all of which are zero, the following inequality holds:

$$3x_1^2 + 3x_2^2 + 3x_3^2 + 2x_1x_2 + 2x_1x_3 + 2x_2x_3 > 0. \qquad (27)$$

Let $q(x)$ denote the left side of the desired inequality (27), and let A be the 3×3 symmetric matrix

$$A = \begin{bmatrix} 3 & 1 & 1 \\ 1 & 3 & 1 \\ 1 & 1 & 3 \end{bmatrix}. \qquad (28)$$

Then

$$q(x) = (x, Ax),$$

as one easily checks. Hence to apply Theorem 1.2, we must compute the characteristic roots of A. But

$$A = 2I_3 + J, \qquad (29)$$

where J is the 3×3 matrix all of whose entries are 1. The characteristic polynomial of J is

$$\det(\lambda I_3 - J) = \lambda^2(\lambda - 3),$$

as one computes directly from the definition of the determinant. Thus the characteristic roots of J are 0, 0, and 3, and from (29) the characteristic roots of A are 2, 2, and 5. Hence, by Theorem 1.2, $q(x)$ is positive for all nonzero x.

Definition 1.1. (Congruence). *Let A and B be two $n \times n$ symmetric matrices. We say that A and B are **congruent** (or B is congruent to A) if there exists a nonsingular matrix P such that*

$$P^T A P = B. \qquad (30)$$

A symmetric matrix is said to be **positive definite** *if all its characteristic roots are positive and* **negative definite** *if all its characteristic roots are negative. If the characteristic roots are simply nonnegative, we say that A is* **positive semidefinite**. *If there are positive and negative characteristic roots of A, we say that A is* **indefinite**.

Observe that if $B = P^T A P$ and P is nonsingular, then $A = (P^{-1})^T B P^{-1}$. Moreover, if $B = P^T A P$ and $A = Q^T C Q$, where Q is nonsingular, then $B = P^T Q^T C Q P = (QP)^T C (QP)$. The matrix QP is nonsingular since both Q and P are. We have proved the following elementary facts:

    (i) any matrix is congruent to itself;

   (ii) if B is congruent to A, then A is congruent to B;

  (iii) if B is congruent to A and A is congruent to C, then B is congruent to C.

The fundamental theorem concerning these concepts is called *Sylvester's law of inertia*.

Theorem 1.3. *Two n × n symmetric matrices are congruent if and only if they have precisely the same number of positive, negative, and zero characteristic roots, respectively.*

Proof. Let A and B be the two symmetric matrices. Suppose that $B = P^T A P$, where P is an $n \times n$ nonsingular matrix. Now suppose that A has p positive and q negative characteristic roots; say $\lambda_1, \ldots, \lambda_p$ are the positive ones and $\lambda_{p+1}, \ldots, \lambda_{p+q}$ are the negative ones. As we know from Theorem 3.5, Chapter 4, there exists a nonsingular orthogonal matrix U such that

$$U^T A U = \begin{bmatrix} \lambda_1 & & & & & & \\ & \ddots & & & & \mathbf{0} & \\ & & \lambda_p & & & & \\ & & & \lambda_{p+1} & & & \\ & & & & \ddots & & \\ & \mathbf{0} & & & \lambda_{p+q} & & \\ & & & & & 0 & \\ & & & & & & \ddots \\ & & & & & & & 0 \end{bmatrix}. \tag{31}$$

Thus the rank of A is $p + q$ and, since $B = P^T A P$, it follows that the rank of B is also $p + q$. The next step in this argument is to define an integer k associated with the matrix A as follows: k is the dimension of a subspace W of $V_n(R)$ of largest dimension for which the quadratic function $q(x) = (x, Ax)$ is positive for all nonzero vectors x in W. Let $u_1, \ldots, u_n$ be the characteristic vectors of A corresponding to the characteristic roots $\lambda_1, \ldots, \lambda_n$, respectively. As we know from Theorems 2.1 and 3.5 in Chapter 4, $u_1, \ldots, u_n$ are, in fact, the columns of the orthogonal matrix U appearing in (31). Since U is orthogonal, $U^T U = I_n$, and this equality, when written in terms of the standard inner product in $V_n(R)$, takes the form

$$(u_i, u_j) = \delta_{ij}, \qquad i, j = 1, \ldots, n. \tag{32}$$

We shall now show that the quadratic function $q(x) = (x, Ax)$ is positive for every nonzero vector x in $\langle u_1, \ldots, u_p \rangle$. For, let

$$x = \sum_{i=1}^{p} c_i u_i.$$

Then,

$$Ax = \sum_{i=1}^{p} c_i A u_i$$

$$= \sum_{i=1}^{p} c_i \lambda_i u_i,$$

and hence

$$q(x) = (x, Ax)$$

$$= \left(\sum_{i=1}^{p} c_i u_i, \sum_{j=1}^{p} \lambda_j c_j u_j \right)$$

$$= \sum_{i,j=1}^{p} c_i c_j \lambda_j (u_i, u_j)$$

$$= \sum_{i,j=1}^{p} c_i c_j \lambda_j \delta_{ij}$$

$$= \sum_{i=1}^{p} c_i^2 \lambda_i$$

$$\geq 0. \tag{33}$$

The equality $q(x) = 0$ can hold if and only if

$$c_1 = c_2 = \cdots = c_p = 0,$$

as we see from (33). In other words, $q(x)$ is positive for any nonzero vector x in the p-dimensional subspace $\langle u_1, \ldots, u_p \rangle$. Now, it follows from the definition of the integer k that

$$p \leq k. \tag{34}$$

On the other hand, suppose the inequality in (34) were strict, i.e., $p < k$. This would imply the existence of a subspace W of dimension k for which $q(x) > 0$ for all nonzero vectors x in W. Consider the subspace in $V_n(R)$ given by

$$V = \langle u_{p+1}, \ldots, u_n \rangle. \tag{35}$$

Recall that $u_{p+1}, \ldots, u_n$ are the characteristic vectors corresponding to $\lambda_{p+1}, \ldots, \lambda_n$, respectively, and moreover, $\lambda_{p+1}, \ldots, \lambda_n$ are the nonpositive characteristic roots of A. Observe that

$$\dim V = n - p,$$

and hence, from Theorem 6.5(c), Chapter 1, W and V must intersect in some nonzero vector x; for,

$$\dim V + \dim W = n - p + k$$
$$> n - p + p$$
$$= n.$$

Now, since x is in V,

$$x = \sum_{j=1}^{n-p} d_j u_{p+j},$$

and hence, in precisely the same way that we derived (33), we see that

$$q(x) = \sum_{j=1}^{n-p} d_j^2 \lambda_{p+j}$$
$$\leq 0, \tag{36}$$

because $\lambda_{p+1}, \ldots, \lambda_n$ are nonpositive. On the other hand, $x \in W$ and thus $q(x)$ is positive. This contradicts (36), and therefore we must abandon the assumption that $p < k$; hence $p = k$. We have proved that the number of positive characteristic roots of the symmetric matrix A is precisely equal to the dimension of a subspace W of largest dimension for which $q(x) = (x, Ax) > 0$ for all nonzero x in W. Recall now that

$$B = P^T A P,$$

where P is nonsingular. Consider the totality W' of vectors $y = P^{-1}x$, where $x \in W$. Let $w_1, \ldots, w_k$ be a basis of W and suppose that $P^{-1}w_1, \ldots, P^{-1}w_k$ are linearly dependent, i.e., there exist constants $c_1, \ldots, c_k$, not all zero, such that

$$\sum_{i=1}^{k} c_i P^{-1} w_i = 0. \tag{37}$$

Now multiply both sides of (37) by P to obtain

$$0 = P \sum_{i=1}^{k} c_i P^{-1} w_i$$

$$= \sum_{i=1}^{k} c_i P P^{-1} w_i$$

$$= \sum_{i=1}^{k} c_i w_i. \tag{38}$$

But the linear independence of $w_1, \ldots, w_k$ implies that all the c_i are zero. It follows, then, that dim $W' = k$. Let $y \in W'$, i.e., $y = P^{-1}x$ for some $x \in W$. Then, by Theorem 1.1,

$$(y, By) = (P^{-1}x, BP^{-1}x)$$

$$= (P^{-1}x, P^T A P P^{-1}x)$$

$$= (P P^{-1}x, Ax)$$

$$= (x, Ax)$$

$$\geq 0, \tag{39}$$

and the inequality in (39) is strict unless x is the zero vector. We have proved that if B is congruent to A, i.e., $B = P^T A P$, then there exists a k-dimensional subspace on which the quadratic function (y, By) is positive.

On the other hand, since $A = (P^{-1})^T B P^{-1}$, A is congruent to B. Hence we can conclude that both B and A have k positive characteristic roots. Moreover, we know that B and A have the same rank, and thus B is congruent to a diagonal matrix of the following type (analogously to (31)):

$$
\begin{bmatrix}
\mu_1 & & & & & & & \\
& \ddots & & & & \mathbf{0} & & \\
& & \mu_p & & & & & \\
& & & \mu_{p+1} & & & & \\
& & & & \ddots & & & \\
& & & & & \mu_{p+q} & & \\
& & & & & & 0 & \\
\mathbf{0} & & & & & & \ddots & \\
& & & & & & & 0
\end{bmatrix}
\tag{40}
$$

We now assert that the matrices (40) and (31) are both congruent to the same diagonal matrix,

$$
\begin{bmatrix}
1 & & & & & & & \\
& 1 & & & & & & \\
& & 1 & & & \mathbf{0} & & \\
& & & \ddots & & & & \\
& & & & 1 & & & \\
& & & & -1 & & & \\
& & & & & \ddots & & \\
& & & & & & -1 & \\
\mathbf{0} & & & & & & 0 & \\
& & & & & & & \ddots \\
& & & & & & & & 0
\end{bmatrix},
\tag{41}
$$

in which there are p ones and q minus ones. This is seen by pre- and post-multiplying the matrix (31) by the diagonal matrix whose first p main diagonal entries are

$$
\frac{1}{\sqrt{\lambda_1}}, \ldots, \frac{1}{\sqrt{\lambda_p}},
$$

whose next q entries are

$$\frac{1}{\sqrt{-\lambda_{p+1}}}, \cdots, \frac{1}{\sqrt{-\lambda_{p+q}}},$$

and whose last $n - (p + q)$ main diagonal entries are 1, and similarly for the matrix (40). We have proved that if A and B are congruent, they have precisely the same number of positive, negative, and zero characteristc roots, respectively, and hence are congruent to the same matrix (41). It follows that they are congruent to one another.

In the proof of Theorem 1.3 we showed that a symmetric matrix A with p positive characteristic roots and q negative characteristic roots is congruent to the matrix (41). The mechanism of the proof required knowing the characteristic roots of A, but we can find the matrix (41) to which A is congruent without knowing the characteristic roots of A. In order to do this we must see what happens to a matrix when we pre- and postmultiply it by P^T and P, where P is a nonsingular matrix. As we know from Theorem 4.3, Chapter 2, any nonsingular matrix P is the product of elementary matrices, and therefore we can write

$$P = E_1 \cdots E_m,$$

in which the E_i are elementary matrices. Thus

$$P^T = E_m^T \cdots E_1^T,$$

and we can write

$$P^T A P = E_m^T \cdots E_1^T A E_1 \cdots E_m. \tag{42}$$

We see from (42) that what happens to a matrix under congruence depends on what happens to it when it is post- and premultiplied by an elementary matrix and its transpose.

Theorem 1.4. *If E is an elementary matrix, then $B = E^T A E$ is the matrix obtained from A by performing the elementary operation corresponding to E on the columns of A followed by performing the same elementary operation on the rows of AE.*

Proof. This is proved very easily by observing that

$$B = E^T(AE).$$

Set $C = AE$ and then

$$E^T C = (C^T E)^T.$$

Now, $C^T E$ is the matrix that results from performing the elementary operation on the columns of C^T, but the columns of C^T are the rows of C. Thus, taking the transpose of $C^T E$ gives us the matrix whose rows are the rows of C after the elementary operation has been performed on them.

For example, suppose E is an elementary 3-square matrix corresponding to the type III operation which adds to column one c times column three:

$$E = \begin{bmatrix} 1 & 0 & 0 \\ 0 & 1 & 0 \\ c & 0 & 1 \end{bmatrix}.$$

Then

$$E^T A E = \begin{bmatrix} 1 & 0 & c \\ 0 & 1 & 0 \\ 0 & 0 & 1 \end{bmatrix} \begin{bmatrix} a_{11} & a_{12} & a_{13} \\ a_{21} & a_{22} & a_{23} \\ a_{31} & a_{32} & a_{33} \end{bmatrix} \begin{bmatrix} 1 & 0 & 0 \\ 0 & 1 & 0 \\ c & 0 & 1 \end{bmatrix}$$

$$= \begin{bmatrix} 1 & 0 & c \\ 0 & 1 & 0 \\ 0 & 0 & 1 \end{bmatrix} \begin{bmatrix} a_{11} + ca_{13} & a_{12} & a_{13} \\ a_{21} + ca_{23} & a_{22} & a_{23} \\ a_{31} + ca_{33} & a_{32} & a_{33} \end{bmatrix}$$

$$= \begin{bmatrix} a_{11} + ca_{13} + ca_{31} + c^2 a_{33} & a_{12} + ca_{32} & a_{13} + ca_{33} \\ a_{21} + ca_{23} & a_{22} & a_{23} \\ a_{31} + ca_{33} & a_{32} & a_{33} \end{bmatrix}.$$

If we assume that the matrix A is symmetric, then it follows that the matrix $E^T A E$ is symmetric:

$$(E^T A E)^T = E^T A^T E^{TT}$$

$$= E^T A E.$$

We can use Theorem 1.4 to describe a constructive method for finding a diagonal matrix congruent to a given symmetric matrix A. We proceed as follows. Suppose first that A has a nonzero entry along the main diagonal, say a_{ii}. If a_{11} is zero, we can first interchange rows one and i and then interchange columns one and i to bring a_{ii} to the (1,1) position. Then by a series of type II operations we can annihilate all the entries in the first column below the $(1, 1)$ position. We then perform the same sequence of operations on the columns of the resulting matrix. By Theorem 1.4, this is a congruence operation and gives us a symmetric matrix of the form

$$
C = \begin{bmatrix} c_{11} & 0 & \cdots & 0 \\ \hline 0 & & & \\ \vdots & & D & \\ 0 & & & \end{bmatrix},
$$

where D is an $(n - 1)$-square matrix. We can reduce D by congruence operations on C which involve neither the first column nor the first row of C. The matrix D can then be reduced to diagonal form, as can be seen by an elementary induction on the size of the matrix involved. The argument thus far has depended on the existence of a nonzero main diagonal entry. Suppose, then, that the original matrix A has a nonzero entry a_{ij}, $i > j$, but that every main diagonal element is 0. Perform the following congruence operation on the matrix A: add row i to row j and add column i to column j. Since every main diagonal element of A is 0, this will result in a matrix B with the number $2a_{ij}$ appearing in the (j, j) position. But we are now reduced to the previous case, in which the main diagonal has a nonzero element in it and the argument can be completed as before. We summarize these results in the following theorem.

Theorem 1.5. *If A is an $n \times n$ symmetric matrix, then there exists a nonsingular matrix P such that $P^T A P$ is a diagonal matrix, i.e., all the off-diagonal elements are zero.*

We illustrate the theorem with the following example. Let

$$
A = \begin{bmatrix} 9 & 5 & 2 \\ 5 & 3 & 1 \\ 2 & 1 & 1 \end{bmatrix}. \tag{43}
$$

First interchange rows one and three and columns one and three to obtain

$$
\begin{bmatrix} 1 & 1 & 2 \\ 1 & 3 & 5 \\ 2 & 5 & 9 \end{bmatrix}, \tag{44}
$$

which puts a 1 in the (1, 1) position. In the matrix (44), subtract row one from row two, and then subtract column one from column two to produce the matrix

$$\begin{bmatrix} 1 & 0 & 2 \\ 0 & 2 & 3 \\ 2 & 3 & 9 \end{bmatrix}. \tag{45}$$

Now subtract twice row one from row three, and then subtract twice column one from column three to produce

$$\begin{bmatrix} 1 & 0 & 0 \\ 0 & 2 & 3 \\ 0 & 3 & 5 \end{bmatrix}. \tag{46}$$

Multiply row and column three of (46) by 2 to produce the matrix

$$\begin{bmatrix} 1 & 0 & 0 \\ 0 & 2 & 6 \\ 0 & 6 & 10 \end{bmatrix}. \tag{47}$$

The purpose of this last congruence operation is to prepare the (2, 3) and (3, 2) entries for annihilation, using only elementary operations involving integers. (We do not have to do this, of course; we could have immediately subtracted $\frac{3}{2}$ times row two from row three and $\frac{3}{2}$ times column two from column three in (46).) Subtract 3 times row two from row three and then subtract 3 times column two from column three to obtain

$$\begin{bmatrix} 1 & 0 & 0 \\ 0 & 2 & 0 \\ 0 & 0 & -8 \end{bmatrix}. \tag{48}$$

We have thus reduced the original matrix A to diagonal form. Since we are talking about real numbers here, we could continue to reduce the matrix (48) to a matrix having only 1 or -1 on the main diagonal. Thus we can multiply row two and column two of (48) by $1/\sqrt{2}$ and row three and column three by $1/\sqrt{8}$ to obtain the matrix

$$\begin{bmatrix} 1 & 0 & 0 \\ 0 & 1 & 0 \\ 0 & 0 & -1 \end{bmatrix}. \tag{49}$$

Theorem 1.6. *If A is a nonzero n-square real symmetric matrix, then there exists a nonsingular matrix P such that $P^T A P$ has the following form:*

$$P^T A P = D = \begin{bmatrix} 1 & & & & & & & \\ & \ddots & & & & 0 & & \\ & & 1 & & & & & \\ & & & -1 & & & & \\ & & & & \ddots & & & \\ & & 0 & & & -1 & & \\ & & & & & & 0 & \\ & & & & & & & \ddots \\ & & & & & & & & 0 \end{bmatrix}.$$

There are p ones and q minus ones in D. The integer p is the number of positive characteristic roots of A and the integer q is the number of negative characteristic roots of A. The integer p + q is the rank of A.

Proof. As we saw before in Theorem 1.3, the matrix A is congruent to a diagonal matrix [see (31)] in which there are p positive characteristic roots and q negative roots on the main diagonal. Perform the following congruence operations on (31): multiply row i and then column i by $1/\sqrt{\lambda_i}$, $i = 1, \ldots, p$; multiply row i and then column i by $1/\sqrt{-\lambda_i}$, $i = p + 1, \ldots$, $p + q$.

For example, we know that the matrix (43) has two positive characteristic roots and one negative characteristic root and is nonsingular, by looking at the matrix (48) which is congruent to (43). Theorem 1.6 is very remarkable, since computing characteristic roots of a general $n \times n$ symmetric matrix is out of the question, whereas determining a diagonal matrix congruent to it is entirely feasible.

Quiz
Answer *true* or *false*:
1. If A and B are n-square real matrices and A is symmetric, then $B^T A B$ is symmetric.
2. If A is symmetric, then A^2 is symmetric.
3. If A^2 is symmetric, then A is symmetric.
4. If A and B are $n \times n$ real symmetric matrices, then AB is symmetric.

5. If A and B are $n \times n$ real symmetric matrices, then $A + B$ is symmetric.
6. If A is an $n \times n$ real matrix, then $A + A^T$ is symmetric.
7. If A and B are $n \times n$ real matrices, then $AB^T + BA^T$ is symmetric.
8. If the 3×3 symmetric matrix A is congruent to the diagonal matrix

$$\begin{bmatrix} 1 & 0 & 0 \\ 0 & 0 & 0 \\ 0 & 0 & -1 \end{bmatrix},$$

then A has one positive, one negative, and one zero characteristic root.
9. If x and y are in $V_n(R)$, then $(x, y) = (y, x)$. (See formula (15).)
10. Using the standard inner product in $V_3(R)$, the vectors $(1, 0, 1)$ and $(-1, 1, 1)$ are orthogonal.

Exercises

1. If P is the matrix

$$\begin{bmatrix} 1 & 2 & 3 \\ 4 & 5 & 6 \\ 7 & 8 & 9 \end{bmatrix},$$

then find the matrix Q such that $(Px, y) = (x, Qy)$ for all 3-tuples x and y [see Theorem 1.1].

2. Construct an argument to show that the following two matrices are not congruent:

$$\begin{bmatrix} 1 & 0 & 0 \\ 0 & 0 & 0 \\ 0 & 0 & -1 \end{bmatrix}, \qquad \begin{bmatrix} 1 & 0 & 0 \\ 0 & 0 & 0 \\ 0 & 0 & 1 \end{bmatrix}.$$

3. Let the matrix P be

$$\begin{bmatrix} -1 & 2 \\ 2 & -4 \end{bmatrix}.$$

Show that the set of all points x in $V_2(R)$ for which $(Px, x) = 0$ consists of points on a straight line.

4. Identify the curve in $V_2(R)$ given by the equation $q(x) = (x, Ax) = 1$, where

$$A = \begin{bmatrix} -1 & 2 \\ 2 & -1 \end{bmatrix}.$$

5. Write down the 3×3 matrix B obtained from

$$A = \begin{bmatrix} 1 & 0 & 1 \\ 2 & -2 & 3 \\ 1 & 1 & -1 \end{bmatrix}$$

by performing the following sequence of elementary row operations and corresponding column operations:

   (i) interchange row one and row three;
   (ii) add to row two -2 times row three;
   (iii) multiply row one by 5.

6. Show that any congruence operation of type I on a matrix A, (i.e., a permutation of the rows followed by the same permutation of the columns) leaves the main diagonal of A intact except for the order in which the entries appear.

7. Show that if A and B are $n \times n$ congruent matrices, then $\det(AB) \geq 0$.

8. Show that if the $n \times n$ symmetric matrix A is congruent to the identity matrix I_n, then the trace of A is positive.

5.2. ABSTRACT INNER PRODUCTS

In Section 1.5 of Chapter 1, we discussed in some detail the idea of an inner product for vectors in the plane. In Theorem 5.1 we proved most of the familiar geometric properties that one usually associates with the length of a vector and the angle between vectors. In Section 4.3, Chapter 4, we defined the standard inner product for the vector space $V_n(R)$. This was used in Section 5.1 as a technical device to enable us to study quadratic functions in general. In the present section we shall introduce a general notion of inner product for vectors in an arbitrary vector space, and we shall be concerned with proving some of the elementary properties that such a quadratic function must possess. These, in fact, will look exactly like the contents of Theorem 5.1 in Chapter 1. To give the student a somewhat different idea of how an inner product may enter the scene, we shall start by considering some examples.

Let V denote the set of all polynomial functions $p(t)$ of degree at most n, defined for $0 \leq t \leq 1$. In other words, a typical element of V has the following appearance:

$$p(t) = \alpha_0 + \alpha_1 t + \alpha_2 t^2 + \cdots + \alpha_n t^n, \tag{1}$$

in which $\alpha_0, \alpha_1, \ldots, \alpha_n$ are real numbers. It is quite easy to see that V is a vector space of dimension $n + 1$. In fact, V has the following set of polynomials as a basis: $\{1, t, t^2, \ldots, t^n\}$. Given two such polynomials in V, call them p and q, we define the following number:

$$(p, q) = \int_0^1 p(t)q(t) \, dt. \tag{2}$$

Now, the number (p, q) has a variety of fascinating properties:

$$(p, q) = (q, p), \tag{3}$$

$$(\alpha p, q) = \alpha(p, q), \tag{4}$$

where α is a number;

$$(p + q, w) = (p, w) + (q, w), \tag{5}$$

where $w \in V$;

$$(p, p) \geq 0, \tag{6}$$

with equality holding in (6) if and only if p is the zero polynomial; and

$$|(p, q)| \leq \|p\| \|q\|, \tag{7}$$

where $\|p\| = (p, p)^{1/2}$, in which equality can hold if and only if one of p and q is a numerical multiple of the other. We shall prove (6), for example. However, rather than get deeply involved in special proofs for some of the other properties (3) through (7), we shall instead see that they follow from quite general theorems concerning the inner product. Thus consider

$$(p, p) = \int_0^1 p(t)p(t)\, dt$$

$$= \int_0^1 (p(t))^2\, dt. \tag{8}$$

The function p^2 is nonnegative for every value of t in the interval from 0 to 1, and from (8) we see that (p, p) just represents the area under the graph of p^2 in the interval from 0 to 1. Thus $(p, p) \geq 0$, and the only way in which this area can be equal to zero is for the nonnegative function p^2 to be zero, i.e., for p to be zero.

As another example of a vector space with an inner product, consider the set of $n \times n$ matrices with real number entries. With each pair of such matrices A and B define (A, B) by

$$(A, B) = \text{tr}(B^T A). \tag{9}$$

We assert that the following properties hold for this "inner product" of matrices:

$$(A, B) = (B, A),$$
$$(\alpha A, B) = \alpha(A, B),$$
$$(A + B, C) = (A, C) + (B, C),$$
$$(A, A) \geq 0,$$

with equality if and only if $A = 0$;

$$|(A, B)| \leq \|A\| \|B\|,$$

where $\|A\| = (A, A)^{1/2}$ and equality holds if and only if one of A and B is a scalar multiple of the other. In the preceding, α is a number and A, B, and C are real matrices.

We compute that

$$\begin{aligned}
(A + B, C) &= \text{tr}(C^T(A + B)) \\
&= \text{tr}(C^T A) + \text{tr}(C^T B) \\
&= (A, C) + (B, C).
\end{aligned}$$

Also, consider the proof of the first property:

$$\begin{aligned}
(A, B) &= \text{tr}(B^T A) \\
&= \text{tr}((B^T A)^T) \\
&= \text{tr}(A^T B) \\
&= (B, A).
\end{aligned}$$

Observe that the properties listed for the inner products (p, q) in the first example and (A, B) in the second example are formally identical. We are therefore led to make the following definition.

Definition 2.1. (*Inner product*). *Let V be a vector space over the complex numbers. A complex-valued function defined on pairs of vectors and denoted by (u, v) is called an **inner product** on V if it has the following properties:*

(i) $(u, v) = \overline{(v, u)}$ *for all vectors u and v;*

(ii) $(\alpha u, v) = \alpha(u, v)$ *for all vectors u and v and all numbers α;*

(iii) $(u, v + w) = (u, v) + (u, w)$ *for all vectors u, v, and w;*

(iv) $(u, u) \geq 0$ *for all vectors u, with equality if and only if $u = 0$.*

The vector space V together with the inner product is called a **unitary space**. *In the event that the vector space V is over the real numbers and the function (u, v) is a real-valued function, then the vector space V together with the real inner product is called a* **euclidean space**.

There are some special words and notation used to describe the properties of the inner product. Property (i) is called *conjugate symmetry*, (ii) is *homogeneity*, (iii) is *linearity*, and (iv) is *positive definiteness*. Thus in words, an inner product is a positive definite conjugate symmetric bilinear function. It is not important for us to use this language. An inner product is just an item which satisfies the above list of properties. It will be noted that in our definition the properties are slightly modified versions of what appeared in examples, e.g., (i) involves the complex conjugate. (It does not occur, of course, if we are talking about a euclidean space.) The reasons for this will become clear if we consider the following situation. Suppose that we were to define the inner product of two vectors x and y in $V_2(C)$ as follows:

$$(x, y) = x_1 y_1 + x_2 y_2. \tag{10}$$

If we want to think of (x, x) as something like the square of the "length" of a vector, we would have the following rather distressing circumstance: let $x = (1, i)$, and compute that

$$(x, x) = 1 \cdot 1 + i \cdot i$$
$$= 1 - 1$$
$$= 0.$$

In other words, the vector $x = (1, i)$ is certainly not the zero vector $(0, 0)$, and yet its length squared, i.e., (x, x), is zero. If, instead of (10), we define the inner product of x and y by

$$(x, y) = x_1 \bar{y}_1 + x_2 \bar{y}_2,$$

then

$$(x, x) = x_1 \bar{x}_1 + x_2 \bar{x}_2$$
$$= |x_1|^2 + |x_2|^2$$
$$\geq 0.$$

Moreover, equality can hold in this last inequality if and only if $x_1 = x_2 = 0$, i.e., x is the zero vector.

Since we want to talk about vector spaces over the complex numbers and introduce a notion of distance between vectors in such spaces, it is important for us to insist that property (iv) in Definition 2.1 holds. We see that if property (i) were not true in general, then we might have a bit of trouble with (iv). In fact, it would not even necessarily be the case that (u, u) is real, much less nonnegative. Let us modify one of our preceding examples to satisfy the axioms in Definition 2.1. Suppose, then, that the vector space V in question is the set of all n-square matrices with complex number entries, in which, of course, addition is ordinary matrix addition and scalar multiplication is the usual multiplication of a matrix by a scalar. Now, in analogy with (9), define (A, B) by

$$(A, B) = \text{tr}(B^*A). \tag{11}$$

We verify properties (i) through (iv):

(i)
$$(A, B) = \text{tr}(B^*A)$$
$$= \overline{\text{tr}((B^*A)^*)}$$
$$= \overline{\text{tr}(A^*B)}$$
$$= \overline{(B, A)};$$

(ii)
$$\overline{(\alpha A, B)} = \text{tr}(B^*\alpha A)$$
$$= \text{tr}(\alpha B^*A)$$
$$= \alpha \, \text{tr}(B^*A)$$
$$= \alpha(A, B);$$

(iii)
$$(A, B + C) = \text{tr}((B + C)^*A)$$
$$= \text{tr}((B^* + C^*)A)$$
$$= \text{tr}(B^*A + C^*A)$$
$$= \text{tr}(B^*A) + \text{tr}(C^*A)$$
$$= (A, B) + (A, C);$$

(iv) $(A, A) = \mathrm{tr}(A^*A)$

$$= \sum_{i=1}^{n} (A^*A)_{ii}$$

$$= \sum_{i=1}^{n} \sum_{k=1}^{n} (A^*)_{ik} A_{ki}$$

$$= \sum_{i=1}^{n} \sum_{k=1}^{n} \overline{A_{ki}} A_{ki}$$

$$= \sum_{i=1}^{n} \sum_{k=1}^{n} |A_{ki}|^2$$

$$\geq 0.$$

Moreover,

$$\sum_{i=1}^{n} \sum_{k=1}^{n} |A_{ki}|^2 = 0$$

if and only if $A_{ki} = 0$, $k = 1, \ldots, n$, $i = 1, \ldots, n$, i.e., A is the zero matrix. Thus the formula (11) does indeed define an inner product on the space of n-square matrices over the complex numbers.

If we consider the pictorial representation of the vector space $V_2(R)$ or $V_3(R)$, where R is the set of real numbers, and we use the standard inner product, then the number

$$(x - y, x - y)^{1/2} \tag{12}$$

has an obvious geometric meaning. For if $x = (x_1, x_2)$ and $y = (y_1, y_2)$, then the number given in (12) is

$$((x_1 - y_1, x_2 - y_2), (x_1 - y_1, x_2 - y_2))^{1/2} = ((x_1 - y_1)^2 + (x_2 - y_2)^2)^{1/2}. \tag{13}$$

The number in (13) is, of course, just the distance in the plane between the points (x_1, x_2) and (y_1, y_2), i.e., it is just the "length" of the vector $x - y$. Similar remarks hold true, of course, for the vector space of 3-tuples of real numbers. We are therefore led to make the following notational conventions. If u is a vector in a space V equipped with an inner product (x, y), then we define the *length* of u to be the number $(u, u)^{1/2}$. We denote this by

$$\|u\| = (u, u)^{1/2}. \tag{14}$$

The length of u is also called the *norm* of u. If $\|u\| = 1$, we say that u is a *unit vector*. We see, from property (iv) in Definition 2.1 and (14), that $\|u\| = 0$ if and only if $u = 0$. If x and y are two vectors in V, then the *distance* between x and y is defined to be

$$\|x - y\|.$$

Once again, we see that the distance between x and y can be zero if and only if $x = y$.

Consider the two nonzero vectors u and v in Fig. 3. The unit vectors

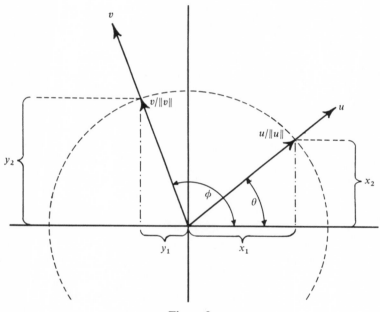

Figure 3

$u/\|u\|$ and $v/\|v\|$ point in the same direction as u and v, of course, but with their "heads" on the unit circle. Let $(x_1, x_2) = u/\|u\|$ and $(y_1, y_2) = v/\|v\|$. Then

$$\cos \theta = x_1,$$
$$\sin \theta = x_2,$$
$$\cos \phi = y_1,$$
$$\sin \phi = y_2.$$

Hence

$$\cos(\phi - \theta) = \cos\phi\cos\theta + \sin\phi\sin\theta$$

$$= y_1 x_1 + y_2 x_2$$

$$= (\frac{v}{\|v\|}, \frac{u}{\|u\|}). \tag{15}$$

Thus we see that the number $(v/\|v\|, u/\|u\|)$ is a measure of the cosine of the angle between the two vectors v and u. Moreover, if v and u are perpendicular vectors, then $(\phi - \theta) = 90°$, therefore $\cos(\phi - \theta) = 0$, and hence $(v/\|v\|, u/\|u\|) = 0$. But since $\|v\|$ and $\|u\|$ are just numbers, we see that v and are u perpendicular if and only if (v, u) is zero. Thus for a general vector space V equipped with an inner product (x, y), we are led to define the *cosine of the angle* between any two vectors to be

$$(\frac{v}{\|v\|}, \frac{u}{\|u\|}). \tag{16}$$

Of course, if either one of v or u is the zero vector, then $(v, u) = 0$ (why?), and we regard every vector as being perpendicular to the zero vector. In general, if

$$(v, u) = 0, \tag{17}$$

we say that v and u are *perpendicular* or *orthogonal*.

Consider the following example. Suppose we wish to find the distance from the point $(1, 2)$ to the line $L : y = x - 3$. (Here (x, y), etc., denotes a point, not an inner product!) We can write the line $y = x - 3$ in the following way. A point (x, y) lies on this line if and only if

$$(x, y) = (x, x - 3)$$

$$= (x, x) + (0, -3)$$

$$= x(1, 1) + (0, -3).$$

The square of the distance from the point $(1, 2)$ to the line L is given by

$$\|x(1, 1) + (0, -3) - (1, 2)\|^2, \tag{18}$$

in which x is chosen to minimize (18). Now, (18) is equal to

$$\|x(1, 1) + (-1, -5)\|^2 = \|(x - 1, x - 5)\|^2$$
$$= (x - 1)^2 + (x - 5)^2$$
$$= x^2 - 2x + 1 + x^2 - 10x + 25$$
$$= 2x^2 - 12x + 26$$
$$= 2(x^2 - 6x + 13).$$

This function of x is clearly minimal at $x = 3$, and the value for $x = 3$ is 8. Hence the distance from the point to the line is

$$\sqrt{8} = 2\sqrt{2}.$$

In (7) we stated without proof an inequality which relates the inner product of two vectors to the product of their lengths. The same inequality appears in Chapter 1, Theorem 5.1(f), and its proof is explicitly exhibited for the vector space $V_2(R)$. At this point, we can give a very general proof of this theorem for arbitrary unitary spaces. This, then, is one of the most important and useful facts occurring in this subject.

Theorem 2.1. **(Cauchy-Schwarz inequality).** *Let V be a unitary space with inner product (x, y). Then*

$$|(x, y)| \leq \|x\| \, \|y\| \tag{19}$$

for any two vectors x and y. Equality holds in (19) if and only if x and y are linearly dependent.

Proof. Clearly (19) is equality if either x or y is the zero vector. Thus let us assume that neither x nor y is zero. We write

$$(x, y) = |(x, y)|c,$$

where c is a complex number whose absolute value is 1. Let r be any real number and consider

$$\|c^{-1}x + ry\|^2. \tag{20}$$

The expression (20) is, of course, a nonnegative number whatever r may be. We compute that

$$0 \leq \|c^{-1}x + ry\|^2$$
$$= (c^{-1}x + ry, c^{-1}x + ry)$$
$$= c^{-1}\overline{c^{-1}}(x, x) + c^{-1}r(x, y) + r\overline{c^{-1}}(y, x) + r^2(y, y)$$
$$= \|x\|^2 + r^2\|y\|^2 + r\{c^{-1}(x, y) + \overline{c^{-1}(x, y)}\}. \qquad (21)$$

In the calculation (21), we have repeatedly used the properties of the inner product given in Definition 2.1, e.g., $(x, y) = \overline{(y, x)}$, $(y, c^{-1}x) = \overline{c^{-1}}(y, x)$, etc. Recall that c was so chosen that $(x, y) = |(x, y)|c$, and therefore $c^{-1}(x, y) = |(x, y)|$. Hence the expression

$$\{c^{-1}(x, y) + \overline{c^{-1}(x, y)}\}$$

appearing in (21) is precisely equal to

$$2|(x, y)|.$$

We conclude from (21) that

$$0 \leq \|x\|^2 + r^2\|y\|^2 + 2r|(x, y)| \qquad (22)$$

for any real number r. Now, the right side of (22) is a quadratic polynomial in r. (We are regarding x and y as being fixed vectors, of course.) Question: how can a quadratic with real number coefficients be nonnegative for all real numbers r? Answer: this can only happen if the roots of the quadratic are either both equal or both nonreal numbers. In other words, the graph of the quadratic cannot cross over the horizontal axis. But as we know, the roots of a quadratic are:

(i) *both equal if and only if the discriminant is zero*;

(ii) *both nonreal numbers if and only if the discriminant is negative.*

The discriminant of the quadratic in (22) is

$$4|(x, y)|^2 - 4\|x\|^2\|y\|^2. \qquad (23)$$

Hence we know that the expression (23) is always nonpositive. This is the inequality (19). Now, to have equality in (19) we know that there would have to exist an r_0 such that the quadratic in (22) is zero for the value $r = r_0$. But the quadratic in (22) is just (20) and, substituting $r = r_0$ in (20), we have

$$c^{-1}x + r_0 y = 0.$$

This is, of course, the statement that x and y are linearly dependent. On the other hand, if x and y are linearly dependent, say $y = dx$ (we are assuming neither x nor y is zero), we compute that

$$|(x, y)| = |(x, dx)|$$
$$= |d(x, x)|$$
$$= |d| \, \|x\|^2,$$

whereas

$$\|x\| \, \|y\| = \|x\| \, \|dx\|$$
$$= |d| \, \|x\|^2.$$

Hence, if x and y are linearly dependent, the equality in (19) does hold and the proof is complete.

Let us now consider some examples of Theorem 2.1. Let the unitary space V in Theorem 2.1 be the vector space of n-tuples of complex numbers, $V_n(C)$. We check that the standard inner product (u, v) is an inner product. We recall that

$$(u, v) = \sum_{i=1}^{n} u_i \bar{v}_i, \tag{24}$$

where $u = (u_1, \ldots, u_n)$, $v = (v_1, \ldots, v_n)$. Now for (24) we verify properties (a) through (d) in Definition 2.1:

(i)
$$(v, u) = \sum_{i=1}^{n} v_i \bar{u}_i$$

$$= \overline{\sum_{i=1}^{n} u_i \bar{v}_i}$$

$$= \overline{(u, v)};$$

(ii)
$$(\alpha u, v) = \sum_{i=1}^{n} (\alpha u_i) \bar{v}_i$$

$$= \alpha \sum_{i=1}^{n} u_i \bar{v}_i$$

$$= \alpha(u, v);$$

(iii)
$$(u, v + w) = \sum_{i=1}^{n} u_i \overline{(v_i + w_i)}$$

$$= \sum_{i=1}^{n} u_i (\overline{v_i} + \overline{w_i})$$

$$= \sum_{i=1}^{n} u_i \overline{v_i} + \sum_{i=1}^{n} u_i \overline{w_i}$$

$$= (u, v) + (u, w);$$

(iv)
$$(u, u) = \sum_{i=1}^{n} u_i \overline{u_i}$$

$$= \sum_{i=1}^{n} |u_i|^2$$

$$\geq 0.$$

Moreover, equality can hold in the preceding inequality if and only if every $u_i = 0$, i.e., $u = 0$. We are now in a position to apply directly the Cauchy-Schwarz inequality to this inner product:

$$\left| \sum_{i=1}^{n} u_i \overline{v_i} \right| = |(u, v)|$$

$$\leq \|u\| \, \|v\|$$

$$= (u, u)^{1/2} (v, v)^{1/2}$$

$$= \left(\sum_{i=1}^{n} u_i \overline{u_i} \right)^{1/2} \left(\sum_{i=1}^{n} v_i \overline{v_i} \right)^{1/2}$$

$$= \left(\sum_{i=1}^{n} |u_i|^2 \right)^{1/2} \left(\sum_{i=1}^{n} |v_i|^2 \right)^{1/2}. \tag{25}$$

For example, if we were to take $u_i \neq 0$, $i = 1, \ldots, n$, and $v_i = \overline{u_i^{-1}}$, $i = 1, \ldots, n$, we would have from (25) that

$$\left| \sum_{i=1}^{n} u_i \overline{v_i} \right| = \left| \sum_{i=1}^{n} u_i u_i^{-1} \right|$$

$$= n$$

$$\leq \left(\sum_{i=1}^{n} |u_i|^2 \right)^{1/2} \left(\sum_{i=1}^{n} \left| \frac{1}{u_i} \right|^2 \right)^{1/2}.$$

In other words, if we set $a_i = |u_i|^2 > 0$, we can conclude that

$$\sum_{i=1}^{n} a_i \sum_{i=1}^{n} \frac{1}{a_i} \geq n^2.$$

Thus a sum of n positive numbers times the sum of the reciprocals of these numbers is always at least n^2.

Quiz

Answer *true* or *false*:

1. In the space of 2-tuples of complex numbers; $V_2(C)$,

$$(x, y) = x_1 y_1 + x_2 y_2$$

   is an inner product.

2. The sum of the reciprocals of the first n positive integers is at least $2n/(n+1)$.

3. The function

$$(x, y) = 2x_1 y_1 + 3x_2 y_2$$

   is an inner product in the space of 2-tuples of real numbers, $V_2(R)$.

4. In the vector space in Question 3, the function

$$(x, y) = x_1 y_1$$

   is an inner product.

5. In the vector space in Question 3, the function

$$(x, y) = x_1 y_1 - x_2 y_2$$

   is an inner product.

6. In the vector space in Question 3, the function

$$(x, y) = x_1 y_2 + x_2 y_1$$

   is an inner product.

7. If p and q are polynomials of degree at most n with real coefficients, then

$$\int_0^1 p(t)q(t)\, dt \leq \int_0^1 p^2(t)\, dt \int_0^1 q^2(t)\, dt.$$

   [*Hint:* See formula (8).]

8. The distance from the point $(0, 1)$ to the line $y = 7x + 3$ is $\sqrt{26}$.

9. If (x, y) is an inner product in V and c is any positive number, then $c(x, y)$ is an inner product also.

10. If (x, y) is an inner product in V, then the function that associates to each pair of vectors the number $(1 + \|x\|)(x, y)$ is also an inner product in V.

Exercises

1. Let V be the vector space of polynomials with real coefficients of degree at most n. Prove that the $n + 1$ polynomials $\{1, t, t^2, \ldots, t^n\}$ constitute a basis of V and hence the dimension of V is $n + 1$.

2. Show that in the vector space $V_2(R)$, the Cauchy-Schwarz inequality has the following geometrical interpretation: the area of a parallelogram is less than or equal to the product of the lengths of two adjacent sides.

3. In $V_3(R)$ find a basis consisting of two mutually perpendicular unit vectors for the subspace consisting of all points (x_1, x_2, x_3) for which $x_1 + x_2 + x_3 = 0$.

4. Show that if V is a unitary space and $u_1, \ldots, u_k$ are mutually orthogonal non-zero vectors, then these vectors are linearly independent.

5. Let A be an n-square complex matrix. Show that

$$\operatorname{tr}(A^*A) \geq 0,$$

with equality holding if and only if A is the zero matrix.

6. Show that if A is an n-square matrix and

$$\operatorname{tr}(AX) = 0$$

for all $n \times n$ matrices X, then A is the zero matrix.

7. Show that the Cauchy-Schwarz inequality implies that if A and B are any two complex matrices, then

$$|\operatorname{tr}(B^*A)|^2 \leq \operatorname{tr}(A^*A) \operatorname{tr}(BB^*).$$

8. In $V_3(R)$ let $u = (1, 0, 1)$, $v = (0, 2, -1)$. Find a unit vector w perpendicular to both u and v. Use the standard inner product.

9. Let $u_1, \ldots, u_n$ be a basis of mutually orthogonal unit vectors of the unitary space V. Show that the zero vector is the only vector which is perpendicular to every one of u_i, $i = 1, \ldots, n$.

Answers and Solutions to Quizzes and Selected Exercises

CHAPTER 1

Section 1.1

Quiz

1. *False.*	**5.** *False.*	**8.** *True.*
2. *True.*	**6.** *True.*	**9.** *True.*
3. *True.*	**7.** *True.*	**10.** ~~*False.*~~ *True*
4. *True.*		

Exercises

2. If $\sqrt{2} + \sqrt{3}$ were a rational number, then $(\sqrt{2} + \sqrt{3})^2 = 5 + 2\sqrt{6}$ would also be rational. Thus $\sqrt{6}$ would be rational, say, $\sqrt{6} = p/q$, where p and q are positive integers with no common divisors greater than 1. Then $6q^2 = p^2$, so that p^2 and hence p would be even, $p = 2r$. Then $6q^2 = 4r^2$, $3q^2 = 2r^2$, and hence q would be even also. But then p and q would have a common factor of 2, a contradiction.

Section 1.2

Quiz

1. *True.*	**5.** *True.*	**8.** *True.*
2. *False.*	**6.** *False.*	**9.** *False.*
3. *True.*	**7.** *False.*	**10.** *True.*
4. *False.*		

Exercises

5. The functions are:

$$f_1(x_1) = x_1, \qquad f_1(x_2) = x_2, \qquad f_1(x_3) = x_3;$$
$$f_2(x_1) = x_2, \qquad f_2(x_2) = x_3, \qquad f_2(x_3) = x_1;$$
$$f_3(x_1) = x_3, \qquad f_3(x_2) = x_1, \qquad f_3(x_3) = x_2;$$
$$f_4(x_1) = x_2, \qquad f_4(x_2) = x_1, \qquad f_4(x_3) = x_3;$$
$$f_5(x_1) = x_3, \qquad f_5(x_2) = x_2, \qquad f_5(x_3) = x_1;$$
$$f_6(x_1) = x_1, \qquad f_6(x_2) = x_3, \qquad f_6(x_3) = x_2.$$

6. There are $3^3 = 27$ different functions. For, there are the three possible values $x_1, x_2,$ and x_3 for each of $f(x_1), f(x_2),$ and $f(x_3)$.

Section 1.3

Quiz

1. *False.*	**5.** *True.*	**8.** *False.*
2. *True.*	**6.** *False.*	**9.** *True.*
3. *True.*	**7.** *True.*	**10.** *True.*
4. *True.*		

Exercises

1. (c) A point (y_1, y_2) lies on the image of the curve $x_1^2 - x_2^2 = 0$ if and only if $y_1 y_2 = (x_1 + x_2)(x_1 - x_2) = 0$. Thus the image is the pair of coordinate axes.

4. Set $P = (x_1, x_2)$, $P' = (x_1', x_2')$, $Q = (y_1, y_2)$, $Q' = (y_1', y_2')$. Let d_1 be the distance from P to P' and d_2 the distance from Q to Q'. Then

$$d_1^2 = (x_1 - x_1')^2 + (x_2 - x_2')^2$$

and

$$d_2^2 = (y_1 - y_1')^2 + (y_2 - y_2')^2$$
$$= ((x_1 - x_1')\cos\theta - (x_2 - x_2')\sin\theta)^2 + ((x_1 - x_1')\sin\theta + (x_2 - x_2')\cos\theta)^2$$
$$= (x_1 - x_1')^2(\cos^2\theta + \sin^2\theta) + (x_2 - x_2')^2(\sin^2\theta + \cos^2\theta)$$
$$= (x_1 - x_1')^2 + (x_2 - x_2')^2$$
$$= d_1^2.$$

Section 1.4

Quiz

1. *False.*	**5.** *True.*	**8.** *True.*
2. *True.*	**6.** *True.*	**9.** *True.*
3. *True.*	**7.** *True.*	**10.** *False.*
4. *False.*		

Exercises

3.

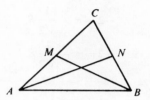

Let ABC be the triangle and let M and N be the midpoints of AC and BC, respectively. Define vectors u and v by $u_A = B$ and $v_A = C$. Observe that $u \nparallel v$; otherwise B and C would be collinear with A. Define a vector w by $w_B = M$. Then, by Exercise 1, $\overrightarrow{BM} = \overrightarrow{AM} - \overrightarrow{AB}$ or $w = \frac{1}{2}v - u$. Hence, by Example 4.4(b), any point on the median BM is given by $(u + sw)_A = (u + s(\frac{1}{2}v - u))_A$ for some number s. Now, by Example 4.4(a), any point on the median AN is given by $(t(u + v))_A$ for some number t. The point of intersection of the two medians lies on both lines and therefore it is given by

$$(u + s(\tfrac{1}{2}v - u))_A = (t(u + v))_A,$$

i.e.,

$$u + s(\tfrac{1}{2}v - u) = t(u + v).$$

We can rewrite the above equation in the form

$$(1 - s - t)u = (t - \tfrac{1}{2}s)v.$$

Now, $u \nparallel v$, and therefore both sides of the preceding equation must vanish; i.e., we must have

$$1 - s - t = 0,$$
$$t - \tfrac{1}{2}s = 0.$$

These equations yield $s = 2t = \frac{2}{3}$.

Section 1.5

Quiz

1. *False.*	**5.** *False.*	**8.** *False.*
2. *True.*	**6.** *True.*	**9.** *True.*
3. *True.*	**7.** *False.*	**10.** *True.*
4. *False.*		

Exercises

4. Observe that $u = [-2, -2]$, $z = [1, 0]$, and $w = [1/\sqrt{2}, -1/\sqrt{2}]$. We want α and β to satisfy

$$-2 = \alpha + \frac{1}{\sqrt{2}}\beta,$$

$$-2 = \quad -\frac{1}{\sqrt{2}}\beta.$$

Then $\alpha = -4$, $\beta = 2\sqrt{2}$.

5. Since u and v are nonzero nonparallel vectors, w can be written uniquely in the form $w = \alpha u + \beta v$ [see Theorem 4.2]. Hence $(w, u) = (\alpha u + \beta v, u) = \alpha(u, u) + \beta(v, u) = \alpha$ and, similarly, $(w, v) = \beta$.

Section 1.6

Quiz

1. *True.*	**5.** *True.*	**8.** *False.*
2. *False.*	**6.** *False.*	**9.** *False.*
3. *False.*	**7.** *True.*	**10.** *True.*
4. *True.*		

Exercises

1. Let W be the subspace and let $v_1, \ldots, v_k$ be a basis of W. According to Theorem 6.4(b), if $u_1, \ldots, u_r$ are linearly independent, it follows that $r \le k$. Hence if $r = k + 1$, the vectors $u_1, \ldots, u_r$ must be linearly dependent.

2. It is easy to check that X is closed under addition and scalar multiplication. That is, if $x_1 + \cdots + x_4 = 0$ and $y_1 + \cdots + y_4 = 0$, then $(x_1 + y_1) + \cdots + (x_4 + y_4) = 0$ and $cx_1 + \cdots + cx_4 = 0$. Hence $(x_1, \ldots, x_4) + (y_1, \ldots, y_4) \in X$ and $c(x_1, \ldots, x_4) \in X$. The vectors $(1, -1, 0, 0)$, $(0, 0, 1, -1)$, and $(1, 0, 0, -1)$ are in X and they constitute a linearly independent set. For,

$$c_1(1, -1, 0, 0) + c_2(0, 0, 1, -1) + c_3(1, 0, 0, -1) = (0, 0, 0, 0)$$

implies that $c_1 + c_3 = 0$, $-c_1 = 0$, $c_2 = 0$, and $-c_2 - c_3 = 0$, i.e., $c_1 = c_2 = c_3 = 0$. Thus dim $X \ge 3$. On the other hand, X is not all of $V_4(C)$, so that, by Theorem 6.5(b), dim $X < \dim V_4(C) = 4$. Hence dim $X = 3$ and the above vectors are a basis of X.

6. Following the hint, let dim $U = n$, dim $V = m$, and, by Theorem 6.4(b), let $w_1, \ldots, w_r, u_1, \ldots, u_{n-r}$ be a basis of U and $w_1, \ldots, w_r, v_1, \ldots, v_{m-r}$ be a basis of V. The space $U + V$ is spanned by the vectors $w_1, \ldots, w_r, u_1, \ldots, u_{n-r}, v_1, \ldots, v_{m-r}$ and there are $r + n - r + m - r = n + m - r$ of these. Now, suppose that $a_1, \ldots, a_r, b_1, \ldots, b_{n-r}, c_1, \ldots, c_{m-r}$ are scalars for which

$$a_1 w_1 + \cdots + a_r w_r + b_1 u_1 + \cdots + b_{n-r} u_{n-r} + c_1 v_1 + \cdots + c_{m-r} v_{m-r} = 0.$$

Let $w = \sum_{i=1}^{r} a_i w_i$, $u = \sum_{i=1}^{n-r} b_i u_i$, and $v = \sum_{i=1}^{m-r} c_i v_i$, so that $w + u + v = 0$.

Hence $u = -w - v \in V$, so that $u \in U \cap V$. But then $\sum_{i=1}^{n-r} b_i u_i$ is a linear combination of $w_1, \ldots, w_r$, and since $w_1, \ldots, w_r, u_1, \ldots, u_{n-r}$ are linearly independent, $b_1 = \cdots = b_{n-r} = 0$. Similarly, $c_1 = \cdots = c_{m-r} = 0$ and hence $w = 0$. But then $a_1 = \cdots = a_r = 0$ and we have proved that $w_1, \ldots, w_r, u_1, \ldots, u_{n-r}, v_1, \ldots, v_{m-r}$ are linearly independent. Hence $\dim(U + V) = n + m - r = \dim U + \dim V - \dim(U \cap V)$.

7. Suppose $u \in \langle a, b \rangle \cap \langle c, d \rangle$. Then

$$u = \alpha a + \beta b$$
$$= \gamma c + \delta d$$

for some scalars, α, β, γ, and δ, i.e.,

$$u = \alpha(1, 2, -1, 1) + \beta(1, -2, -1, 3)$$
$$= \gamma(1, 2, 3, 0) + \delta(2, 2, 2, 2).$$

We have

$$\begin{aligned}
\alpha + \beta &= \gamma + 2\delta, \\
2\alpha - 2\beta &= 2\gamma + 2\delta, \\
-\alpha - \beta &= 3\gamma + 2\delta, \\
\alpha + 3\beta &= \quad\ 2\delta.
\end{aligned}$$

Adding the first and the third equations we get

$$0 = 4\gamma + 4\delta,$$

and therefore $\delta = -\gamma$. Thus the second equation yields

$$\alpha = \beta.$$

Since

$$\begin{aligned}
u &= \alpha(1, 2, -1, 1) + \beta(1, -2, -1, 3) \\
&= \alpha(2, 0, -2, 4), \\
u &= \gamma(1, 2, 3, 0) + \delta(2, 2, 2, 2) \\
&= \gamma(-1, 0, 1, -2) \\
&= -\tfrac{1}{2}\gamma(2, 0, -2, 4),
\end{aligned}$$

we see that u is a multiple of the vector $v = (2, 0, -2, 4)$ which can be taken as a basis for $\langle a, b \rangle \cap \langle c, d \rangle$.

By Exercise 6 the dimension of the space $U = \langle a, b \rangle + \langle c, d \rangle$ cannot exceed 3. If we could find three linearly independent vectors in U, then we would know that $\dim U = 3$ and that the three vectors form a basis for U.

Now, the vectors $a - b = (0, 4, 0, -2), a - c = (0, 0, -4, 1)$, and $c = (1, 2, 3, 0)$ are all in U. Suppose that

$$\lambda(0, 4, 0, -2) + \mu(0, 0, -4, 1) + \nu(1, 2, 3, 0) = 0,$$

i.e.,

$$(\nu, 4\lambda + 2\nu, -4\mu + 3\nu, -2\lambda + \mu) = 0.$$

Clearly, we must have $\nu = \lambda = \mu = 0$. The vectors $a - b$, $a - c$, and c are therefore linearly independent and, by Theorem 6.5(a), they form a basis of U.

CHAPTER 2

Section 2.1

Quiz

1. *False.*	**5.** *False.*	**8.** *True.*
2. *True.*	**6.** *False.*	**9.** *True.*
3. *True.*	**7.** *True.*	**10.** *False.*
4. *False.*		

Exercises

1. By Theorem 1.1, ST is given by $z = Cx$, in which $C = BA$. Then

$$C = [2 \quad 5 \quad 0] \begin{bmatrix} 1 & 0 \\ 0 & 2 \\ -3 & 5 \end{bmatrix} = [2 \quad 10].$$

5. Let

$$B = \begin{bmatrix} b_{11} & b_{12} \\ b_{21} & b_{22} \end{bmatrix}.$$

Then

$$AB = \begin{bmatrix} b_{11} - b_{21} & b_{12} - b_{22} \\ b_{11} & b_{12} \end{bmatrix}.$$

Thus $AB = I_2$ implies

$$b_{11} - b_{21} = 1,$$
$$b_{12} - b_{22} = 0,$$
$$b_{11} = 0,$$
$$b_{12} = 1.$$

Hence $b_{21} = -1$, $b_{22} = 1$, and

$$B = \begin{bmatrix} 0 & 1 \\ -1 & 1 \end{bmatrix}.$$

6. Let

$$C = \begin{bmatrix} c_{11} & c_{12} \\ c_{21} & c_{22} \end{bmatrix}.$$

Then $CA = I_2$ implies

$$c_{11} - c_{12} = 1,$$
$$-c_{11} = 0,$$
$$c_{21} - c_{22} = 0,$$
$$-c_{21} = 1.$$

It follows that $c_{12} = 1$, $c_{22} = 1$, and $C = B$.

9. The ith row of AB is by definition of matrix product

$$\left(\sum_{k=1}^{n} a_{ik} b_{k1}, \sum_{k=1}^{n} a_{ik} b_{k2}, \dots, \sum_{k=1}^{n} a_{ik} b_{kp} \right).$$

The product $A_{(i)} B$ is just

$$[a_{i1} \quad a_{i2} \cdots a_{in}] \begin{bmatrix} b_{11} & \cdots & b_{1p} \\ \vdots & & \vdots \\ b_{n1} & \cdots & b_{np} \end{bmatrix}$$

$$= \left(\sum_{k=1}^{n} a_{ik} b_{k1}, \sum_{k=1}^{n} a_{ik} b_{k2}, \dots, \sum_{k=1}^{n} a_{ik} b_{kp} \right).$$

Hence $(AB)_{(i)} = A_{(i)}B$. Similarly, $(AB)^{(j)} = AB^{(j)}$.

Section 2.2

Quiz

1. *True.*	**5.** *True.*	**8.** *True.*
2. *True.*	**6.** *True.*	**9.** *True.*
3. *True.*	**7.** *True.*	**10.** *True.*
4. *True.*		

Exercises

3. $A(B + C) = AB + AC$. Now

$$B + C = \begin{bmatrix} 0 & 2 \\ 1 & 2 \\ 0 & -1 \end{bmatrix} + \begin{bmatrix} -1 & 2 \\ 0 & 4 \\ 3 & 6 \end{bmatrix}$$

$$= \begin{bmatrix} -1 & 4 \\ 1 & 6 \\ 3 & 5 \end{bmatrix}.$$

Then $A(B + C)$ is

$$\begin{bmatrix} 1 & 2 & 3 \\ 4 & 5 & 6 \end{bmatrix} \begin{bmatrix} -1 & 4 \\ 1 & 6 \\ 3 & 5 \end{bmatrix} = \begin{bmatrix} 10 & 31 \\ 19 & 76 \end{bmatrix}.$$

4. We have

$$AA^T = \begin{bmatrix} a_{11}^2 + a_{12}^2 + a_{13}^2 & a_{11}a_{21} + a_{12}a_{22} + a_{13}a_{23} \\ a_{11}a_{21} + a_{12}a_{22} + a_{13}a_{23} & a_{21}^2 + a_{22}^2 + a_{23}^2 \end{bmatrix}.$$

If $AA^T = 0$, we have

$$a_{11}^2 + a_{12}^2 + a_{13}^2 = 0,$$
$$a_{21}^2 + a_{22}^2 + a_{23}^2 = 0.$$

Therefore, $a_{11} = a_{12} = a_{13} = a_{21} = a_{22} = a_{23} = 0$ and $A = 0$.

Section 2.3

Quiz

1. *False.*   **5.** *True.*   **8.** *False.*

2. *False.*   **6.** *False.*   **9.** *True.*

3. *True.*   **7.** *True.*   **10.** *True.*

4. *False.*

Exercises

1. The augmented matrix $[A : b]$ is

$$\begin{bmatrix} 2 & 3 & -1 & 1 & -1 \\ 3 & 2 & -2 & 2 & 1 \\ 5 & 0 & -4 & 4 & 5 \end{bmatrix}.$$

Performing the necessary row operations on $[A : b]$ to reduce A to Hermite normal form, we obtain

$$\begin{bmatrix} 1 & 0 & -\frac{4}{5} & \frac{4}{5} & 1 \\ 0 & 1 & \frac{1}{5} & -\frac{1}{5} & -1 \\ 0 & 0 & 0 & 0 & 0 \end{bmatrix}.$$

Thus the general solution to the system is

$$(x_1, x_2, x_3, x_4) = (1 + \tfrac{4}{5}x_3 - \tfrac{4}{5}x_4, -1 - \tfrac{1}{5}x_3 + \tfrac{1}{5}x_4, x_3, x_4)$$
$$= (1, -1, 0, 0) + x_3(\tfrac{4}{5}, -\tfrac{1}{5}, 1, 0) + x_4(-\tfrac{4}{5}, \tfrac{1}{5}, 0, 1).$$

3. The reduction to Hermite normal form proceeds as follows:

$$\begin{bmatrix} 1 & 3 & 2 \\ -1 & -1 & -1 \\ 2 & 3 & -2 \end{bmatrix} \rightarrow \begin{bmatrix} 1 & 3 & 2 \\ 0 & 2 & 1 \\ 0 & -3 & -6 \end{bmatrix} \rightarrow \begin{bmatrix} 1 & 3 & 2 \\ 0 & 1 & \frac{1}{2} \\ 0 & -3 & -6 \end{bmatrix} \rightarrow \begin{bmatrix} 1 & 0 & \frac{1}{2} \\ 0 & 1 & \frac{1}{2} \\ 0 & 0 & -\frac{9}{2} \end{bmatrix}$$

$$\rightarrow \begin{bmatrix} 1 & 0 & \frac{1}{2} \\ 0 & 1 & \frac{1}{2} \\ 0 & 0 & 1 \end{bmatrix} \rightarrow \begin{bmatrix} 1 & 0 & 0 \\ 0 & 1 & 0 \\ 0 & 0 & 1 \end{bmatrix}.$$

7. Let the columns of A^{-1} be denoted by x, y, and z. Since $AA^{-1} = I_3$, we must have

$$Ax = e_1,$$
$$Ay = e_2,$$
$$Az = e_3,$$

where e_1, e_2, and e_3 are the columns of I_3, i.e., $e_1 = (1, 0, 0)$, $e_2 = (0, 1, 0)$, and $e_3 = (0, 0, 1)$. We now solve the above systems by the method used in the text, that is, we perform the elementary operations used to reduce A to its Hermite normal form (see Exercise 3) on the augmented matrices $[A : e_1]$, $[A : e_2]$, and $[A : e_3]$. Thus we obtain

$$x = (-\tfrac{5}{9}, \tfrac{4}{9}, \tfrac{1}{9}), \qquad y = (-\tfrac{4}{3}, \tfrac{2}{3}, -\tfrac{1}{3}), \qquad z = (\tfrac{1}{9}, \tfrac{1}{9}, -\tfrac{2}{9}),$$

$$A^{-1} = \begin{bmatrix} -\frac{5}{9} & -\frac{4}{3} & \frac{1}{9} \\ \frac{4}{9} & \frac{2}{3} & \frac{1}{9} \\ \frac{1}{9} & -\frac{1}{3} & -\frac{2}{9} \end{bmatrix}.$$

Section 2.4

Quiz

1. *True.* **5.** *True.* **8.** *False.*

2. *False.* **6.** *False.* **9.** *True.*

3. *True.* **7.** *True.* **10.** *True.*

4. *True.*

Exercises

2. Performing a sequence of elementary row operations we have:

$$\begin{bmatrix} 1 & 0 & -1 & 2 & 5 \\ 0 & 0 & 0 & 1 & 1 \\ 1 & -1 & -1 & 2 & 3 \end{bmatrix} \rightarrow \begin{bmatrix} 1 & 0 & -1 & 2 & 5 \\ 1 & -1 & -1 & 2 & 3 \\ 0 & 0 & 0 & 1 & 1 \end{bmatrix} \rightarrow \begin{bmatrix} 1 & 0 & -1 & 2 & 5 \\ 0 & -1 & 0 & 0 & -2 \\ 0 & 0 & 0 & 1 & 1 \end{bmatrix}$$

$$\rightarrow \begin{bmatrix} 1 & 0 & -1 & 2 & 5 \\ 0 & 1 & 0 & 0 & 2 \\ 0 & 0 & 0 & 1 & 1 \end{bmatrix} \rightarrow \begin{bmatrix} 1 & 0 & -1 & 0 & 3 \\ 0 & 1 & 0 & 0 & 2 \\ 0 & 0 & 0 & 1 & 1 \end{bmatrix}.$$

This last matrix is in Hermite normal form and has rank 3.

3. We reduce the matrix to its Hermite normal form:

$$
\begin{bmatrix} 1 & 0 & 0 & 1 \\ 0 & 1 & 1 & 0 \\ 0 & 1 & -1 & 0 \\ -1 & 0 & 0 & 1 \end{bmatrix}
\rightarrow
\begin{bmatrix} 1 & 0 & 0 & 1 \\ 0 & 1 & 1 & 0 \\ 0 & 1 & -1 & 0 \\ 0 & 0 & 0 & 2 \end{bmatrix}
\rightarrow
\begin{bmatrix} 1 & 0 & 0 & 1 \\ 0 & 1 & 1 & 0 \\ 0 & 0 & -2 & 0 \\ 0 & 0 & 0 & 2 \end{bmatrix}
\rightarrow
\begin{bmatrix} 1 & 0 & 0 & 1 \\ 0 & 1 & 1 & 0 \\ 0 & 0 & 1 & 0 \\ 0 & 0 & 0 & 2 \end{bmatrix}
$$

$$
\rightarrow
\begin{bmatrix} 1 & 0 & 0 & 1 \\ 0 & 1 & 0 & 0 \\ 0 & 0 & 1 & 0 \\ 0 & 0 & 0 & 2 \end{bmatrix}
\rightarrow
\begin{bmatrix} 1 & 0 & 0 & 1 \\ 0 & 1 & 0 & 0 \\ 0 & 0 & 1 & 0 \\ 0 & 0 & 0 & 1 \end{bmatrix}
\rightarrow
\begin{bmatrix} 1 & 0 & 0 & 0 \\ 0 & 1 & 0 & 0 \\ 0 & 0 & 1 & 0 \\ 0 & 0 & 0 & 1 \end{bmatrix},
$$

and we perform the same sequence of elementary row operations on I_4:

$$
\begin{bmatrix} 1 & 0 & 0 & 0 \\ 0 & 1 & 0 & 0 \\ 0 & 0 & 1 & 0 \\ 0 & 0 & 0 & 1 \end{bmatrix}
\rightarrow
\begin{bmatrix} 1 & 0 & 0 & 0 \\ 0 & 1 & 0 & 0 \\ 0 & 0 & 1 & 0 \\ 1 & 0 & 0 & 1 \end{bmatrix}
\rightarrow
\begin{bmatrix} 1 & 0 & 0 & 0 \\ 0 & 1 & 0 & 0 \\ 0 & -1 & 1 & 0 \\ 1 & 0 & 0 & 1 \end{bmatrix}
\rightarrow
\begin{bmatrix} 1 & 0 & 0 & 0 \\ 0 & 1 & 0 & 0 \\ 0 & \frac{1}{2} & -\frac{1}{2} & 0 \\ 1 & 0 & 0 & 1 \end{bmatrix}
$$

$$
\rightarrow
\begin{bmatrix} 1 & 0 & 0 & 0 \\ 0 & \frac{1}{2} & \frac{1}{2} & 0 \\ 0 & \frac{1}{2} & -\frac{1}{2} & 0 \\ 1 & 0 & 0 & 1 \end{bmatrix}
\rightarrow
\begin{bmatrix} 1 & 0 & 0 & 0 \\ 0 & \frac{1}{2} & \frac{1}{2} & 0 \\ 0 & \frac{1}{2} & -\frac{1}{2} & 0 \\ \frac{1}{2} & 0 & 0 & \frac{1}{2} \end{bmatrix}
\rightarrow
\begin{bmatrix} \frac{1}{2} & 0 & 0 & -\frac{1}{2} \\ 0 & \frac{1}{2} & \frac{1}{2} & 0 \\ 0 & \frac{1}{2} & -\frac{1}{2} & 0 \\ \frac{1}{2} & 0 & 0 & \frac{1}{2} \end{bmatrix}.
$$

The last matrix is the required inverse.

CHAPTER 3

Section 3.1

Quiz

1. *False.*	**5.** *False.*	**8.** *False.*
2. *False.*	**6.** *True.*	**9.** *False.*
3. *True.*	**7.** *True.*	**10.** *False.*
4. *True.*		

Exercises

3. The matrix A has the following form:

$$
A = \begin{bmatrix}
b_{11} + c_{11} & b_{12} + c_{12} & b_{13} + c_{13} & \cdots & b_{1n} + c_{1n} \\
a_{21} & a_{22} & a_{23} & \cdots & a_{2n} \\
\vdots & \vdots & \vdots & & \vdots \\
a_{n1} & a_{n2} & a_{n3} & \cdots & a_{nn}
\end{bmatrix}.
$$

We also have $a_{ij} = b_{ij} = c_{ij}$, $i = 2, \ldots, n$, $j = 1, \ldots, n$. Expanding $\det(A)$ by the first row we have

$$\det(A) = \sum_{j=1}^{n} (-1)^{1+j}(b_{1j} + c_{1j}) \det(A(1 \mid j))$$

$$= \sum_{j=1}^{n} (-1)^{1+j}b_{1j} \det(A(1 \mid j)) + \sum_{j=1}^{n} (-1)^{1+j}c_{1j} \det(A(1 \mid j)).$$

Now $A(1 \mid j) = B(1 \mid j) = C(1 \mid j)$, $j = 1, \ldots, n$, and hence

$$\sum_{j=1}^{n} (-1)^{1+j}b_{1j} \det(A(1 \mid j)) = \sum_{j=1}^{n} (-1)^{1+j}b_{1j} \det(B(1 \mid j))$$

$$= \det(B).$$

Similarly,

$$\sum_{j=1}^{n} (-1)^{1+j}c_{1j} \det(A(1 \mid j)) = \det(C)$$

and thus

$$\det(A) = \det(B) + \det(C).$$

4. If $n = 2$, then

$$\det(A) = \det\left(\begin{bmatrix} 1 & 1 \\ r_1 & r_2 \end{bmatrix}\right)$$

$$= r_2 - r_1.$$

If $n = 3$, then

$$\det(A) = \det\left(\begin{bmatrix} 1 & 1 & 1 \\ r_1 & r_2 & r_3 \\ r_1^2 & r_2^2 & r_3^2 \end{bmatrix}\right)$$

$$= \det\left(\begin{bmatrix} 1 & 0 & 0 \\ r_1 & r_2 - r_1 & r_3 - r_1 \\ r_1^2 & r_2^2 - r_1^2 & r_3^2 - r_1^2 \end{bmatrix}\right)$$

$$= \det\left(\begin{bmatrix} r_2 - r_1 & r_3 - r_1 \\ r_2^2 - r_1^2 & r_3^2 - r_1^2 \end{bmatrix}\right)$$

$$= (r_2 - r_1)(r_3 - r_1)\det\left(\begin{bmatrix} 1 & 1 \\ r_2 + r_1 & r_3 + r_1 \end{bmatrix}\right)$$

$$= (r_2 - r_1)(r_3 - r_1)(r_3 - r_2).$$

Section 3.2

Quiz

1. *False.*

2. *False.*

3. *True.*

4. *True.*

5. *True.*

6. *False.*

7. *True.*

8. *True.*

9. *True.*

10. *True.*

Exercises

4. We want to find numbers x and y such that the rank of the matrix

$$A = \begin{bmatrix} x & 1 & 3 & 2 \\ 1 & -1 & 1 & 1 \\ 1 & 2 & 2 & y \end{bmatrix},$$

whose rows are the three given vectors, is less than 3. By Theorem 2.4, all sub-determinants of A of order 3 must be zero. Thus we must have

$$\det\left(\begin{bmatrix} x & 1 & 3 \\ 1 & -1 & 1 \\ 1 & 2 & 2 \end{bmatrix}\right) = -4x + 8$$
$$= 0$$

and therefore $x = 2$. Also

$$\det\left(\begin{bmatrix} 1 & 3 & 2 \\ -1 & 1 & 1 \\ 2 & 2 & y \end{bmatrix}\right) = 4y - 4$$
$$= 0$$

and thus $y = 1$. It is easy to see that with these values for x and y, the rank of A is 2.

6. Suppose first that A is nonsingular. Then $\det(A) \neq 0$. We have

$$A \text{ adj } A = \det(A)I_n$$

and therefore

$$\det(A)\det(\text{adj } A) = (\det(A))^n.$$

Hence

$$\det(\text{adj } A) = (\det(A))^{n-1}.$$

Now suppose that $\det(A) = 0$. Then

$$A \text{ adj } A = 0.$$

We have to prove that

$$\det(\text{adj } A) = 0$$

(see Quiz question 10). Suppose that $\det(\text{adj } A) \neq 0$ and thus, by Theorem 2.2, adj A is nonsingular. But then

$$A(\text{adj } A)(\text{adj } A)^{-1} = 0,$$

i.e.,

$$A = 0,$$

which is impossible if $\det(\text{adj } A) \neq 0$.

7. Since A and B are nonsingular, AB is nonsingular and hence $\text{adj}(AB) = (AB)^{-1}\det(AB) = B^{-1}A^{-1}\det(A)\det(B) = \det(B)B^{-1}\det(A)A^{-1} = \text{adj}B\,\text{adj}A$.

8. We have A adj $A = \det(A)I_n$. Computing the adjugate of both sides and using the results of Exercise 7, we have

$$\text{adj}(\text{adj } A)\text{adj } A = \text{adj}(\det(A)I_n).$$

But, by Exercise 5, $\text{adj}(\det(A)I_n) = \det(A)^{n-1}$ adj $I_n = \det(A)^{n-1}I_n$. Hence

$$\text{adj}(\text{adj } A)\text{adj } A = \det(A)^{n-1}I_n,$$

and, since adj $A = A^{-1}\det(A)$, we have

$$\text{adj}(\text{adj } A)A^{-1}\det(A) = \det(A)^{n-1}I_n,$$
$$\text{adj}(\text{adj } A) = A\det(A)^{n-2}.$$

CHAPTER 4

Section 4.1

Quiz

1. *True.*   **5.** *True.*   **8.** *True.*

2. *True.*   **6.** *False.*   **9.** *False.*

3. *False.*   **7.** *True.*   **10.** *True.*

4. *False.*

Exercises

5. The matrices E_{ij}, in which $j \geq i$, form a basis for T_n, since they are obviously linearly independent and span T_n. There are $(n^2 + n)/2$ of these matrices. Hence $\dim T_n = (n^2 + n)/2$.

6. We compute:

$$T(E_{11}) = T\left(\begin{bmatrix} 1 & 0 \\ 0 & 0 \end{bmatrix}\right) = \begin{bmatrix} 2 & 0 \\ 0 & 0 \end{bmatrix} = 2E_{11},$$

$$T(E_{12}) = \begin{bmatrix} 0 & 1 \\ 1 & 0 \end{bmatrix} = E_{12} + E_{21},$$

$$T(E_{21}) = \begin{bmatrix} 0 & 1 \\ -1 & 0 \end{bmatrix} = E_{12} - E_{21},$$

$$T(E_{22}) = \begin{bmatrix} 0 & 0 \\ 0 & 3 \end{bmatrix} = 3E_{22}.$$

Hence

$$[T]_G^G = \begin{bmatrix} 2 & 0 & 0 & 0 \\ 0 & 1 & 1 & 0 \\ 0 & 1 & -1 & 0 \\ 0 & 0 & 0 & 3 \end{bmatrix}.$$

7. We have

$$T(F_1) = \begin{bmatrix} 2 & 0 \\ 0 & 3 \end{bmatrix} = \tfrac{5}{2}F_1 - \tfrac{1}{2}F_2,$$

$$T(F_2) = \begin{bmatrix} 2 & 0 \\ 0 & -3 \end{bmatrix} = -\tfrac{1}{2}F_1 + \tfrac{5}{2}F_2,$$

$$T(F_3) = \begin{bmatrix} 0 & 2 \\ 0 & 0 \end{bmatrix} = F_3 + F_4,$$

$$T(F_4) = \begin{bmatrix} 0 & 0 \\ 2 & 0 \end{bmatrix} = F_3 - F_4.$$

Thus

$$B = \begin{bmatrix} \tfrac{5}{2} & -\tfrac{1}{2} & 0 & 0 \\ -\tfrac{1}{2} & \tfrac{5}{2} & 0 & 0 \\ 0 & 0 & 1 & 1 \\ 0 & 0 & 1 & -1 \end{bmatrix}.$$

Let $C = [I_U]_H^G$, where $U = M_2(R)$. We compute

$$I_U(F_1) = E_{11} + E_{22},$$
$$I_U(F_2) = E_{11} - E_{22},$$
$$I_U(F_3) = E_{12} + E_{21},$$
$$I_U(F_4) = E_{12} - E_{21}.$$

Thus

$$C = \begin{bmatrix} 1 & 1 & 0 & 0 \\ 0 & 0 & 1 & 1 \\ 0 & 0 & 1 & -1 \\ 1 & -1 & 0 & 0 \end{bmatrix}.$$

Section 4.2

Quiz

1. *False.*   **5.** *False.*   **8.** *True.*

2. *True.*   **6.** *False.*   **9.** *False.*

3. *True.*   **7.** *False.*   **10.** *False.*

4. *False.*

Exercises

2. All the row sums of B are equal to 2. Therefore 2 is a characteristic root of B and $(1, 1, 1, 1)$ is a corresponding characteristic vector. Let

$$P = \begin{bmatrix} 1 & 0 & 0 & 0 \\ 1 & 1 & 0 & 0 \\ 1 & 0 & 1 & 0 \\ 1 & 0 & 0 & 1 \end{bmatrix}.$$

Then

$$P^{-1} = \begin{bmatrix} 1 & 0 & 0 & 0 \\ -1 & 1 & 0 & 0 \\ -1 & 0 & 1 & 0 \\ -1 & 0 & 0 & 1 \end{bmatrix}.$$

We compute

$$P^{-1}BP = \begin{bmatrix} 2 & -1 & 2 & 0 \\ 0 & 0 & -2 & 2 \\ 0 & 1 & -1 & -1 \\ 0 & 3 & -1 & -1 \end{bmatrix}.$$

Let

$$B_1 = \begin{bmatrix} 0 & -2 & 2 \\ 1 & -1 & -1 \\ 3 & -1 & -1 \end{bmatrix}.$$

Then

$$\det(\lambda I_3 - B_1) = \lambda^3 + 2\lambda^2 - 4\lambda - 8$$
$$= (\lambda + 2)^2(\lambda - 2).$$

Characteristic vectors corresponding to -2 and 2 can be computed as in Example 2.3. We find that $(0, 1, 1)$ and $(1, 0, 1)$ are characteristic vectors of B_1 corresponding to -2 and 2, respectively. Let

$$Q_1 = \begin{bmatrix} 0 & 1 & 0 \\ 1 & 0 & 0 \\ 1 & 1 & 1 \end{bmatrix}.$$

Then

$$Q_1^{-1}B_1Q_1 = \begin{bmatrix} -2 & 0 & -1 \\ 0 & 2 & 2 \\ 0 & 0 & -2 \end{bmatrix}.$$

Let

$$Q = \left[\begin{array}{c|ccc} 1 & 0 & 0 & 0 \\ \hline 0 & 0 & 1 & 0 \\ 0 & 1 & 0 & 0 \\ 0 & 1 & 1 & 1 \end{array} \right]$$

and set $S = PQ$. Then

$$S^{-1}BS = \begin{bmatrix} 2 & 2 & -1 & 0 \\ 0 & -2 & 0 & -1 \\ 0 & 0 & 2 & 2 \\ 0 & 0 & 0 & -2 \end{bmatrix},$$

which is upper triangular.

4. Let A have p nonzero characteristic roots, $\lambda_1, \ldots, \lambda_p$. According to Theorem 2.4, we can find an upper triangular matrix T similar to A in which $\lambda_1, \ldots, \lambda_p$ appear in positions $(1, 1), \ldots, (p, p)$:

$$T = \begin{bmatrix} \lambda_1 & * & \cdots & & & * \\ 0 & \ddots & & & & \vdots \\ \vdots & & \lambda_p & & * & \\ & & & 0 & \ddots & \\ 0 & \cdots & & & & 0 \end{bmatrix}.$$

The $p \times p$ submatrix in the upper left corner of T has nonzero determinant $\prod_{i=1}^{p} \lambda_i$. Hence, according to Theorem 2.3, Chapter 3, $r = \rho(A) = \rho(T) \geq p$.

8. Suppose that A is nonsingular. Then $A^{-1}(AB)A = (A^{-1}A)(BA) = I_n(BA) = BA$.

Section 4.3

Quiz

1. *False.*　　　　　**5.** *True.*　　　　　**8.** *False.*

2. *True.*　　　　　**6.** *False.*　　　　　**9.** *True.*

3. *True.*　　　　　**7.** *True.*　　　　　**10.** *True.*

4. *True.*

Exercises

4. Let

$$U = \begin{bmatrix} u_{11} & u_{12} \\ u_{21} & u_{22} \end{bmatrix}$$

be a 2×2 orthogonal matrix. Then the rows and columns are mutually perpendicular unit vectors (Theorem 3.4). Thus $u_{11}^2 + u_{21}^2 = 1$ and $u_{12}^2 + u_{22}^2 = 1$. Set $u_{11} = \cos\theta$, $u_{21} = \sin\theta$, $u_{12} = \sin\phi$, $u_{22} = \cos\phi$, where $0 \leq \theta \leq 2\pi$, $0 \leq \phi \leq 2\pi$. Then $0 = u_{11}u_{12} + u_{21}u_{22} = \cos\theta\sin\phi + \sin\theta\cos\phi = \sin(\phi + \theta)$. Hence $\phi + \theta = k\pi$, where $k = 0, 1, 2, 3, 4$. Therefore $u_{12} = \sin\phi = \sin(k\pi - \theta) = \sin k\pi\cos\theta - \cos k\pi\sin\theta = -\cos k\pi\sin\theta = (-1)^{k+1}\sin\theta$ and $u_{22} = \cos\phi = \cos(k\pi - \theta) = \cos k\pi\cos\theta + \sin k\pi\sin\theta = (-1)^k\cos\theta$. Thus

$$U = \begin{bmatrix} \cos\theta & (-1)^{k+1}\sin\theta \\ \sin\theta & (-1)^k\cos\theta \end{bmatrix},$$

which always has the indicated form.

7. We have

$$\det(\lambda I_3 - A) = \det\left(\begin{bmatrix} \lambda - 2 & 0 & -1 \\ 0 & \lambda - 2 & 1 \\ -1 & 1 & \lambda - 1 \end{bmatrix}\right)$$

$$= \lambda^3 - 5\lambda^2 + 6\lambda$$

$$= \lambda(\lambda - 2)(\lambda - 3).$$

Thus the characteristic roots of A are 0, 2, and 3. We find that the corresponding unit charactertstic vectors are $(1/\sqrt{6})(1, -1, -2), (1/\sqrt{2})(1, 1, 0)$, and $(1/\sqrt{3})(1, -1, 1)$, respectively. We therefore set

$$U = \begin{bmatrix} \dfrac{1}{\sqrt{6}} & \dfrac{1}{\sqrt{2}} & \dfrac{1}{\sqrt{3}} \\ -\dfrac{1}{\sqrt{6}} & \dfrac{1}{\sqrt{2}} & -\dfrac{1}{\sqrt{3}} \\ -\dfrac{2}{\sqrt{6}} & 0 & \dfrac{1}{\sqrt{3}} \end{bmatrix}.$$

Then $U^*AU = \operatorname{diag}(0, 2, 3)$.

CHAPTER 5

Section 5.1

Quiz

1. *True.*   **5.** *True.*   **8.** *True.*

2. *True.*   **6.** *True.*   **9.** *True.*

3. *False.*   **7.** *True.*   **10.** *True.*

4. *False.*

Exercises

4. As in the case of the equation (3), we set $y = Px$,

$$P = \begin{bmatrix} \cos\theta & -\sin\theta \\ \sin\theta & \cos\theta \end{bmatrix},$$

in $q(x) = (x, Ax) = 1$. Now

$$P^{-1} = \begin{bmatrix} \cos\theta & \sin\theta \\ -\sin\theta & \cos\theta \end{bmatrix}$$

and hence

$$\begin{aligned}
q(P^{-1}y) &= q(y_1\cos\theta + y_2\sin\theta, -y_1\sin\theta + y_2\cos\theta) \\
&= -(y_1\cos\theta + y_2\sin\theta)^2 - (-y_1\sin\theta + y_2\cos\theta)^2 \\
&\quad + 4(y_1\cos\theta + y_2\sin\theta)(-y_1\sin\theta + y_2\cos\theta) \\
&= -y_1^2 - y_2^2 + 4[-y_1^2\cos\theta\sin\theta + y_2^2\sin\theta\cos\theta \\
&\quad + y_1y_2(\cos^2\theta - \sin^2\theta)] \\
&= y_1^2(-1 - 4\cos\theta\sin\theta) + y_2^2(-1 + 4\sin\theta\cos\theta) \\
&\quad + 4y_1y_2(\cos^2\theta - \sin^2\theta).
\end{aligned}$$

If we choose $\theta = \pi/4$, we have

$$1 = q(P^{-1}y)$$
$$= -3y_1^2 + y_2^2$$

or

$$y_2^2 - 3y_1^2 = 1.$$

This curve is, of course, a hyperbola. Thus the original curve, $q(x) = (x, Ax) = 1$, is a hyperbola, since it is just obtained from the curve $y_2^2 - 3y_1^2 = 1$ by a rotation about the origin through $\pi/4$.

6. Let the congruence operation permute the ith and the jth rows. Then the diagonal entries are unchanged except that a_{ii} is replaced by a_{ji} and a_{jj} is replaced by a_{ij}. The new matrix is therefore of the form

$$\begin{bmatrix} \ddots & & & \\ & a_{ji} & \cdots & a_{jj} \\ & \vdots & \ddots & \vdots \\ & a_{ii} & \cdots & a_{ij} \\ & & & \ddots \end{bmatrix}.$$

The permutation of the ith and the jth columns will restore a_{jj} and a_{ii} to the main diagonal: a_{jj} will be in the (i, i) position and a_{ii} in the (j, j) position.

7. If $B = P^T A P$, then $AB = AP^T A P$ and

$$\det(AB) = \det(A)\det(P^T)\det(A)\det(P)$$
$$= (\det(A)\det(P))^2$$
$$\geq 0.$$

8. If A is congruent to I_n, then there exists a nonsingular P such that

$$A = P^T I_n P$$
$$= P^T P.$$

Therefore

$$\text{tr}(A) = \sum_{i=1}^{n} a_{ii}$$
$$= \sum_{i=1}^{n} \sum_{t=1}^{n} (P^T)_{it} p_{ti}$$
$$= \sum_{i=1}^{n} \sum_{t=1}^{n} p_{ti}^2$$
$$> 0,$$

since obviously not all $p_{ti} = 0$ (P is nonsingular).

Section 5.2

Quiz

1. *False.* **5.** *False.* **8.** *False.*
2. *True.* **6.** *False.* **9.** *True.*
3. *True.* **7.** *False.* **10.** *False.*
4. *False.*

Exercises

1. Let $P_n(R)$ denote the space of polynomials with real coefficients of degree not exceeding n. Let $p(t) = \sum_{j=0}^{n} a_j t^j$ be any polynomial in $P_n(R)$. Then, by definiton, $p(t) \in \langle 1, t, \ldots, t^n \rangle$. Clearly, any linear combination of $1, t, \ldots, t^n$ is in $P_n(R)$. Hence $P_n(R) = \langle 1, t, \ldots, t^n \rangle$. It remains to prove that $1, t, \ldots, t^n$ are linearly independent. Suppose that

$$\sum_{j=0}^{n} c_j t^j = 0$$

for some real numbers c_j. The above equation states that a polynomial is equal to 0. This can happen only if all coefficients are 0, i.e., only if $c_0 = c_1 = \cdots = c_n$. Thus $1, t, \ldots, t^n$ are linearly independent and therefore form a basis.

2. Let $OPQS$ be a parallelgram in a plane. Refer the plane to axes of coordinates so that O is the origin, P is on the x-axis, and S and Q are in the first quadrant. Let P' be the point on the positive part of the y-axis such that $OP' = OP$.

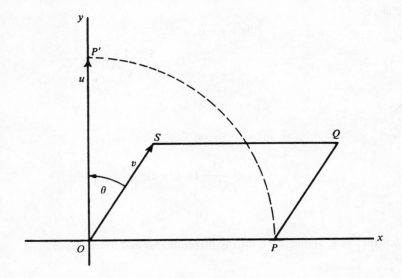

Let u and v be vectors in the plane represented by $\overrightarrow{OP'}$ and $\overrightarrow{OS}$ (see Section 1.4) and let θ be the angle between them. By formula (4), Section 1.5,

$$\|u\| \, \|v\| \cos \theta = (u, v).$$

Now, $\|u\| = OP = OP'$, $\|v\| = OS$, while $\cos \theta = \cos(90° - \angle POS) = \sin(\angle POS)$. We know from elementary trigonometry that the area of parallel-ogram $OPQS$ is $OP \times OS \times \sin(\angle POS)$. Thus

$$\text{area of } OPQS = \|u\| \, \|v\| \cos \theta$$
$$= (u, v).$$

But by the Cauchy-Schwarz inequality

$$(u, v) \leq \|u\| \, \|v\|.$$

The result follows.

3. Let V denote the subspace. Then V consists of all vectors in $V_3(R)$ of the form $(a_1, + a_2, -a_1, - a_2)$. Let $u = (1, -1, 0)$ and $v = (1, 0, -1)$. We assert that u and v form a basis of V. For,

$$(a_1, + a_2, -a_1, - a_2) = a_1 u + a_2 v$$

and clearly u and v are linearly independent. We now use the Gram-Schmidt process (see Section 4.3) to find the required orthonormal basis. Let

$$u' = \frac{1}{\|u\|} u$$

$$= \frac{1}{\sqrt{2}} (1, -1, 0);$$

and

$$w = v - (v, u')u'$$

$$= (1, 0, -1) - \frac{1}{\sqrt{2}} \cdot \frac{1}{\sqrt{2}} (1, -1, 0)$$

$$= (\tfrac{1}{2}, \tfrac{1}{2}, -1).$$

Set

$$w' = \frac{1}{\|w\|} w$$

$$= \frac{1}{\sqrt{3/2}} (\tfrac{1}{2}, \tfrac{1}{2}, -1)$$

$$= \frac{1}{\sqrt{6}} (1, 1, -2).$$

Unit vectors u' and w' are mutually perpendicular and form a basis of V.

4. Suppose that $c_1, \ldots, c_k$ are complex numbers for which

$$\sum_{t=1}^{k} c_t u_t = 0.$$

For a fixed j, $1 \leq j \leq k$, compute the inner product of both sides of the preceding equality with u_j:

$$\sum_{t=1}^{k} c_t(u_t, u_j) = 0.$$

Now, $(u_t, u_j) = 0$ if $t = j$. Hence the left side reduces to $c_j \|u_j\|^2$, i.e., $c_j = 0$.

5. We have verified in the text that $(A, B) = \text{tr}(B^*A)$ is an inner product for n-square complex matrices. Hence $\text{tr}(A^*A) = (A, A) \geq 0$, with equality holding if and only if A is the zero matrix.

6. In particular, set $X = A^*$ and, since $\text{tr}(AA^*) = \text{tr}(A^*A)$, we can use Exercise 5 to complete the argument.

7. By (11), $(A, B) = \text{tr}(B^*A)$ defines an inner product on the space of all n-square matrices and, with respect to this inner product,

$$\|A\|^2 = \text{tr}(A^*A).$$

Therefore, by the Cauchy-Schwarz inequality,

$$|\text{tr}(B^*A)|^2 \leq \text{tr}(A^*A)\text{tr}(B^*B).$$

But

$$\text{tr}(B^*B) = \sum_{i=1}^{n} \sum_{t=1}^{n} \bar{b}_{ti} b_{ti}$$

$$= \sum_{i=1}^{n} \sum_{t=1}^{n} |b_{ti}|^2$$

$$= \text{tr}(BB^*).$$

Hence

$$|\text{tr}(B^*A)|^2 \leq \text{tr}(A^*A)\text{tr}(BB^*).$$

8. Let $z = (a, b, c)$ be a vector perpendicular to u and to v. Then

$$(u, z) = a + c = 0,$$

$$(v, z) = 2b - c = 0.$$

Thus $z = (-2b, b, 2b)$ and the required unit vector w is $(-\frac{2}{3}, \frac{1}{3}, \frac{2}{3})$.

9. Let $v = \sum_{j=1}^{n} c_j u_j$ be a vector perpendicular to every one of the u_i, $i = 1, \ldots, n$. Then

$$(u_i, v) = (u_i, \sum_{j=1}^{n} c_j u_j)$$
$$= \sum_{j=1}^{n} \bar{c}_j (u_i, u_j)$$
$$= \bar{c}_i$$
$$= 0$$

for $i = 1, \ldots, n$. Thus $v = 0$.

Indexes

Index of Symbols

Index

263